i-Ready® Classroom
Mathematics

Grade 7 • Volume 1

NOT FOR RESALE

978-1-7280-1300-8
©2021–Curriculum Associates, LLC
North Billerica, MA 01862
No part of this book may be reproduced
by any means without written permission
from the publisher.
All Rights Reserved. Printed in USA.
7 8 9 10 11 12 13 14 15   22 21

BTS21

801757

Curriculum Associates

Contents

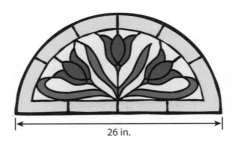

26 in.

UNIT
2

Numbers and Operations

Add and Subtract Rational Numbers

Contents (continued)

UNIT 3

Numbers and Operations

Multiply and Divide Rational Numbers

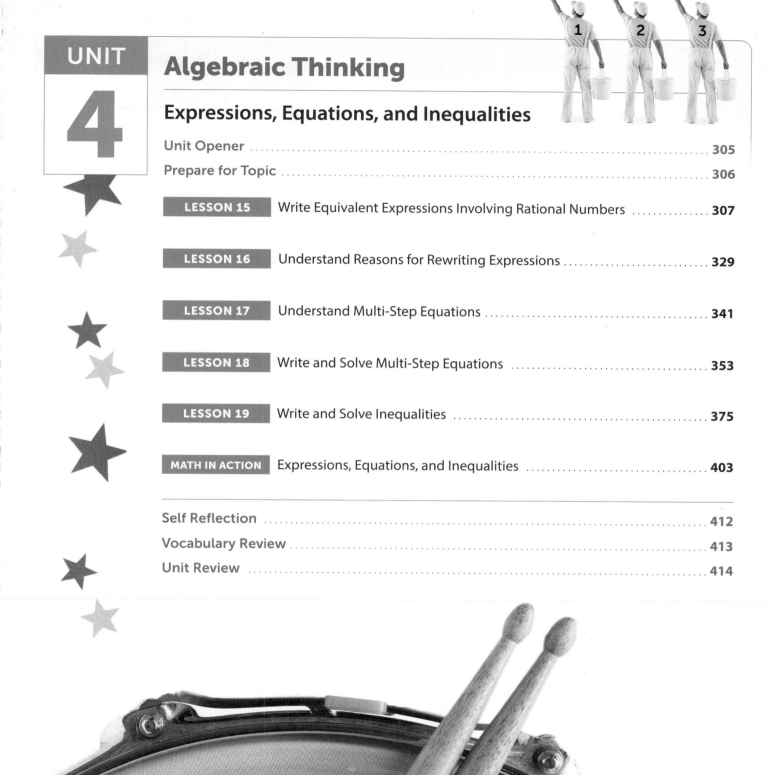

UNIT 4

Algebraic Thinking

Expressions, Equations, and Inequalities

Contents (continued)

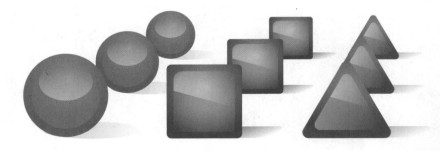

UNIT 5

Proportional Reasoning

Percents and Statistical Samples

Average Sleep
7.9% of day

UNIT 6

Geometry

Solids, Triangles, and Angles

Contents (continued)

Unit 1

Proportional Relationships

Ratios, Rates, and Circles

✓ **Self Check**

Before starting this unit, check off the skills you know below. As you complete each lesson, see how many more skills you can check off!

I can . . .	Before	After
Find actual distance given a scale drawing.	☐	☐
Find actual area given a scale drawing.	☐	☐
Draw a scale drawing at a different scale.	☐	☐
Find unit rates with complex fractions.	☐	☐
Identify proportional relationships and the constant of proportionality.	☐	☐
Write an equation to represent a proportional relationship.	☐	☐
Interpret graphs of proportional relationships.	☐	☐
Find the circumference and area of circles.	☐	☐
Make connections between representations of proportional relationships by explaining how they are similar and different.	☐	☐

Prepare for Ratios, Rates, and Circles

➤ **You have learned to reason about ratio concepts and equivalent ratios. Find the ratio of G : H for each group below. Write the letter of the group in the correct column of the table.**

a. GGGGHHH   **e.** GGGHHHH   **i.** GGGGGHH

b. GHGHGHG   **f.** HHGGHHG   **j.** HHHHHHG

c. GHGGGGG   **g.** GHHHHHG   **k.** GGGHGGH

d. HGHHHHH   **h.** HGHGHGH   **l.** HHGHHGH

Ratios of G : H					
1 : 6	**3 : 4**	**2 : 5**	**6 : 1**	**4 : 3**	**5 : 2**
				a	

Find the ratio of G : H for the group below. Which column in the table above does this ratio belong to?

G H G H G H G H G G H G H G H G G G G H H

Write your own GH group that has one of the ratios in the table. Then meet with a partner to discuss which column each ratio belongs to.

Dear Family,

This week your student is learning about scale drawings. In a **scale drawing**, the size of an original figure changes, but its shape does not change.

Here are some examples of scale drawings that you may be familiar with.

- A floor plan is a scale drawing of the actual layout of space in a building.
- A state road map is a scale drawing of the actual roads in the state.

Scale drawings are typically used when objects are either too small or too large to be shown at their actual sizes. Floor plans and maps are drawn smaller than actual size. Suppose a floor plan is drawn so that 1 inch on the floor plan represents an actual distance of 3 feet. For that floor plan, the **scale** is 1 in. to 3 ft.

Your student will be solving scale drawing problems like the one below.

> The scale from an actual volcano to a drawing of the volcano is 50 m to 5 cm. The height of the drawing of the volcano is 25 cm. How tall is the actual volcano?

➤ **ONE WAY** to find the height is to use a double number line.

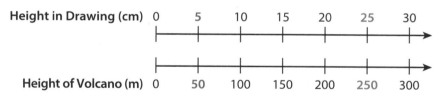

➤ **ANOTHER WAY** is to use a **scale factor**.

The scale from the drawing to the actual volcano is 5 cm for every 50 m, so the scale factor from the drawing to the volcano is $\frac{50}{5}$, or **10**.

Multiply the height of the model by the scale factor: $25 \times \mathbf{10} = 250$.

Using either method, the height of the actual volcano is 250 m.

 Use the next page to start a conversation about scale.

Activity Thinking About Scale Around You

➤ **Do this activity together to investigate scale in the real world.**

Have you ever taken a long road trip and come across some large roadside attractions?

The world's largest cowboy boots are a sculpture in Texas. They are over 35 feet tall! A cowboy boot is normally just 12 inches, or 1 foot, tall.

Gift shops often have models of buildings that fit in the palm of your hand. In Washington, D.C., you can get a Lincoln Memorial model that is 6.5 inches tall. The actual memorial is 80 feet tall! These giant and tiny models are scale copies of real-life objects.

? Where do you see scale drawings and scale copies in the world around you?

Explore Scale Drawings

Previously, you learned about ratios and rates. In this lesson, you will learn about scale drawings.

➤ **Use what you know to try to solve the problem below.**

A geodesic dome is a dome made of triangles. To make a model of a geodesic dome, Ayana needs a smaller triangle that is the same shape as △*A*. Which of these triangles could she use? Show how you know.

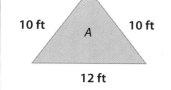

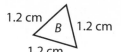 

 TRY IT

 Math Toolkit double number lines, grid paper, ribbon, yarn

DISCUSS IT

Ask: How did you begin to solve the problem?

Share: At first I thought . . .

 Learning Target   SMP 1, SMP 2, SMP 3, SMP 4, SMP 5, SMP 6, SMP 7, SMP 8
Solve problems involving scale drawings of geometric figures, including computing actual lengths and areas from a scale drawing and reproducing a scale drawing at a different scale.

CONNECT IT

1 **Look Back** Which of the triangles could be the same shape as △A? Explain.

2 **Look Ahead** △D is a **scale drawing** of △A. A scale drawing of a figure is larger or smaller than the original figure but has the same exact shape. The **scale** is the ratio between the side lengths of the original figure and the side lengths of the scale drawing. To make a scale drawing of a figure, you can multiply each length of the original figure by a **scale factor** to get the corresponding length in the scale drawing. You can think of the scale factor as a unit rate.

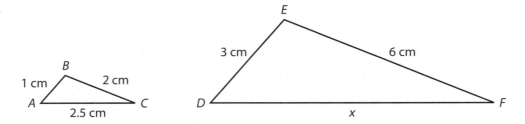

a. Explain why the scale from △ABC to △DEF could be 1 : 3.

b. Explain why the scale factor from △ABC to △DEF is 3.

c. What is the value of x? Describe two different ways you can find it.

3 **Reflect** Yukio says the scale from △DEF to △ABC is 3 : 1. Is Yukio correct? Explain.

Prepare for Solving Problems Involving Scale

1 Think about what you know about ratios and unit rates. Fill in each box. Use words, numbers, and pictures. Show as many ideas as you can.

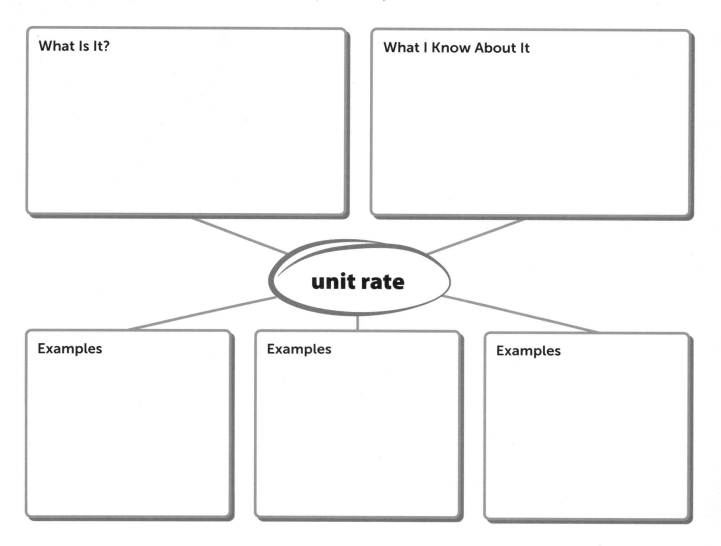

| What Is It? | What I Know About It |

unit rate

| Examples | Examples | Examples |

2 Limes are on sale. The sale price is 8 limes for $2.00. Why could the unit rate be 4 or 0.25?

3 A museum sells postcards of famous paintings. The postcards must be the same shape as the painting. Below are three options for the size of the postcard.

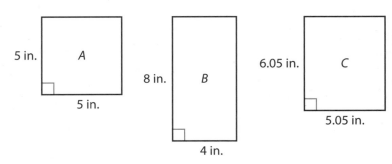

painting of George Washington

a. Which postcard could be the same shape as the painting? Show your work.

SOLUTION _____

b. Check your answer to problem 3a. Show your work.

Develop Using Scale to Find Distances

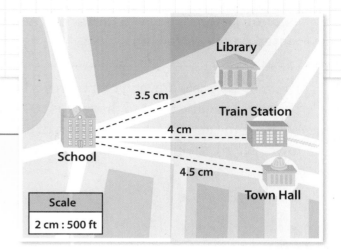

Library

Train Station

3.5 cm

4 cm

School

4.5 cm

Town Hall

Scale

2 cm : 500 ft

➤ **Read and try to solve the problem below.**

This map is a scale drawing of the streets in a town. The scale from the town to the map is 500 ft to 2 cm. What are the actual distances, in feet, of the library, town hall, and train station from the school?

 TRY IT

 Math Toolkit double number lines, grid paper, ribbon, yarn

DISCUSS IT

Ask: What did you do first to find the actual distances?

Share: I knew that . . . so I decided to . . .

➤ **Explore different ways to find actual lengths based on scale drawings.**

This map is a scale drawing of the streets in a town. The scale from the town to the map is 500 ft to 2 cm. What are the actual distances, in feet, of the library, town hall, and train station from the school?

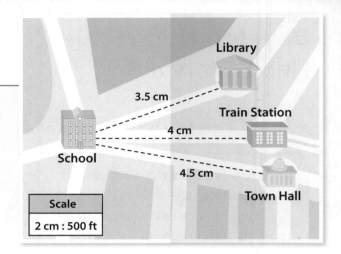

Model It

You can use a double number line to find the actual distances.

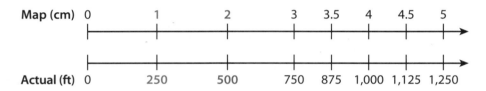

Model It

You can use a scale factor to find the actual distances.

Map (cm)	Actual (ft)
2	500
1	250

You can multiply each distance on the map by the scale factor, **250**.

Library: 3.5 × **250**

Train Station: 4 × **250**

Town Hall: 4.5 × **250**

➤ **Use the problem from the previous page to help you understand how to find actual lengths from a scale drawing.**

1 How far, in feet, are the library, town hall, and train station from the school?

2 Look at the first **Model It**. How does the double number line show the scale factor you can use to find an actual distance, given the distance on the map?

3 Look at the second **Model It**. How is a scale factor like a unit rate?

4 Suppose you have a scale drawing and know its scale. How can you use the scale drawing to find an actual length?

5 The actual distance between the library and train station is 500 ft. Explain how you could find the distance between them in centimeters on the map.

6 **Reflect** Think about all the models and strategies you have discussed today. Describe how one of them helped you better understand how to solve the **Try It** problem.

Apply It

➤ **Use what you learned to solve these problems.**

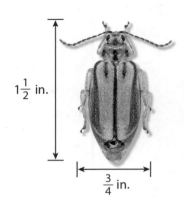

$1\frac{1}{2}$ in.

$\frac{3}{4}$ in.

7 A scientist who studies insects enlarges a photograph of an elm leaf beetle. Every 2 in. in the photograph represents 8 mm on the actual beetle. The length of the beetle in the photograph is $1\frac{1}{2}$ in. The width of the beetle in the photograph is $\frac{3}{4}$ in. What are the length and width of the actual beetle? Show your work.

SOLUTION _____

8 On a map, 2 cm represents 30 mi. The actual distance between two towns is 75 mi. What is the distance between the towns on the map? Show your work.

SOLUTION _____

9 Tyrone makes a scale drawing of his backyard. The scale from the backyard to the drawing is 2 ft to 1 in. The width of the patio on the drawing is 8 in. What is the width of Tyrone's actual patio? Show your work.

SOLUTION _____

Practice Using Scale to Find Distances

➤ **Study the Example showing how to use a scale drawing to find an actual distance. Then solve problems 1–5.**

Example

Colin makes a scale drawing of his bedroom. Every inch in his drawing represents 10 feet in his actual bedroom. The drawing is 1.25 in. wide and 1.5 in. long. How wide and long is his actual bedroom?

You can use a scale factor to find the dimensions.

The scale from the drawing to the bedroom is 1 in. to 10 ft, so the scale factor from the drawing to the bedroom is $\frac{10}{1}$, or **10**.

$1.25 \times 10 = 12.5$ $1.5 \times 10 = 15$

Colin's bedroom is 12.5 ft wide and 15 ft long.

---

1 A drawing of a basement uses the same scale as the Example. The basement is 28 ft wide and 35 ft long. How wide and long is the drawing? Show your work.

SOLUTION _____

2 Efia draws this scale drawing of two famous landmarks. Each inch in the drawing represents 400 ft on the actual landmark. Approximately how much taller is the actual Eiffel Tower than the actual Space Needle? Show your work.

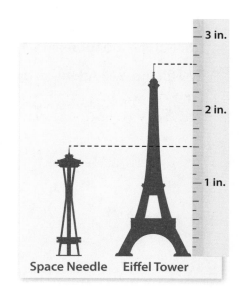

Space Needle   Eiffel Tower

SOLUTION _____

LESSON 1 Solve Problems Involving Scale   **13**

3 The photo shows a small coin. The scale from the actual coin to the photo is 8 mm to 2 cm. In the photo, the distance across the coin is 3.25 cm. What is the distance across the actual coin? Show your work.

3.25 cm

SOLUTION _____

4 In a photograph, Alison stands next to her brother Caleb. Alison is 4 cm tall in the photograph. Her actual height is 60 in. Caleb is 3.2 cm tall in the photograph. What is his actual height? Show your work.

SOLUTION _____

5 Adoncia makes a scale drawing of the front of the Lincoln Memorial. She uses a scale of 15 ft in the monument to 1 in. in the drawing. The front of the monument is about 80 ft high and 200 ft long. Will Adoncia's drawing fit on an $8\frac{1}{2}$ in.-by-11 in. sheet of paper? Explain.

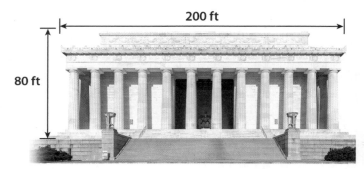

Lincoln Memorial

Develop Using Scale to Find Areas

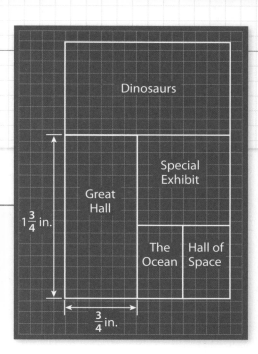

➤ **Read and try to solve the problem below.**

A blueprint for the floor of a natural history museum is shown. The scale of the museum to the blueprint is 20 yd to 1 in. What is the area of the floor of the actual Great Hall?

  TRY IT   **Math Toolkit** double number lines, grid paper, ribbon, yarn

➤ **Explore different ways to find actual areas from a scale drawing.**

A blueprint for the floor of a natural history museum is shown. The scale of the museum to the blueprint is 20 yd to 1 in. What is the area of the floor of the actual Great Hall?

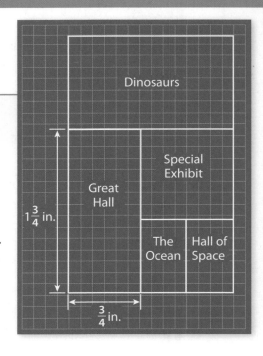

Model It

You can use a table of equivalent ratios to find the actual dimensions.

Blueprint (in.)	1	$\frac{1}{4}$	$\frac{3}{4}$	$1\frac{3}{4}$
Actual (yd)	20	5	15	35

The actual floor is 35 yd long and 15 yd wide.

Area of floor = 35 × 15

Model It

You can use a scale factor to find the area of the actual floor.

The scale from the blueprint to the museum is 20 : 1. So, the scale factor is **20**.

Length of actual floor: 1.75 × **20**

Width of actual floor: 0.75 × **20**

Area = ℓw

= (1.75 × **20**)(0.75 × **20**)

➤ **Use the problem from the previous page to help you understand how to find actual areas from a scale drawing.**

1 What is the area of the floor of the actual Great Hall?

2 Look at the second **Model It**. What does the scale factor mean in this situation?

3 The scale from the museum to the drawing is 20 yd : 1 in. Another scale from the museum to the drawing is 400 yd² : 1 in.². Explain why.

4 The area of the Great Hall in the blueprint is $1\frac{5}{16}$ in.². Why does multiplying the blueprint area by the scale factor 20 not give the area of the floor of the actual Great Hall?

5 How is finding an actual area from the area in a scale drawing similar to finding an actual length from a length in a scale drawing? How is it different?

6 **Reflect** Think about all the models and strategies you have discussed today. Describe how one of them helped you better understand the relationship between an actual area and the area in a scale drawing.

Apply It

➤ **Use what you learned to solve these problems.**

7 The scale from a playground to a scale drawing of the playground is 4 meters per centimeter. The length of the drawing of the playground is 5.3 cm and the width is 3.8 cm. What is the area of the actual playground? Show your work.

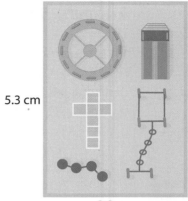

5.3 cm

3.8 cm

scale drawing of a playground

SOLUTION _____

8 A square has an area of 144 ft^2. In a scale drawing of the square, each inch represents 6 ft. What is the area of the square in the drawing?

A 5,184 in.^{2}

B 24 in.^{2}

C 6 in.^{2}

D 4 in.^{2}

9 Below is a scale drawing of the side of a ramp at a skateboard park. The scale from the drawing to the actual ramp is 2 cm to 12 in. What is the area of the actual side of the ramp? Show your work.

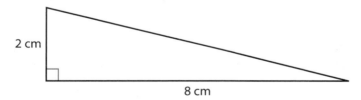

2 cm

8 cm

SOLUTION _____

Practice Using Scale to Find Areas

➤ **Study the Example showing how to find an actual area from a scale drawing. Then solve problems 1–4.**

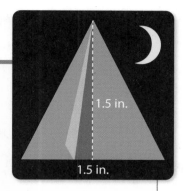

Example

A camping supply store uses a tent as its logo. The store makes a sign with the logo on it. The scale from the actual logo to the logo on the sign is 1 in. to 2 ft. What is the area of the logo on the sign?

You can use the scale factor to find the actual dimensions. The scale factor from the logo to the sign is $\frac{2}{1}$, or **2**.

$$A = \frac{1}{2} bh$$
$$= \frac{1}{2}(1.5 \times 2)(1.5 \times 2)$$
$$= 4.5$$

The area of the logo on the sign is 4.5 ft^2.

---

1 Employees of the store in the Example wear shirts with the logo on the back. The scale from the original logo in inches to the shirt in inches is 1 : 8. What is the area of the logo on their shirts? Show your work.

SOLUTION _____

2 Dr. Gordon has a scale drawing of a building site. The drawing uses the scale 2 in. on the drawing for every 100 ft on the building site. Dr. Gordon marks a 6 in.-by-3.2 in. section of the drawing to show the section she will search. What is the area of the section she will search? Show your work.

SOLUTION _____

LESSON 1 Solve Problems Involving Scale   **19**

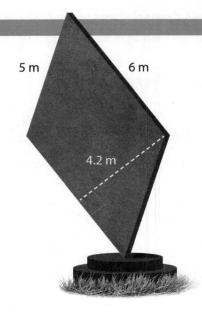

5 m   6 m

4.2 m

3 An artist makes a scale drawing of a parallelogram-shaped sculpture. The scale is 10 cm on the drawing for every 8 m on the sculpture. What is the area of the scale drawing? Show your work.

SOLUTION _____

4 On a map, each centimeter represents 50 m.

a. The area of a rectangular park on the map is 6 cm². Tameka says that to find the area of the actual park, she can multiply the area of the park on the map by 2,500. Do you agree or disagree? Explain.

b. The area of a square sports arena is 10,000 m². What are the dimensions of the sports arena on the map? Show your work.

SOLUTION _____

c. The area of a parallelogram on the map is 5 cm². What is the area of the actual parallelogram? Explain why you can find the area without knowing the dimensions of the parallelogram.

Develop Redrawing a Scale Drawing

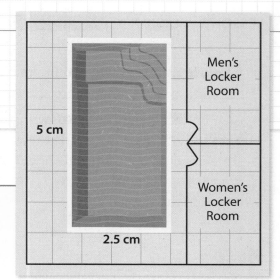

Men's Locker Room

5 cm

2.5 cm

Women's Locker Room

➤ **Read and try to solve the problem below.**

An architect makes a scale drawing of a recreation center. The scale from the actual center to the drawing is 6 m to 1 cm. Make another scale drawing of the pool using 5 m to 1 cm as the scale from the recreation center to the drawing.

 TRY IT **Math Toolkit** double number lines, grid paper, ribbon, rulers, yarn

DISCUSS IT

Ask: How did you start to figure out the dimensions of the new drawing?

Share: I knew . . . so I . . .

➤ **Explore different ways to make a new drawing with a different scale.**

An architect makes a scale drawing of a recreation center. The scale from the actual center to the drawing is 6 m to 1 cm. The pool in the scale drawing is 2.5 cm wide and 5 cm long. Make another scale drawing of the pool using 5 m to 1 cm as the scale from the recreation center to the drawing.

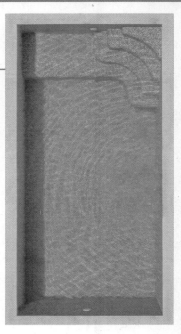

Model It

You can use double number lines to find the dimensions.

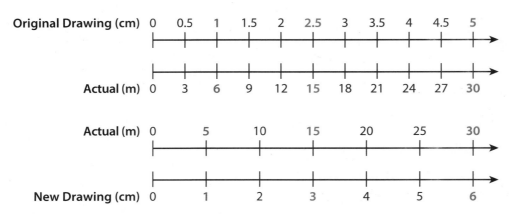

Analyze It

You can reason about how the scales in each drawing are related.

Original Drawing Scale:

actual recreation center to drawing is **6 m** to **1 cm**

New Drawing Scale:

actual recreation center to drawing is **5 m** to **1 cm**

So, the scale from the original drawing to the new drawing is **6 : 5**.

CONNECT IT

➤ **Use the problem from the previous page to help you understand how to reproduce a scale drawing using a different scale.**

1 What are the dimensions of the pool in the new drawing?

2 Look at **Model It**. How are the two double number lines related?

3 Look at **Analyze It**. How do the dimensions of the pool in the original drawing compare to those in the new drawing?

4 The new drawing is a scale drawing of both the actual pool and the original drawing. Why?

5 **Reflect** Think about all the models and strategies you have discussed today. Describe how one of them helped you better understand how to solve the **Try It** problem.

Apply It

➤ **Use what you learned to solve these problems.**

6 The drawing at the right is a plan for an apartment. The length of each square on the grid represents 1 cm. The scale from the apartment to the drawing is 8 ft to 1 cm. Draw another scale drawing of the apartment using a scale from the apartment to the drawing of 4 ft to 1 cm. Justify why your drawing is accurate.

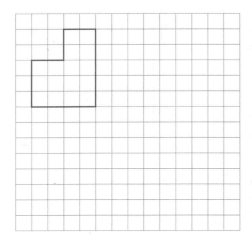

7 The image at the right is a four-square court from a scale plan of a park. The scale from the actual court to the drawing is 8 ft to 1 cm. Draw another scale drawing of the court using a scale from the actual court to the new drawing of 12 ft to 1 cm. Justify why your drawing is accurate.

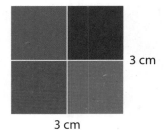

3 cm

3 cm

8 A design for a playground includes a sandbox. The length of a square on the grid represents 1 in. The scale from the playground to the drawing is 12 in. to 1 in. Draw another scale drawing of the sandbox using a scale from the playground to the new drawing of 20 in. to 1 in. Justify why your drawing is accurate.

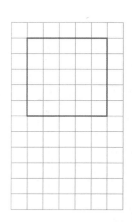

Practice Redrawing a Scale Drawing

➤ **Study the Example showing how to redraw a scale drawing using a different scale. Then solve problems 1–5.**

Example

Luke and Isabella make scale drawings of a fountain. The scale from the fountain to Isabella's drawing is 6 m to 3 cm. The height of the fountain in Isabella's drawing is 5 cm. The scale from the fountain to Luke's drawing is 5 m to 2 cm. What is the height of the fountain in Luke's drawing?

Isabella's scale is 6 m to 3 cm, so the scale factor from her drawing to the actual fountain is $\frac{6}{3}$, or **2**.

Since 5×2 is 10, the actual fountain is 10 m tall.

Luke's scale is 5 m to 2 cm.

The actual fountain is 10 m tall. Since 10 is 5×2, the scale factor from Luke's drawing to the actual fountain is 2.

Since 2×2 is 4, the height of the fountain in Luke's drawing is 4 cm.

1 The width of the fountain in Luke's drawing from the Example is 2 cm. What is the width of the fountain in Isabella's scale drawing? Show your work.

SOLUTION _____

2 The scale from an actual triangle to the drawing at the right is 30 : 1. The scale from the same triangle to Jorge's drawing of the triangle is 10 : 1. Is this drawing or Jorge's drawing larger? Explain your answer.

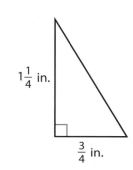

$1\frac{1}{4}$ in.

$\frac{3}{4}$ in.

3 The drawing shows three octagons.

a. Is octagon *B* a scale drawing of octagon *A*? Explain.

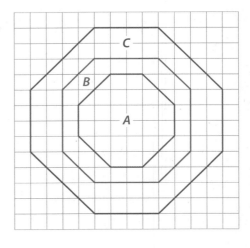

b. Is octagon *C* a scale drawing of octagon *A*? Explain.

4 The length of each square on the grid represents 1 cm. The scale from an actual rectangle to the drawing is 24 in. to 1 cm. Make a new scale drawing where each centimeter represents 16 in. Label the length and width of your drawing in centimeters.

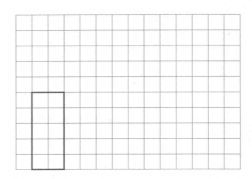

5 The perimeter of a pool is 150 m. The rectangle at the right is a scale drawing of the pool. The length of each square on the grid represents 1 cm. Draw another scale drawing of the pool using the scale 25 m to 2 cm. Explain why your drawing is accurate.

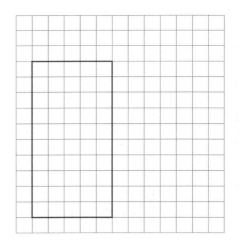

Refine Solving Problems Involving Scale

➤ **Complete the Example below. Then solve problems 1–9.**

Example

Demarco tiles a bathroom floor. He has a scale drawing in which the side length of each unit square represents 2 ft. Demarco uses square tiles that are $\frac{1}{2}$ ft wide. How many tiles does Demarco need?

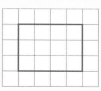

Look how you could show your work using the scale.

Area of the floor in square feet: $(4 \times 2)(3 \times 2) = 48$

Since $\frac{1}{2} \times \frac{1}{2} = \frac{1}{4}$, each tile has an area of $\frac{1}{4}$ ft².

So, it takes 4 tiles to cover each square foot.

SOLUTION _____

Apply It

1 On one map of a town, the scale from the town to the map is 12 mi to 3 cm. The school is 2.5 cm from the grocery store on this map. On a different map of the same town, the scale from the town to the map is 12 mi to 2 cm. The school is 1.5 cm from the library on that map. Is the grocery store or library closer to the school? Show your work.

SOLUTION _____

2 Nautical flags are used to communicate on ships. Kimani uses the scale drawing at the right to sew a nautical *Z* flag. The scale from her flag to the drawing is 20 : 1. Each color is $\frac{1}{4}$ of the flag. How many square inches of each color of fabric does Kimani need? Show your work.

$1\frac{1}{2}$ in.

$1\frac{1}{2}$ in.

CONSIDER THIS...
There is more than one way to solve this problem.

PAIR/SHARE
How can you convert the area to square feet?

SOLUTION _____

3 The scale from a garden to this drawing is 8 ft to 1 cm. The scale from the same garden to another drawing is 2 ft to 1 cm. What are the lengths of the base and height of the garden in the other scale drawing?

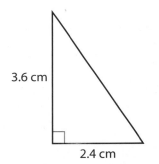

3.6 cm

2.4 cm

A 0.6 cm and 0.9 cm

B 1.2 cm and 1.8 cm

C 4.8 cm and 7.2 cm

D 9.6 cm and 14.4 cm

Kamal chose A as the correct answer. How might he have gotten that answer?

CONSIDER THIS...
In the other scale drawing, how many centimeters represent 8 ft?

PAIR/SHARE
What would be the length of the base and the height if the new scale were 1 cm for every 16 ft?

4 The scale from a map to actual distance is 2.5 cm to 620 mi. The distance on the map between Chicago and Boston is about 3.5 cm. What is the approximate distance, in miles, between Chicago and Boston? Show your work.

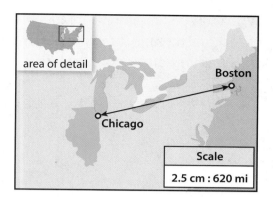

SOLUTION _____

5 On a scale drawing of the front of a square earring, each side of the earring is 3.2 cm. The scale from the earring to the drawing is 4 mm to 2 cm. What is the area of the front of the actual earring?

A 6.4 mm²

B 12.8 mm²

C 20.48 mm²

D 40.96 mm²

6 The image at the right is a scale drawing of a parking lot. The length of each square on the grid represents 0.5 cm. The actual parking lot has a perimeter of 84 m. Draw another scale drawing of the parking lot using a scale from the parking lot to the drawing of 2 m to 1 cm. Justify why your drawing is accurate.

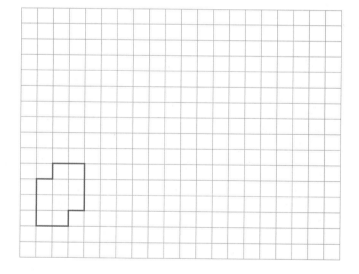

George Washington's
head at Mt. Rushmore

7 Adela paints a mural of Mount Rushmore. She uses the scale 6 ft to 1 ft from the actual monument to the mural. On Adela's mural, how much wider is George Washington's mouth than his eye? Show your work.

11 ft

18 ft

SOLUTION _____

8 The scale from a square park to a drawing of the park is 5 m to 1 cm. The actual park has an area of 1,600 m^2. What is the area of the drawing of the park? Show your work.

SOLUTION _____

9 **Math Journal** Jada will draw two scale drawings of the same object on 1-cm grid paper. Each centimeter will represent a greater distance in the second drawing than in the first. Jada claims that the lengths in the second drawing will be longer than the lengths in the first drawing. Do you agree? Give an example of a scale and a measurement to support your answer.

✓ **End of Lesson Checklist**

☐ **INTERACTIVE GLOSSARY** Find the entry for *scale drawing*. Rewrite the definition in your own words.

☐ **SELF CHECK** Go back to the Unit 1 Opener and see what you can check off.

Dear Family,

This week your student is learning how to find unit rates for ratios when at least one of the quantities is a fraction.

Your student is also learning how to interpret complex fractions. A **complex fraction** is a fraction that has another fraction in the numerator, the denominator, or both. For example, $\frac{\frac{2}{3}}{8}$ is a complex fraction. You can read this as $\frac{2}{3}$ *over 8*. Your student will be solving problems with ratios of fractions like the one below.

> Malcolm is making a costume. He wants to buy red fabric. Red sequin fabric costs \$14 for 2 yards and red velvet fabric costs \$2 for $\frac{1}{3}$ yard. Which fabric is less expensive?

➤ **ONE WAY** to find a unit rate is to use a double number line.

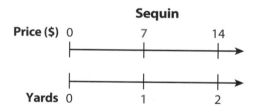

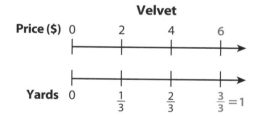

➤ **ANOTHER WAY** is to use division.

Sequin Fabric

Cost in dollars per yard is $\frac{14}{2}$.

$$\frac{14}{2} = 14 \div 2$$

$$= 7$$

Velvet Fabric

Cost in dollars per yard is $\frac{2}{\frac{1}{3}}$.

$$\frac{2}{\frac{1}{3}} = 2 \div \frac{1}{3}$$

$$= 2 \cdot 3$$

$$= 6$$

Both ways show that the sequin fabric costs \$7 per yard and the velvet fabric costs \$6 per yard. So, the velvet fabric is less expensive!

 Use the next page to start a conversation about ratios of fractions.

Activity Thinking About Ratios of Fractions Around You

➤ **Do this activity together to investigate ratios of fractions in the real world.**

One of the greatest snowfalls was in Colorado in 1921. It snowed 87 inches in $27\frac{1}{2}$ hours. That is an average of more than 3 inches per hour!

In 2017, a town in Alaska got 15 inches of snow in $1\frac{1}{2}$ hours. That might not sound like much snow, but it snowed at a rate of 10 inches per hour!

? Where else do you see ratios with fractions in the world around you?

Explore Unit Rates for Ratios with Fractions

Previously, you learned about unit rates. In this lesson, you will learn about unit rates for ratios with fractions.

➤ **Use what you know to try to solve the problem below.**

Grace weaves a rug that is $\frac{1}{3}$ yard wide and 2 yards long. She wants to weave a rug that uses the same design but is 1 yard wide. How long will the rug be?

 TRY IT

 Math Toolkit double number lines, fraction bars, fraction tiles, grid paper

DISCUSS IT

Ask: What did you do first to find the length?

Share: I knew . . . so I . . .

 Learning Target SMP 1, SMP 2, SMP 3, SMP 4, SMP 5, SMP 6, SMP 7
Compute unit rates associated with ratios of fractions, including ratios of lengths, areas and other quantities measured in like or different units.

CONNECT IT

1 Look Back How long is the rug that is 1 yard wide? Explain how you know.

2 Look Ahead Grace's original rug has a length of 2 yards and a width of $\frac{1}{3}$ yard. You can write the ratio of length to width as $2 : \frac{1}{3}$. To find the unit rate, you can start with the **complex fraction** $\frac{2}{\frac{1}{3}}$. Fractions in which the numerator, the denominator, or both are also fractions are called *complex fractions*.

  a. You can simplify a complex fraction by dividing. Since a fraction bar represents division, you can think of $\frac{2}{\frac{1}{3}}$ as $2 \div \frac{1}{3}$. Then you can divide to simplify. What is the unit rate for the length to width of Grace's rug?

  b. Rewrite the complex fraction $\frac{\frac{1}{8}}{\frac{4}{9}}$ as a division expression using $\div$.

  c. What is the quotient of $\frac{\frac{1}{8}}{\frac{4}{9}}$?

  d. Suppose a bug travels $\frac{1}{2}$ mile in 12 minutes. Write a complex fraction you could use to find the speed of the bug in miles per minute. What is the bug's speed in miles per minute?

3 Reflect Are $\frac{1}{\frac{3}{4}}$ and $\frac{\frac{1}{3}}{4}$ equivalent fractions? Explain.

Prepare for Finding Unit Rates Involving Ratios of Fractions

1 Think about what you know about ratios and comparisons. Fill in each box. Use words, numbers, and pictures. Show as many ideas as you can.

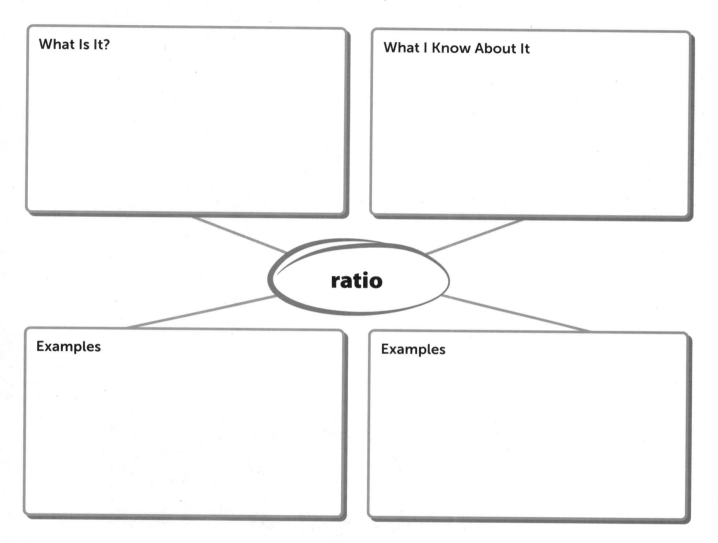

What Is It?

What I Know About It

ratio

Examples

Examples

2 On a bookshelf there are 5 paperback books and 3 hardcover books. Is the ratio of books to hardcover books 5 : 3? Explain.

3 Muna is making a scale drawing of a gecko. The gecko is $\frac{1}{2}$ inch wide and 5 inches long.

a. She decides to make her drawing of the gecko 1 inch wide. How long will the drawing be? Show your work.

SOLUTION _____

b. Check your answer to problem 3a. Show your work.

Develop Solving Problems with Unit Rates for Ratios with Two Fractions

National Park Trail #126

Julio hikes the first $\frac{1}{2}$ mile of the trail in $\frac{1}{4}$ hour.

➤ **Read and try to solve the problem below.**

Julio and Kyle hike along the same trail. Kyle hikes the first 6 miles in 2 hours. Who hikes more quickly?

 TRY IT

 Math Toolkit double number lines, fraction bars, fraction tiles, grid paper

DISCUSS IT

Ask: Why did you choose that strategy to find who is hiking more quickly?

Share: I knew . . . so I . . .

➤ **Explore different ways to understand unit rates for ratios with fractions.**

Julio and Kyle hike along the same trail. Julio hikes the first $\frac{1}{2}$ mile of the trail in $\frac{1}{4}$ hour. Kyle hikes the first 6 miles in 2 hours. Who hikes more quickly?

Model It

You can use a double number line to find each speed.

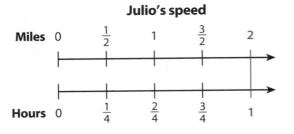

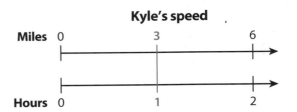

Model It

You can simplify fractions to find each speed.

Julio's Speed

Julio hikes $\frac{1}{2}$ mile in $\frac{1}{4}$ hour.

The unit rate for the ratio $\frac{1}{2} : \frac{1}{4}$ is $\frac{\frac{1}{2}}{\frac{1}{4}}$.

You can think of $\frac{\frac{1}{2}}{\frac{1}{4}}$ as $\frac{1}{2} \div \frac{1}{4}$.

Kyle's Speed

Kyle hikes 6 miles in 2 hours.

The unit rate for the ratio 6 : 2 is $\frac{6}{2}$.

You can think of $\frac{6}{2}$ as $6 \div 2$.

➤ **Use the problem from the previous page to help you understand how to find unit rates for ratios with fractions.**

1 Look at the first **Model It**. Who hikes more quickly? How can you use the double number lines to figure out who is hiking more quickly?

2 What is Julio's speed in hours per mile? Explain how you can use the double number line to find Julio's speed in hours per mile.

3 Look at the second **Model It**. The fraction $\frac{\frac{1}{2}}{\frac{1}{4}}$ describes Julio's speed in miles per hour. What fraction describes Julio's speed in hours per mile? What is his speed in hours per mile?

4 The fraction $\frac{6}{2}$ describes Kyle's speed in miles per hour. What fraction would describe Kyle's speed in hours per mile? What is his speed in hours per mile?

5 Do you need a different strategy to find each speed because one involves fractions? Explain.

6 **Reflect** Think about all the models and strategies you have discussed today. Describe how one of them helped you better understand how to solve the **Try It** problem.

Apply It

➤ **Use what you learned to solve these problems.**

7 A penguin walks south. It completes the first $\frac{1}{3}$ mile in $\frac{1}{5}$ hour and continues walking at the same rate. What is the penguin's speed in miles per hour? Show your work.

SOLUTION _____

8 A maple tree shades an area of $7\frac{1}{2}$ m². In a scale drawing, the maple tree shades an area of $12\frac{1}{2}$ cm². In the scale drawing, how many square centimeters represent 1 m²?

A $\frac{3}{5}$

B $\frac{5}{3}$

C $93\frac{3}{4}$

D 10,000

9 Dalila is mixing paste. For every $1\frac{2}{3}$ cups of water, she uses $2\frac{1}{2}$ cups of flour. How much flour does Dalila need for each cup of water? Show your work.

SOLUTION _____

Practice Solving Problems with Unit Rates for Ratios with Two Fractions

➤ **Study the Example showing how to find the unit rate for a ratio with two fractions. Then solve problems 1–4.**

Example

A baker uses $\frac{3}{4}$ teaspoon of yeast in $\frac{1}{3}$ cup of warm water to make rolls.

How many teaspoons of yeast does the baker use in 1 cup of water?

You can use a double number line to find how many teaspoons of yeast the baker uses in 1 cup of water.

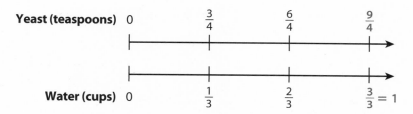

The baker uses $\frac{9}{4}$, or $2\frac{1}{4}$, teaspoons of yeast in 1 cup of water.

1 **a.** In the Example, what is $\dfrac{\frac{3}{4}}{\frac{1}{3}}$ the unit rate for?

b. The baker fits 26 rolls onto a pan that measures $1\frac{5}{8}$ ft². How many square feet does the baker use for each roll? Show your work.

Vocabulary

equivalent ratios
two ratios that express the same comparison. Multiplying both numbers in the ratio $a : b$ by a nonzero number n results in the equivalent ratio $na : nb$.

unit rate
the numerical part of a rate. For example, the rate 3 miles per hour has a unit rate of 3.

SOLUTION _____

2 Kenji mixes $\frac{1}{5}$ pound of clay soil with $\frac{1}{8}$ of a bale of straw to make an adobe brick. How much clay soil will he need to use the whole bale of straw? Show your work.

adobe brick

SOLUTION _____

3 The soccer field at a park is 9,000 square yards. The soccer field takes up $6\frac{2}{5}$ square inches on the map of the park. How many square yards does 1 square inch on the map represent? Show your work.

SOLUTION _____

4 At top cruising speed, a mako shark can swim 4 kilometers in $\frac{1}{10}$ hour. A blue whale can swim 5 kilometers in $\frac{1}{4}$ hour. Which animal swims faster at top cruising speed? How much faster? Show your work.

SOLUTION _____

_____

Refine Finding Unit Rates Involving Ratios of Fractions

➤ **Complete the Example below. Then solve problems 1–9.**

Example

Angela lives 0.6 mile from the park. It takes her $\frac{1}{4}$ hour to walk her dog to the park. How quickly are Angela and her dog walking in miles per hour?

Look at how you could use reciprocals to solve the problem.

The unit rate for miles to hours is $\frac{0.6}{\frac{1}{4}}$.

Instead of dividing 0.6 by $\frac{1}{4}$, I can multiply both the numerator and the denominator by the reciprocal of $\frac{1}{4}$. The reciprocal of $\frac{1}{4}$ is 4.

$$\frac{0.6}{\frac{1}{4}} \cdot \frac{4}{4} = \frac{0.6 \cdot 4}{\frac{1}{4} \cdot 4}$$

SOLUTION _____

CONSIDER THIS . . .
Will it take Angela more or less than 1 hour to walk her dog 3 miles?

PAIR/SHARE
Explain whether or not it is necessary to find the unit rate to solve the problem.

Apply It

1 Felipe has a flower bed with area $\frac{25}{4}$ ft². He expands the flower bed to have area $\frac{75}{4}$ ft². How many square feet of space does the larger flower bed have for every square foot of the smaller flower bed? Show your work.

CONSIDER THIS . . .
Make sure you compare the flower beds in the correct order.

SOLUTION _____

PAIR/SHARE
How can you check your answer?

2 Amare runs $\frac{1}{10}$ mile in $\frac{2}{3}$ minute. What is his speed in miles per minute?

Show your work.

CONSIDER THIS...
Speed in miles per minute means how many miles can Amare go in one minute.

SOLUTION _____

PAIR/SHARE
How else could you solve this problem?

3 Which of the following tables shows a rate greater than 1 kilometer per hour?

CONSIDER THIS...
For a rate greater than 1 kilometer per hour should the number of hours or kilometers be greater?

A

Kilometers	$\frac{1}{5}$	$\frac{1}{4}$	$\frac{1}{3}$	$\frac{1}{2}$
Hours	$\frac{7}{5}$	$\frac{7}{4}$	$\frac{7}{3}$	$\frac{7}{2}$

B

Kilometers	$\frac{3}{4}$	$\frac{6}{4}$	$\frac{9}{4}$	$\frac{12}{4}$
Hours	$\frac{3}{8}$	$\frac{6}{8}$	$\frac{9}{8}$	$\frac{12}{8}$

C

Kilometers	$\frac{2}{3}$	$\frac{4}{3}$	$\frac{6}{3}$	$\frac{8}{3}$
Hours	$\frac{4}{3}$	$\frac{8}{3}$	$\frac{12}{3}$	$\frac{16}{3}$

D

Kilometers	$\frac{1}{4}$	$\frac{1}{2}$	$\frac{3}{4}$	$\frac{3}{2}$
Hours	$\frac{3}{4}$	$\frac{3}{2}$	$\frac{9}{4}$	$\frac{9}{2}$

Hailey chose C as the correct answer. How might she have gotten that answer?

PAIR/SHARE
How would your answer change if you had to find tables that show a rate greater than $\frac{1}{2}$ kilometer per hour?

4. Rani is making rice pudding. She uses $\frac{3}{4}$ cup of white rice for every 2 cups of milk. How many cups of rice does she need when she uses 3 cups of milk? Show your work.

SOLUTION _____

5. For every $\frac{1}{150}$ square mile Xavier mows, Bao mows $\frac{1}{120}$ square mile. How many square miles does Xavier mow for every 1 square mile Bao mows?

A $\frac{3}{4}$

B $\frac{4}{5}$

C $\frac{5}{4}$

D $\frac{15}{12}$

6. Tell whether each statement is *True* or *False*.

	True	False
a. The ratio $\frac{3}{8}$ to $\frac{1}{2}$ has a unit rate of $\frac{3}{16}$.	◯	◯
b. The ratio $9 : \frac{1}{6}$ has a unit rate of 54.	◯	◯
c. The ratio $\frac{2}{5} : \frac{1}{4}$ has a unit rate of $\frac{8}{5}$.	◯	◯
d. The ratio $5\frac{1}{2} : 1\frac{1}{2}$ has a unit rate of $3\frac{2}{3}$.	◯	◯

7 Elisa is practicing her clarinet. She plays $\frac{1}{8}$ of a song in $\frac{1}{2}$ minute. At this rate, she will play a whole song in _____ minutes.

8 Tyler looks at a map on his phone. He zooms in until the map scale for centimeters to kilometers is $0.3 : \frac{1}{5}$. How many centimeters does the map use to show 1 kilometer?

A $\frac{2}{3}$

B $\frac{3}{5}$

C 0.06

D 1.5

9 **Math Journal** Write a word problem you can solve by simplifying a complex fraction. Explain how to find the answer.

✓ End of Lesson Checklist

☐ **INTERACTIVE GLOSSARY** Find the entry for *complex fraction*. Write a definition for a younger student. Show an example.

☐ **SELF CHECK** Go back to the Unit 1 Opener and see what you can check off.

Dear Family,

This week your student is exploring proportional relationships.

Here are some examples of **proportional relationships** that you may be familiar with.

- Ingredients of a recipe are proportional to one another: *you use the same proportions when making smaller or larger batches.*

- The earnings of hourly employees are proportional to the number of hours worked: *a person who works 3 hours will earn 3 times the hourly wage.*

Suppose Ichiro's hourly wage is $15. When he works 4 hours, he earns $60. His hourly wage of $15 does not change. In Ichiro's case, the **constant of proportionality** between amount earned and hours worked is 15. When a relationship is proportional, *constant of proportionality* is another term for *unit rate*.

Your student will be modeling proportional relationships like the one below.

> Jennifer goes apple picking with her family at a nearby farm. Each pound of apples they pick costs $2. The total cost depends on the number of pounds of apples they pick.

➤ **ONE WAY** to represent a proportional relationship is with a table.

Apples (lb)	0	1	2	3	4	5	6	7	8
Cost ($)	0	2	4	6	8	10	12	14	16

➤ **ANOTHER WAY** is to use a double number line.

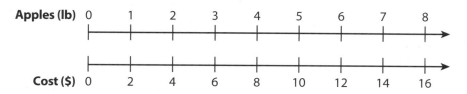

Both representations show that the cost is always twice the number of pounds of apples. That means the constant of proportionality in this situation is 2.

 Use the next page to start a conversation about proportional relationships.

Activity Thinking About Proportional Relationships Around You

➤ **Do this activity together to investigate proportional relationships in the real world.**

Have you ever played a video game and found that a day in the game was shorter than a day in real life? The game designers might have decided that 20 minutes pass in game time for each minute that passes in real time. That would mean that the relationship between real time and game time is a proportional relationship!

? Where else do you see proportional relationships in the world around you?

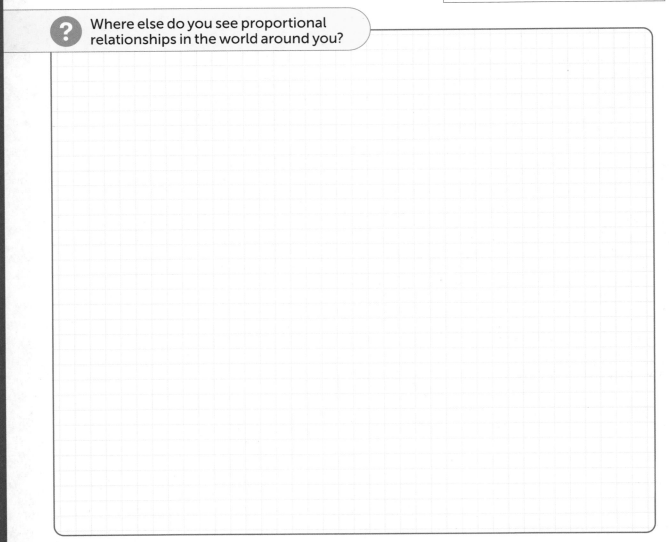

Explore Proportional Relationships

Model It

➤ **Complete the problems about equivalent ratios.**

1 In 1 week, each cat at a shelter eats 7 cans of cat food. The ratio of cans of cat food to cats is 7 : 1.

🗓 **1** cat eats
7 cans per week

a. The number of cans of cat food the shelter needs depends on the number of cats. Show how many cans are needed for different numbers of cats.

Number of Cats	1	2	3			6	7	
Cans of Cat Food	7			28	35			56

b. Are all of the ratios in the table equivalent? Explain.

c. What is the unit rate for cans of cat food per cat?

d. Suppose you know how many cats are at the shelter in any week. How can you find the number of cans of cat food *x* cats will eat?

e. When a group of ratios are equivalent, it means there is a **proportional relationship** between the quantities. At the shelter, is there a proportional relationship between the number of cats and the number of cans of cat food? Explain.

DISCUSS IT

Ask: Every time the number of cats increases by 1, what does the number of cans of cat food increase by?

Share: I notice that when you multiply the number of cats by the unit rate . . .

◎ **Learning Targets**   SMP 2, SMP 3, SMP 7
Recognize and represent proportional relationships between quantities.
• Identify the constant of proportionality (unit rate) in tables, graphs, equations, diagrams, and verbal descriptions of proportional relationships.
• Represent proportional relationships by equations.

Model It

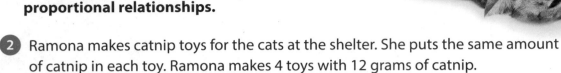

➤ **Complete the problems about representing proportional relationships.**

2 Ramona makes catnip toys for the cats at the shelter. She puts the same amount of catnip in each toy. Ramona makes 4 toys with 12 grams of catnip.

a. Complete the equivalent ratio table to show how many toys Ramona can make with different amounts of catnip.

Number of Toys	Catnip (grams)
0	
	3
2	
	9
4	12
5	

b. Describe the relationship between the number of grams of catnip and the number of toys.

c. What is the unit rate for grams of catnip per toy? How can Ramona find the number of grams of catnip she needs to make a certain number of toys?

d. Write an equation to show the number of grams of catnip, *g*, Ramona needs to make *t* toys.

3 **Reflect** The table shows the hours needed for different numbers of people to clean up after a school dance. Is there a proportional relationship between the quantities in the table? Explain.

Number of People Cleaning	2	3	4	6
Hours Needed to Clean Up	12	9	8	6

Prepare for Understanding Proportional Relationships

1 Think about what you know about equivalent ratios. Fill in each box. Use words, numbers, and pictures. Show as many ideas as you can.

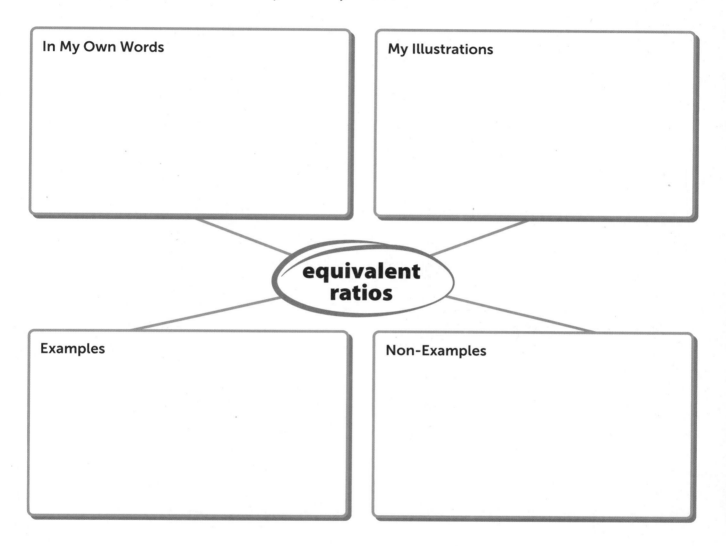

In My Own Words

My Illustrations

equivalent ratios

Examples

Non-Examples

2 Mason says you can find an equivalent ratio by adding the same number to both quantities in a ratio. For example, 2 : 3 is equivalent to 3 : 4 because 2 + 1 = 3 and 3 + 1 = 4. Is Mason correct? Explain your thinking.

➤ **Complete problems 3–4.**

3 Each horse at a ranch eats 20 pounds of hay each day.

a. Complete the table to show how much hay different numbers of horses eat each day.

Number of Horses	1	2				6	
Hay (pounds)	20		60	80	100		140

b. What is the unit rate for pounds of hay per horse?

c. When a group of ratios are equivalent, it means there is a proportional relationship between the quantities. Is there a proportional relationship between the pounds of hay eaten daily and the number of horses? Explain.

4 Tessa plays her favorite song several times. It takes 16 minutes to play it 4 times.

a. Complete the table to find how many minutes it takes Tessa to play the song different numbers of times.

Number of Plays	Minutes
	0
1	
	8
3	
4	16

b. Describe the relationship between the number of minutes Tessa spends playing the song and the number of times she plays it.

c. Once Tessa knows how many times she wants to play the song, how can she find how long it will take her?

d. Write an equation to show the number of minutes, m, Tessa spends playing the song t times.

UNDERSTAND: What does it mean for there to be a proportional relationship between two quantities?

Develop Understanding of Proportional Relationships

Model It: Tables

➤ **Try this problem involving unit rates.**

1 The table shows how many gallons of water Veda uses for showers of different numbers of minutes.

Time (minutes)	1	2	3	4	5	6
Water (gallons)	2	4	6	8	10	12

a. How does the table show a proportional relationship between the length of Veda's shower and the number of gallons of water used?

b. What is the unit rate for gallons of water per minute?

c. When ratios are equivalent, they all have the same unit rate. In a proportional relationship, the unit rate is called the **constant of proportionality**. What is the constant of proportionality for the relationship of gallons of water to minutes of showering?

d. Use the constant of proportionality to write an equation that shows the number of gallons of water used, g, during a shower m minutes long.

e. What is the unit rate for minutes per gallon of water?

f. What is the constant of proportionality for the relationship of minutes of showering to gallons of water? Write an equation that shows the length of a shower in minutes, m, based on using g gallons of water.

DISCUSS IT

Ask: Why are there two constants of proportionality?

Share: It makes sense that there are two constants of proportionality because . . .

Model It: Double Number Lines

➤ **Try this problem about representing proportional relationships.**

2 There is a proportional relationship between the area of a wall and the amount of paint needed to cover it.

    a. What is the constant of proportionality for that relationship? Explain.

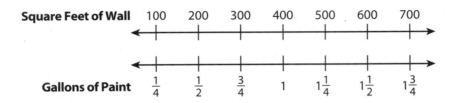

> **DISCUSS IT**
>
> **Ask:** Where can you see a unit rate in the double number line?
>
> **Share:** I can find the constant of proportionality by . . .

    b. Use the constant of proportionality to write an equation that represents the square feet of wall, w, that can be covered by g gallons of paint.

CONNECT IT

➤ **Complete the problems below.**

3 Do the table and the double number line show the same constants of proportionality? How can you tell?

Mugs	1	3	5
Cost ($)	8	24	40

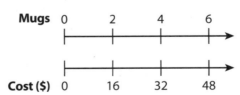

4 Use any model you like to show a proportional relationship with a constant of proportionality of 4.

Practice Understanding Proportional Relationships

➤ Study how the Example shows a proportional relationship. Then solve problems 1–5.

Example

The double number line shows the amount of clay Jamal uses to make different numbers of identical bowls. Is there a proportional relationship between the amount of clay and the number of bowls? If so, what is the constant of proportionality for pounds of clay per bowl?

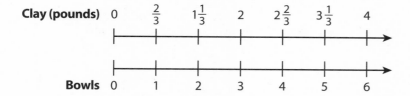

All of the ratios for clay : bowls are equivalent. So, there is a proportional relationship.

All of the ratios have the same rate, $\frac{2}{3}$ pound of clay per bowl. The constant of proportionality is $\frac{2}{3}$.

1 **a.** Write an equation representing the pounds of clay, c, that Jamal from the Example needs to make b bowls.

   b. Explain how to find the amount of clay Jamal needs to make 8 bowls.

2 Zara has paper rectangles of different sizes. Every rectangle is 5 cm longer than it is wide. Is there a proportional relationship between the lengths and widths of these rectangles? Explain.

Vocabulary

constant of proportionality
the unit rate in a proportional relationship.

proportional relationship
the relationship between two quantities where one quantity is a constant multiple of the other quantity.

unit rate
the numerical part of a rate.

3 Miguel mixes plant food with water to feed his plants. The instructions on the plant food say to mix 1 teaspoon of plant food into every 4 cups of water.

a. Write an equation to show the relationship between cups of water, w, and teaspoons of plant food, f.

b. How much plant food should Miguel add to 7 cups of water? Use a model to show your work.

SOLUTION _____

_____

4 The number of laps Jessica runs around the track is proportional to the time she spends running. She runs 12 laps in $\frac{1}{2}$ hour.

a. What is the constant of proportionality for the relationship between number of laps and number of hours? Show your work.

SOLUTION _____

b. Use the constant of proportionality to write an equation to show the relationship between laps Jessica runs, r, and hours she runs, h.

5 A store sells 2 pounds of tomatoes for $7. Write an equation that represents the cost, c, for t pounds of tomatoes.

Refine Ideas About Proportional Relationships

Apply It

➤ **Complete problems 1–5.**

1 **Explain** How do you know that the table and the equation represent the same proportional relationship between *x* and *y*?

x	0	1	2	3	4	5	6
y	0	$\frac{1}{3}$	$\frac{2}{3}$	1	$1\frac{1}{3}$	$1\frac{2}{3}$	2

$$y = \frac{1}{3}x$$

2 **Analyze** Samuel says that his sister's age is proportional to his brother's age. Is Samuel correct? Explain.

	2020	**2025**	**2030**	**2035**
Sister's Age	5	10	15	20
Brother's Age	10	15	20	25

3 **Interpret** Explain what the circled ratio on this double number line means.

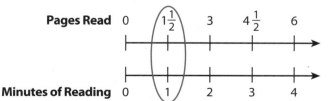

4 Lucía makes braided key chains out of cotton cord. For every 8 feet of cotton cord she has, she can make 3 braided key chains.

PART A Use a model to represent the relationship between the feet of cotton cord and the number of key chains.

PART B Use the model to explain how to find the number of feet of cotton cord Lucía needs to make 5 key chains.

5 **Math Journal** In a baking recipe, there is a proportional relationship between the number of cups of flour and the number of cups of sugar. What does that mean? Tell at least two things you know are true about this relationship.

✓ **End of Lesson Checklist**

☐ **INTERACTIVE GLOSSARY** Find the entry for *constant of proportionality*. Rewrite the definition in your own words.

©Curriculum Associates, LLC   Copying is not permitted.

Dear Family,

This week your student is learning about graphs and equations that can represent proportional relationships.

One way to represent a proportional relationship is with a graph. The graph will be a straight line that goes through the **origin**, or the point (0, 0).

Another way is with an equation that tells you how many *x* you have for every one *y*. The equation for the proportional relationship at the right is $y = 8x$.

Your student will solve problems like the one below.

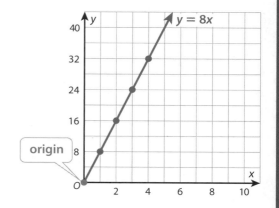

The table compares the number of people who ride a rollercoaster to the number of rollercoaster cars they fill. Is this a proportional relationship?

Cars Filled (*x*)	3	5	6	8
People (*y*)	18	30	36	48

➤ **ONE WAY** to recognize a proportional relationship is with a graph.

Plot the pairs of values as ordered pairs and connect the points. The graph is a straight line that passes through (0, 0), so the relationship is proportional.

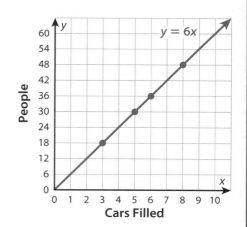

➤ **ANOTHER WAY** to recognize a proportional relationship is to check if the ratios are equivalent.

The ratios 3 : 18, 5 : 30, 6 : 36, and 8 : 48 are all equivalent. In each case, you can multiply the first quantity by 6 to get the second quantity.

Both ways show that the relationship is proportional.

> ▶ Use the next page to start a conversation about proportional relationships.

LESSON 4 Represent Proportional Relationships

Activity Thinking About Proportional Relationships Around You

➤ **Do this activity together to investigate proportional relationships in the real world.**

Have you ever heard or seen a thunderstorm approaching and wondered how far away it was? You can figure this out!

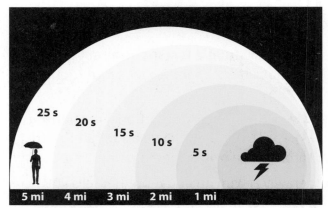

After you see a flash of lightning, count the number of seconds until you hear the next rumble of thunder. For every 5 seconds you count, the storm is 1 mile away.

You can multiply the number of seconds by $\frac{1}{5}$ to find how many miles away the storm is. That means the constant of proportionality for the relationship between time and distance is $\frac{1}{5}$.

? What are other situations around you where one quantity is always a multiple of another quantity?

Explore Graphing Proportional Relationships

Speed:
8 miles per hour

Previously, you learned about the constant of proportionality and proportional relationships. In this lesson, you will learn about how graphs and equations can represent proportional relationships.

➤ **Use what you know to try to solve the problem below.**

Fiona has a goal to ride her bike at a constant speed for 2 hours. To see if she is meeting her goal, she plans to check her distance at 1, 1.5, and 2 hours. She makes a graph to see what these distances should be. What points should she plot for 1.5 and 2 hours?

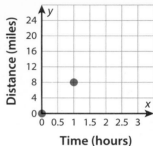

TRY IT

 Math Toolkit double number lines, graph paper

 Learning Targets SMP 1, SMP 2, SMP 3, SMP 4, SMP 5, SMP 6
• Decide whether two quantities are in a proportional relationship.
• Identify the constant of proportionality (unit rate) in graphs and equations of proportional relationships.
• Explain what a point (x, y) on the graph of a proportional relationship means in terms of the situation, with special attention to the points (0, 0) and (1, r) where r is the unit rate.

CONNECT IT

1 **Look Back** What points should Fiona plot on the graph? What do the points represent?

2 **Look Ahead** You can use ratios represented as points to find other equivalent ratios. You can also represent proportional relationships in the coordinate plane.

a. The graph at the right shows a proportional relationship between x and y. Why does this mean all the $x : y$ ratios are equivalent?

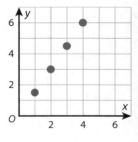

b. How can you move from point $\left(1, \frac{3}{2}\right)$ to $(2, 3)$? How can you move from $\left(1, \frac{3}{2}\right)$ to $\left(3, \frac{9}{2}\right)$?

c. For every x units you move right, how many units do you move up? How can you use this information to find the constant of proportionality?

d. The equation $y = \frac{3}{2}x$ also represents the proportional relationship. How does the equation show the constant of proportionality?

3 **Reflect** How is using a graph to represent a proportional relationship like using a table? How is it different?

Prepare for Representing Proportional Relationships

1 Think about what you know about graphing. Fill in each box. Use words, numbers, and pictures. Show as many ideas as you can.

Word	In My Own Words	Example
x-coordinate		
y-coordinate		
ordered pair		
origin		

2 Fadil says that the ordered pair for the point shown is (7, 5). Explain why Fadil is incorrect.

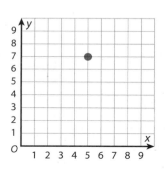

3 Cyrus runs on a track at a constant speed of 200 meters per minute. Later, he makes a graph of his run to show his coach. He puts time on the *x*-axis and distance on the *y*-axis.

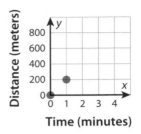

a. What points does he plot to show how far he runs in 8 minutes and 12 minutes?

b. Check your answer to problem 3a. Show your work.

Develop Interpreting Graphs of Proportional Relationships

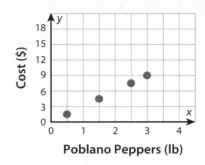

➤ **Read and try to solve the problem below.**

Ignacio is making chiles en nogada to celebrate Mexican Independence Day with his family. Ignacio needs to buy poblano peppers. The local market sells poblano peppers by the pound. How much will 1 pound of peppers cost? How much will 3.5 pounds of peppers cost?

  Math Toolkit double number lines, graph paper

DISCUSS IT

Ask: What was your first step in finding the cost of 1 pound of peppers?

Share: I started by . . .

➤ **Explore different ways to interpret graphs of proportional relationships.**

Ignacio is making chiles en nogada to celebrate Mexican Independence Day with his family. Ignacio needs to buy poblano peppers. The local market sells poblano peppers by the pound. How much will 1 pound of peppers cost? How much will 3.5 pounds of peppers cost?

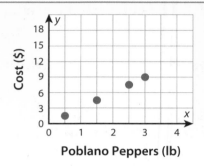

Poblano Peppers (lb)

Model It

You can write an equation that represents a proportional relationship.

The ordered pair (3, 9) shows that it costs $9 to buy 3 pounds of peppers.

$9 ÷ 3 = $3

Each pound of peppers costs $3. That means the constant of proportionality is 3.

You can model this with the equation $y = 3x$.

Model It

You can interpret the graph of a proportional relationship.

Draw a line through the points.

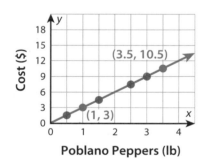

Poblano Peppers (lb)

The line passes through the points (1, 3) and (3.5, 10.5).

➤ **Use the problem from the previous page to help you understand how to interpret graphs of proportional relationships.**

1 Look at the equation in the first **Model It**. How can you use it to find the cost of 1 pound of peppers? Of 3.5 pounds of peppers?

2 Look at the graph in the second **Model It**. What do 1 pound and 3.5 pounds of peppers cost? How can you tell?

3 What does the point (0, 0) represent in this situation? Why is the point (0, 0) part of the graph of any proportional relationship?

4 What does the point (1, 3) tell you?

5 Which point gives the unit rate, or constant of proportionality, in any graph of a proportional relationship? Explain.

6 How could you use the graph of a proportional relationship to find any ratio in the proportional relationship? Why does this work?

7 **Reflect** Think about all the models and strategies you have discussed today. Describe how one of them helped you better understand how to solve the **Try It** problem.

Apply It

➤ **Use what you learned to solve these problems.**

8 Alejandro babysits in the evenings. He makes a graph to show the money he earns. How much money does Alejandro earn for each hour of babysitting? How do you know?

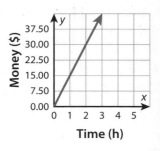

9 Indira makes a graph to show how many pages of her graphic novel she can illustrate each day.

a. What is the constant of proportionality for the relationship between pages and days?

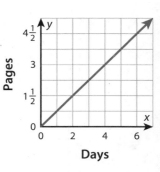

b. Write an equation to show the relationship between pages and days.

10 Ellema's little sisters want box braids. They complain that Ellema braids too slowly. So, she makes a graph to show them how fast she is.

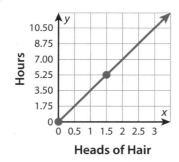

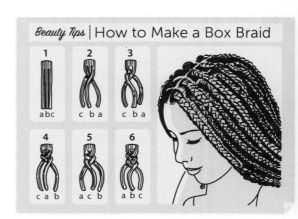

a. What does the point (0, 0) mean?

b. What does the point (1.5, 5.25) mean?

Practice Interpreting Graphs of Proportional Relationships

➤ **Study the Example showing how to interpret a graph of a proportional relationship. Then solve problems 1–5.**

Example

The graph shows the proportional relationship between the pounds of mangos bought and the cost. What do the points (0, 0) and (3, 4.5) mean in this situation? What is the constant of proportionality for this relationship?

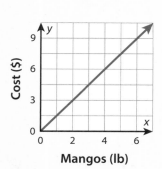

The point (0, 0) means that 0 pounds of mangos cost $0.

The point (3, 4.5) means that 3 pounds of mangos cost $4.50.

Look for the point on the line with the x-coordinate of 1. The y-coordinate of this point is the constant of proportionality. The line passes through the point (1, 1.5). So, the constant of proportionality is 1.5.

---

1 The graph shows the proportional relationship between grams of protein and cups of milk.

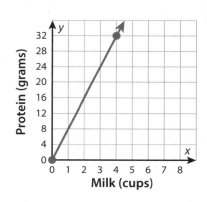

a. What is the constant of proportionality for the relationship between grams of protein and cups of milk?

b. What does the point (0, 0) mean in this situation?

c. What does the point (4, 32) mean in this situation?

2 Both lines on the graph represent proportional relationships. What is the constant of proportionality for each relationship? Explain how you know.

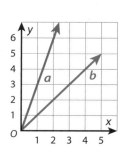

3 Tiana uses the equation $c = 21h$ to figure out the total amount, c, she should charge a customer for babysitting for h hours.

a. What is the constant of proportionality? What does it mean?

b. Tiana charges $94.50 for a job. How long did she babysit for? Show your work.

SOLUTION _____

4 The graph shows the proportional relationship between the minutes Oliver spends reading and the number of pages he reads. Pick two points on the line. What do they mean?

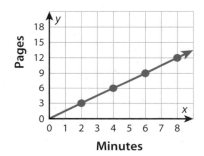

5 The graph models the proportional relationship between pounds of dog food Savanna's dog eats and days. Tell whether each statement is *True* or *False*.

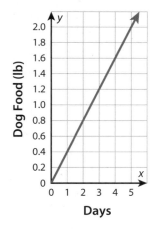

	True	False
a. The point (5, 2) means that Savanna's dog eats 5 pounds of dog food in 2 days.	○	○
b. The constant of proportionality is 0.4.	○	○
c. Savanna's dog eats 4 pounds of dog food in 10 days.	○	○
d. The equation $y = 2x$ represents this relationship.	○	○

Develop Recognizing Graphs of Proportional Relationships

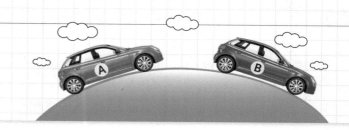

➤ **Read and try to solve the problem below.**

Josephine uses a graph to compare the cost of renting a car at two different companies.

Is the relationship between cost and time proportional at either company? How do you know?

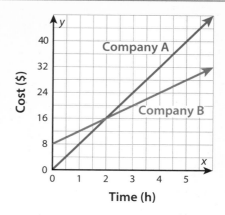

TRY IT

Math Toolkit double number lines, graph paper

➤ **Explore different ways to identify graphs of proportional relationships.**

Josephine uses a graph to compare the cost of renting a car at two different companies.

Is the relationship between cost and time proportional at either company? How do you know?

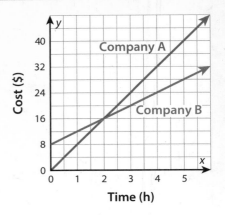

Model It

You can make a table of the ratios from a graph.

Company A	
Time (h)	**Cost ($)**
0	0
1	8
2	16

Company B	
Time (h)	**Cost ($)**
0	8
1	12
2	16

Analyze It

You can analyze a graph.

Look at the shape of the graph and at whether it passes through the origin.

Company A

The graph is a straight line.

The line passes through the origin.

Company B

The graph is a straight line.

The line does not pass through the origin.

➤ **Use the problem from the previous page to help you understand how to identify graphs of proportional relationships.**

1 Is the relationship between cost and time proportional at either company? Explain.

2 How are the graphs representing Company A and Company B alike and different?

3 The graph for Company B does not pass through the origin. Why does that show the relationship between time and cost is not proportional?

4 The graph at the right shows the relationship between cost and time at Company C. How are the graphs for Company A and Company C alike and different?

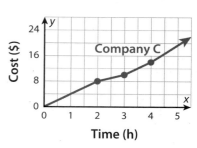

5 Is the relationship between time and cost proportional at Company C? Explain.

6 The graph of a proportional relationship will always be a straight line that passes through the origin. Why?

7 **Reflect** Think about all the models and strategies you have discussed today. Describe how one of them helped you better understand how to decide if two quantities are in a proportional relationship.

Apply It

➤ **Use what you learned to solve these problems.**

8 Six people ride a bus to get to work. The table shows their travel times and distances. Make a graph to represent the situation.

Distance (mi)	1.5	2.0	3.0	2.5	0.5	3.5
Time (min)	12	16	26	20	4	32

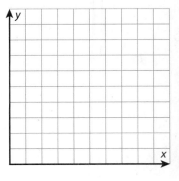

Is there a proportional relationship between the number of minutes and the number of miles? Explain using your graph.

9 How can you describe the relationship between x and y that each line represents?

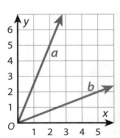

A Line *a* represents a proportional relationship and line *b* represents a non-proportional relationship.

B Line *a* represents a non-proportional relationship and line *b* represents a proportional relationship.

C Lines *a* and *b* both represent proportional relationships.

D Lines *a* and *b* both represent non-proportional relationships.

10 Naomi says that the graph represents a proportional relationship because it is a straight line. Is Naomi's reasoning correct? Explain your answer.

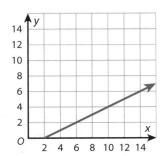

Practice Recognizing Graphs of Proportional Relationships

➤ **Study the Example showing how to decide whether a graph represents a proportional relationship. Then solve problems 1–5.**

Example

The three graphs show different relationships between *x* and *y*. Does each graph show a proportional relationship?

Graph A

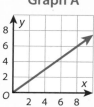

Graph B

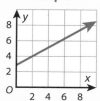

Graph C

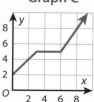

Graph A shows a straight line that passes through the origin. It shows a proportional relationship between *x* and *y*.

Graph B is a straight line, but it does not pass through the origin. It does not show a proportional relationship between *x* and *y*.

Graph C is not a straight line and does not pass through the origin. It does not show a proportional relationship between *x* and *y*.

1 **a.** Is there a change you could make to Graph B from the Example so that it would show a proportional relationship? Explain.

b. Graph C starts at the point (0, 2). If it started at the point (0, 0), would it show a proportional relationship? Explain.

2 Describe the graph of the equation *y* = 6*x*.

Vocabulary

proportional relationship
the relationship between two quantities where one quantity is a constant multiple of the other quantity.

3 Deon plots points to show the time it takes him to swim laps on two days. Is there a proportional relationship between the number of laps and minutes? Explain your answer.

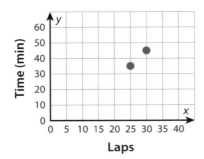

4 Which line is a graph of a proportional relationship? Explain.

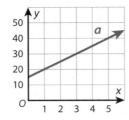 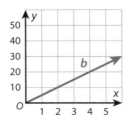

5 Carson is training to run a race. He records the distance and the amount of time he runs each day.

Distance (mi)	2	3.5	3	4.5
Time (min)	18	31.5	27	40.5

Is the relationship between the distance and time he runs proportional? Make a graph and use it to explain your answer.

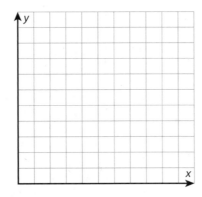

Refine Representing Proportional Relationships

➤ **Complete the Example below. Then solve problems 1–9.**

Example

A straight line passes through the points (0, 0) and $\left(1, \frac{3}{4}\right)$. What is an equation that represents the relationship?

Look at how you could use the constant of proportionality.

The graph of the relationship is a straight line that passes through the origin. That means the relationship is proportional.

Since the line passes through $\left(1, \frac{3}{4}\right)$, $\frac{3}{4}$ is the constant of proportionality.

SOLUTION _____

CONSIDER THIS . . .
Where does the constant of proportionality appear in the equation of a proportional relationship?

PAIR/SHARE
How would this problem change if the points were (0, 0) and (4, 3)?

Apply It

1 Ju-long is making punch. For every 3 cups of juice, he adds 6 cups of seltzer. Graph this relationship. Is there a proportional relationship between the cups of juice and the cups of seltzer? Explain.

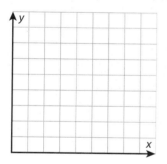

CONSIDER THIS . . .
This punch only has 2 ingredients.

PAIR/SHARE
Does it matter which axis you choose for juice and seltzer?

2 A potter buys clay by weight. The graph shows the relationship between the weight and the cost of the clay.

CONSIDER THIS...
Potters mold clay and then bake it so it turns to ceramic.

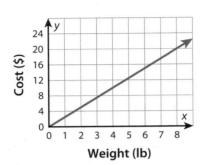

Weight (lb)

a. Is there a proportional relationship between the weight and the cost of clay? Explain your answer.

PAIR/SHARE
Does the point (12.5, 5) have the same meaning as the point (5, 12.5)?

b. What does the point (5, 12.5) mean in this situation?

3 The graph shows the height, *h*, in inches, of a plant after *d* days. Which equation can you use to represent the situation?

CONSIDER THIS...
What can both a graph and an equation tell you about a proportional relationship??

A $h = 4d$

B $h = 6d$

C $h = \frac{3}{2}d$

D $h = \frac{2}{3}d$

Ummi chose C as the correct answer. How might she have gotten that answer?

PAIR/SHARE
Explain how to check if your answer is correct.

4 The graph shows the relationship between the distance Amelia can drive her car and the amount of gas she needs. How much gas will Amelia need for a trip of 125 miles? Show your work.

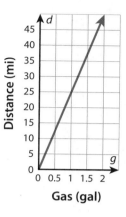

SOLUTION _____

5 Each line represents a proportional relationship. Write an equation for each line. Show your work.

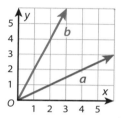

SOLUTION _____

_____

6 Look at the lines. Tell whether each statement is *True* or *False*.

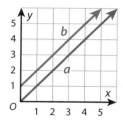

	True	False
a. Line *a* shows a proportional relationship.	○	○
b. Line *b* shows a proportional relationship.	○	○
c. A constant of proportionality for line *a* is 2.	○	○
d. Neither line includes a point that represents the ratio 3 : 4.	○	○

7. The equation for a proportional relationship is $y = 5.8x$. The graph of the relationship passes through the point (1, 5.8) which represents the

_____ .

8. Mindy says that the equations $p = 1.5q$ and $\frac{2}{3}p = q$ both represent the same proportional relationship. Vivian says that cannot be true because the constants of proportionality are different. Which student do you agree with? Explain.

9. **Math Journal** Graph a proportional relationship. Then write an equation that represents the proportional relationship. Explain how to find the constant of proportionality in both your equation and your graph.

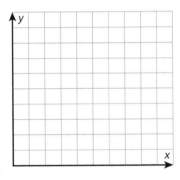

End of Lesson Checklist

- [ ] **INTERACTIVE GLOSSARY** Write a new entry for *identify*. Tell what you do when you *identify* the constant of proportionality for a proportional relationship.

- [ ] **SELF CHECK** Go back to the Unit 1 Opener and see what you can check off.

Dear Family,

This week your student is learning how to solve problems that involve proportional relationships. Your student has already learned about different ways to represent a proportional relationship. A proportional relationship can be represented with a verbal description, a graph, an equation, or a diagram (such as a double number line).

Verbal Description	Graph	Equation
Each pound of bananas costs $0.50.	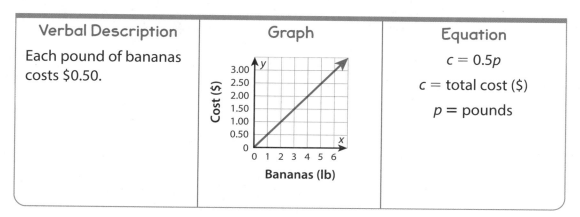	$c = 0.5p$ c = total cost ($) p = pounds

Your student will be solving problems like the one below.

> Charlotte and Sofia are 66 miles apart. They ride their bikes toward each other. They meet after 3 hours of riding. Each girl rides at a constant rate. Charlotte rides at 10 miles per hour. How far does Sofia ride?

Together Sofia and Charlotte ride 66 miles. First find out how far Charlotte rides.

➤ **ONE WAY** is to use a double number line to find how far Charlotte rides.

Time (h)	0	1	2	3

Distance (m)	0	10	20	30

➤ **ANOTHER WAY** is to use an equation to find how far Charlotte rides.

Let m = miles and h = hours.

$$m = 10h$$
$$= 10(3)$$
$$= 30$$

Charlotte rides 30 miles, so Sofia rides 66 miles − 30 miles = 36 miles.

Both ways show that Sofia rides her bike 36 miles.

 Use the next page to start a conversation about proportional relationships.

Activity Thinking About Proportional Relationships Around You

TODAY'S EXCHANGE RATE

US Dollar		1.00
EURO		0.886006
INDIAN RUPEE		69.633798
JAPANESE YEN		111.26608
MEXICAN PESO		0.052
SWISS FRANC		1.006909

➤ **Do this activity together to investigate proportional relationships in the real world.**

Have you ever paid for something using money other than dollars and cents? Different countries use different currencies. Mexico uses the peso and Japan uses the yen.

You exchange dollars for another currency according to the exchange rate. This tells you how many units of the other currency you get for 1 dollar.

? What are other situations where you use proportional relationships?

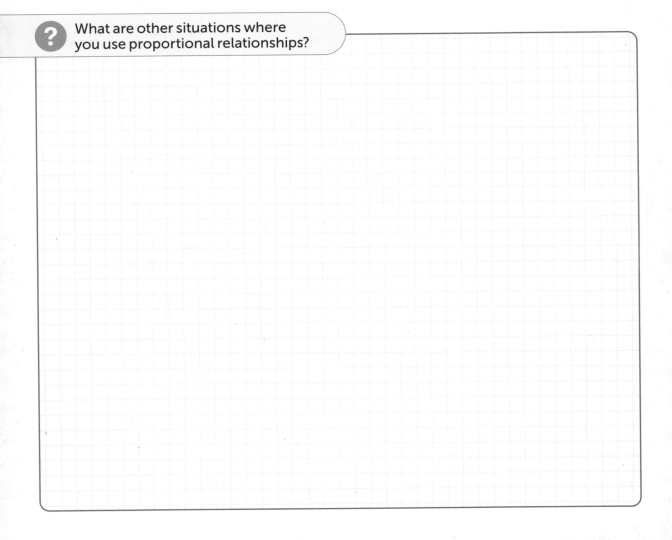

Explore Proportional Relationship Problems

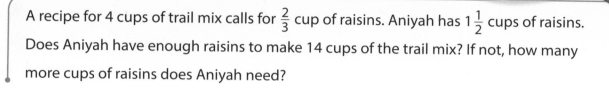

Previously, you learned to identify and model proportional relationships. In this lesson, you will use proportional relationships to solve multi-step problems.

➤ **Use what you know to try to solve the problem below.**

A recipe for 4 cups of trail mix calls for $\frac{2}{3}$ cup of raisins. Aniyah has $1\frac{1}{2}$ cups of raisins. Does Aniyah have enough raisins to make 14 cups of the trail mix? If not, how many more cups of raisins does Aniyah need?

 TRY IT

 Math Toolkit double number lines, graph paper

DISCUSS IT

Ask: How can you explain what the problem is asking in your own words?

Share: The problem is asking . . .

◎ **Learning Targets** SMP 1, SMP 2, SMP 3, SMP 4, SMP 5, SMP 6, SMP 7
• Identify the constant of proportionality (unit rate) in verbal descriptions of proportional relationships.
• Use proportional relationships to solve multistep ratio and percent problems.

CONNECT IT

1 **Look Back** Does Aniyah need more raisins? If so, how much more?

2 **Look Ahead** There is a proportional relationship between the total amount of trail mix and the amount of each ingredient. You can identify constants of proportionality from descriptions of proportional relationships.

a. A recipe for 3 cups of snack mix calls for $\frac{1}{2}$ cup of pretzels. You can describe this as *3 cups of snack mix for every $\frac{1}{2}$ cup of pretzels* and as *$\frac{1}{2}$ cup of pretzels for every 3 cups of snack mix*. Why?

b. How could you describe the relationship in terms of 1 cup of pretzels? What is this constant of proportionality?

c. How could you describe the relationship in terms of 1 cup of snack mix? What is this constant of proportionality?

d. Why are the two constants of proportionality not the same?

e. Suppose you are making 4 cups of snack mix. You want to find how many cups of pretzels you need. Which constant of proportionality would you use? Why?

3 **Reflect** How does knowing the constant of proportionality help you solve problems that involve proportional relationships?

Prepare for Proportional Relationship Problems

1 Think about what you know about proportional relationships and constants of proportionality. Fill in each box. Use words, numbers, and pictures. Show as many ideas as you can.

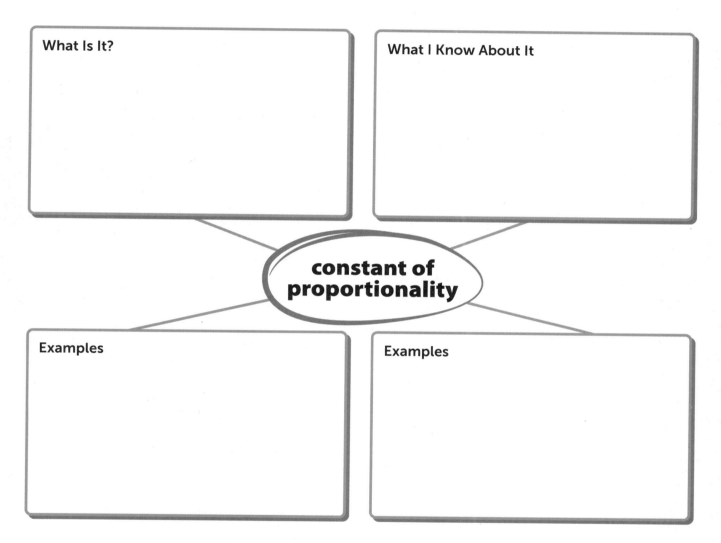

What Is It?

What I Know About It

constant of proportionality

Examples

Examples

2 Hiroaki says that a constant of proportionality must be a whole number and cannot be a fraction or a decimal. Explain why Hiroaki is incorrect.

3 A formula for 6 gallons of light green paint uses $\frac{3}{8}$ gallon of white paint.

Liam has $\frac{9}{16}$ gallon of white paint.

a. Does Liam have enough white paint to make 8 gallons of light green paint? If not, how much more does he need? Show your work.

SOLUTION _____

b. Check your answer to problem 3a. Show your work.

Develop Solving Multi-Step Ratio Problems

➤ **Read and try to solve the problem below.**

Francisca and Elizabeth are participating in a walk-a-thon fundraiser. Each girl walks for 3 hours. How much will they raise together?

Walk-a-thon Fundraiser

Francisca   Elizabeth

$25.50 every $\frac{1}{2}$ hour $14.50 every $\frac{1}{4}$ hour

TRY IT

 Math Toolkit double number lines, graph paper

DISCUSS IT

Ask: What did you do first to find how much the girls raise together?

Share: First, I . . .

LESSON 5 Solve Proportional Relationship Problems **87**

➤ **Explore different ways to solve problems that involve proportional relationships.**

Francisca and Elizabeth are participating in a walk-a-thon fundraiser. For every $\frac{1}{2}$ hour Francisca walks she raises $25.50. For every $\frac{1}{4}$ hour Elizabeth walks she raises $14.50. Each girl walks for 3 hours. How much will they raise together?

Model It

You can identify the constant of proportionality from a verbal description.

Francisca raises **$25.50 every 0.5 hour.**

That means she raises **$51.00 per 1 hour.**

constant of proportionality

Elizabeth raises **$14.50 every 0.25 hour.**

That means she raises **$58.00 per 1 hour.**

constant of proportionality

Model It

You can use equations to model how much Francisca and Elizabeth raise per hour.

Let *m* represent dollars raised per hour. Let *h* represent time in hours.

You can use the equations to find how much money each girl raises in 3 hours.

Francisca	**Elizabeth**
$m = 51h$	$m = 58h$
$= 51(3)$	$= 58(3)$

CONNECT IT

➤ **Use the problem from the previous page to help you understand how to solve problems that involve proportional relationships.**

1 Look at the first **Model It**. How can you identify the constant of proportionality from a verbal description?

2 Look at the second **Model It**. Where is the constant of proportionality in each equation? How can you use it to find how much money each girl raises in 3 hours?

3 How much money do Francisca and Elizabeth raise together? You could use the equation $m = (51 + 58)h$ to find the amount of money they raise together. Why?

4 You have identified constants of proportionality in tables, verbal descriptions, graphs, and equations. Why is this helpful when solving problems that involve proportional relationships?

5 **Reflect** Think about all the models and strategies you have discussed today. Describe how one of them helped you better understand how to solve the **Try It** problem.

Apply It

➤ **Use what you learned to solve these problems.**

6 At a certain bookstore, you get a $5 coupon for every 4 books you buy. What is the least number of books you could buy to get $15 in coupons? Show your work.

SOLUTION _____

7 Swim team members can race or dive. At a meet, 18 members race. The ratio of racers to divers is 6 : 2. How many members are on the team? Show your work.

SOLUTION _____

8 Roberto runs 25 miles. His average speed is 7.4 miles per hour. He takes a break after 13.9 miles. How many more hours does he run? Show your work.

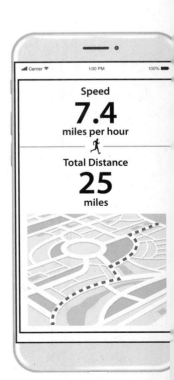

SOLUTION _____

Practice Solving Multi-Step Ratio Problems

➤ **Study the Example showing how to solve problems involving proportional relationships. Then solve problems 1–4.**

white vinegar	$\frac{1}{4}$ cup
rubbing alcohol	$\frac{1}{4}$ cup
water	$1\frac{1}{2}$ cups

Example

Jasmine is making a spray cleaner. She mixes $1\frac{1}{2}$ cups water, $\frac{1}{4}$ cup white vinegar, and $\frac{1}{4}$ cup rubbing alcohol. How much white vinegar would Jasmine need to make 5 cups of the spray cleaner?

Find how much spray cleaner Jasmine makes.

Cups of cleaner: $1\frac{1}{2} + \frac{1}{4} + \frac{1}{4} = 2$

For every **2 cups of spray cleaner**, Jasmine needs $\frac{1}{4}$ cup of white vinegar.

So, for **1 cup of spray cleaner**, Jasmine needs $\frac{1}{4} \div 2 = \frac{1}{8}$ cup of white vinegar.

Then find how much white vinegar Jasmine would need to make **5 cups** of the spray cleaner.

$5 \cdot \frac{1}{8} = \frac{5}{8}$

Jasmine would need $\frac{5}{8}$ cup of white vinegar to make 5 cups of the spray cleaner.

1 **a.** In the Example, what is the constant of proportionality for cups of vinegar to cups of spray cleaner?

b. Jasmine is making more of the spray cleaner. She only wants to use 1 cup of water. How much of the spray cleaner will Jasmine make? Show your work.

SOLUTION _____

2 Kadeem and Quinn both drive 25 miles. Kadeem drives at a constant speed of 50 miles an hour. Quinn drives at a constant speed of 75 miles an hour. Who takes longer to drive the 25 miles? How much longer? Show your work.

SOLUTION _____

3 Pilar and Ravi start at opposite ends of a 55-mile bike trail. They start riding their bikes toward each other at the same time. After 3 hours, they meet. Pilar rides 34 miles before they meet. What is Ravi's average speed? Show your work.

SOLUTION _____

4 Riley finds a recipe for bubble solution that uses 1 cup water, $\frac{1}{4}$ cup dish soap, and 1 tablespoon corn syrup. She uses 2 cups of dish soap. How much water should she use? Show your work.

SOLUTION _____

Refine Solving Proportional Relationship Problems

➤ **Complete the Example below. Then solve problems 1–9.**

Example

In the student council election, 217 students vote. Uma receives 4 votes for every 3 that Paloma receives. How many more votes does Uma receive than Paloma?

Look at how you could use proportional relationships.

Find how many votes Uma, u, and Paloma, p, each receive.

Uma:	Paloma:
$\dfrac{4}{7} = \dfrac{u}{217}$	$\dfrac{3}{7} = \dfrac{p}{217}$
$217\left(\dfrac{4}{7}\right) = u$	$217\left(\dfrac{3}{7}\right) = p$
$124 = u$	$93 = p$

Then find the difference.

SOLUTION _____

CONSIDER THIS . . .
This problem involves more than one proportional relationship.

PAIR/SHARE
How can you check that your answer makes sense?

Apply It

1 Vinh has a recipe for a marinade. The recipe says to mix $\dfrac{3}{8}$ cup olive oil, $\dfrac{1}{4}$ cup soy sauce, and $\dfrac{1}{8}$ cup lime juice. How much olive oil does he need to make 9 cups of the marinade? Show your work.

CONSIDER THIS . . .
A marinade is often used to add a different flavor when cooking.

PAIR/SHARE
Is there a different way you could solve this problem?

SOLUTION _____

2 Neena is listening to a song. It has a consistent beat. She counts 11 beats in 5 seconds. What is the constant of proportionality for the relationship of beats to minutes? Show your work.

CONSIDER THIS . . .
There are 60 seconds in 1 minute.

PAIR/SHARE
Explain why you think your answer is reasonable.

SOLUTION _____

3 Deyvi goes to a carnival with $20.00. He spends $2.00 to get in and the rest on ride tickets. Each ticket is $1.50. How many tickets does Deyvi buy?

A 9 tickets

B 12 tickets

C 13 tickets

D 14 tickets

Bruno chose C as the correct answer. How might he have gotten that answer?

CONSIDER THIS . . .
Can you use the tickets without paying for admission?

PAIR/SHARE
How can you check your answer?

4 Gears A and B turn together. Gear A turns 20 times when Gear B turns 30 times. When Gear A turns 60 times, how many times does Gear B turn? Show your work.

SOLUTION _____

5 In a certain town, in 90 minutes $\frac{1}{2}$ inch of rain falls. It continues at the same rate for a total of 24 hours. Which of the following statements are true about the amount of rain in the 24-hour period? Select all that apply.

A The number of inches of rain is 16 times $\frac{1}{2}$.

B The number of inches of rain is 24 times $\frac{1}{2}$.

C The number of inches of rain is 24 times $\frac{1}{3}$.

D The number of inches of rain is $\frac{1}{2}$ times 36.

E The number of inches of rain is 24 times $1\frac{1}{2}$.

6 Benjamin is planning to make scale drawings of bat wings. He wants all of his drawings to use the same scale. He says he can use the equation $d = 1.5w$ to find the length of a scale drawing, d, based on the length of the bat wing, w. What is the scale factor from bat wing length to scale drawing length? Explain.

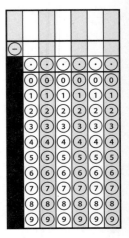

7 Adsila and Carlos volunteer to fill gift boxes for soldiers serving overseas. Both work at a constant rate. They work together for 6 hours and fill 126 boxes. Adsila fills 9 boxes every hour. How many boxes does Carlos fill every hour?

8 Aimee is in charge of buying tickets for a trip to the movies. She can buy tickets at the theater or online. At the theater, 8 tickets cost $60. Online, 6 tickets cost $51. Aimee needs to buy 24 tickets. How much money can Aimee save by buying tickets at the lower price? Show your work.

SOLUTION _____

9 **Math Journal** Write a word problem that involves a proportional relationship and needs more than one step to solve. Show how to solve the problem.

✓ **End of Lesson Checklist**

☐ **INTERACTIVE GLOSSARY** Find the entry for *proportional relationship*. Rewrite the definition in your own words.

☐ **SELF CHECK** Go back to the Unit 1 Opener and see what you can check off.

Dear Family,

This week your student is learning about circumference and area of circles.

Circumference is the distance around a **circle**, or its perimeter. Area is the amount of space inside a circle.

The **radius**, r, is the distance from the **center** of a circle to any point on the circle. The **diameter**, d, is the distance from one side of the circle to the other, passing through the center of the circle.

A special relationship exists between the circumference of a circle and its diameter. No matter the size of the circle, the quotient of $\frac{\text{circumference}}{\text{diameter}}$ is constant. This quotient is called **pi**, and the symbol for pi is π. π represents a decimal that goes on forever without repeating. You can approximate π with a decimal or a fraction.

diameter, d

center

radius, r

$$\pi \approx 3.14, \text{ or } \frac{22}{7}$$

The formulas for the circumference and area of a circle involve π.

Circumference: $C = \pi d$ Area: $A = \pi r^2$

Your student will be solving circumference and area problems like the one below.

A circular traffic sign has diameter 36 inches. How can you measure the traffic sign?

➤ **ONE WAY** to measure the traffic sign is to find its circumference.

$C = \pi d$

   $= \pi(36)$

The circumference is 36π in.

➤ **ANOTHER WAY** to measure the traffic sign is to find its area.

The diameter is 36 in. So, the radius is 18 in.

$A = \pi r^2$

   $= \pi\left(\dfrac{36}{2}\right)^2$

   $= \pi(18)^2$

The area is 324π in.^{2}.

 Use the next page to start a conversation about circumference and area of circles.

Solve Area and Circumference Problems Involving Circles

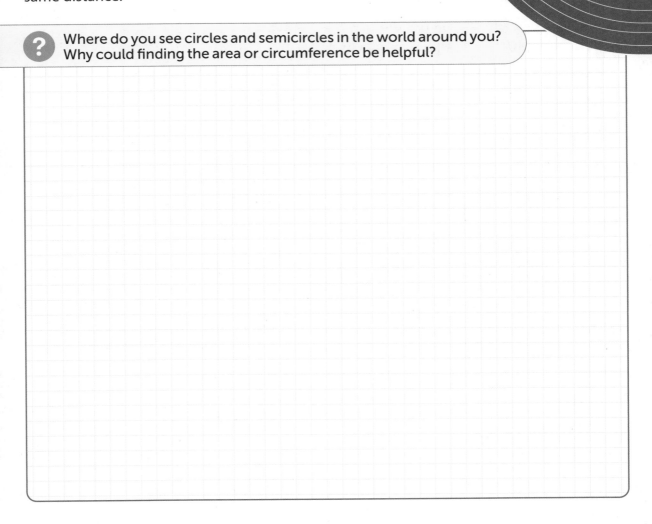

Activity Thinking About Circles Around You

➤ **Do this activity together to investigate circles in the real world.**

Have you ever wondered why runners start at different spots on a track instead of lining up together? This is called a *staggered start*.

Since tracks have semicircles (or half circles) on the ends, if all the runners lined up together, runners in outer lanes would need to run farther than runners in inner lanes. Why? Because the circumference of the outer lane is greater than the circumference of the inner lane.

Staggering starting positions ensures that all runners run the same distance!

? Where do you see circles and semicircles in the world around you? Why could finding the area or circumference be helpful?

Explore Circumference of a Circle

Center pivot irrigation systems water crops with sprinklers.

Previously, you learned about area and perimeter of polygons.
In this lesson, you will learn about the area and circumference of circles.

➤ **Use what you know to try to solve the problem below.**

Hai orders a center pivot irrigation system to water his fields. The system is made up of a line of connected pipes that turn around a center point. Hai's system will be 1,320 feet in length. What is the shape of the space Hai's system will water? What is the longest distance across the watered space?

TRY IT

 Math Toolkit grid paper, string

DISCUSS IT

Ask: How is your strategy similar to mine? How is it different?

Share: My strategy is similar to yours . . . It is different . . .

 Learning Target SMP 1, SMP 2, SMP 3, SMP 4, SMP 5, SMP 6, SMP 7
Know the formulas for the area and circumference of a circle and use them to solve problems; give an informal derivation of the relationship between the circumference and area of a circle.

CONNECT IT

1 **Look Back** What is the shape of the space Hai's system will water? What is the longest distance across the space? How do you know?

2 **Look Ahead** Hai's irrigation system waters in the shape of a **circle**. Every point on the edge of a circle is the same distance from the **center**. The **radius** of Hai's system is 1,320 feet, so the **diameter** is 2,640 feet.

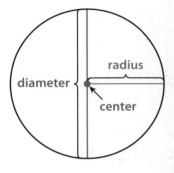

a. The radius of a circle is the distance from the edge to the center. The diameter is the distance across a circle through the center. What is the relationship between the radius and the diameter of any circle?

b. You can draw more than one diameter on a circle. Why?

c. Suppose two different diameters are drawn on a circle. Explain how you can use these diameters to find the center of the circle.

d. The distance around a circle is called the **circumference**. Trace the circumference of the circle. How is the circumference of a circle like the perimeter of a square?

3 **Reflect** You can draw more than one radius on a circle. What must be true about all of the radii? (*Radii* is the plural of *radius*.)

Prepare for Solving Circumference and Area Problems Involving Circles

1 Think about what you know about the area of two-dimensional figures. Fill in each box. Use words, numbers, and pictures. Show as many ideas as you can.

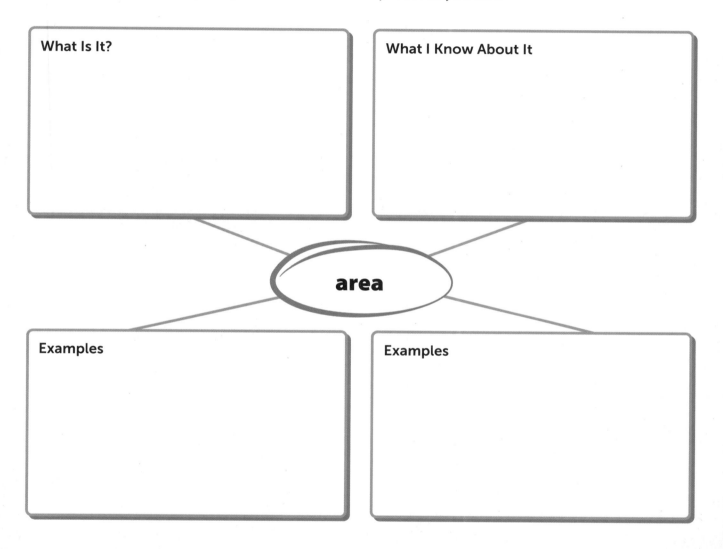

What Is It?

What I Know About It

area

Examples

Examples

2 Is the area of the rectangle 40 feet or 96 square feet? Explain.

12 ft

8 ft

3 Brian orders a center pivot irrigation system to water his fields. The system is made up of a line of connected pipes that turn around a center point. Brian's system will be 1,150 ft long.

a. What is the longest distance across the space the system will water?
Show your work.

SOLUTION _____

b. Check your answer to problem 3a. Show your work.

center pivot irrigation system

Develop Using the Relationship Between a Circle's Circumference and Diameter

➤ **Read and try to solve the problem below.**

Look at the circumference of each of the circles below. What do you think would be the circumference of a circle with diameter 1 cm?

2 cm

$C \approx 6.28$ cm

3 cm

$C \approx 9.42$ cm

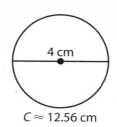

4 cm

$C \approx 12.56$ cm

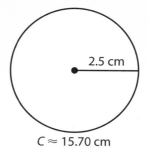

2.5 cm

$C \approx 15.70$ cm

TRY IT

  Math Toolkit compasses, flexible tape measures, rulers, string

DISCUSS IT

Ask: Why did you choose that strategy to find the circumference of a circle with diameter 1 cm?

Share: I chose to use . . . because . . .

➤ **Explore different ways to investigate the relationship between the circumference and diameter of a circle.**

Look at the circumference of each of the circles below. What do you think would be the circumference of a circle with diameter 1 cm?

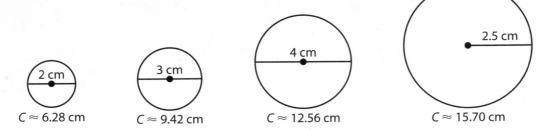

2 cm
C ≈ 6.28 cm

3 cm
C ≈ 9.42 cm

4 cm
C ≈ 12.56 cm

2.5 cm
C ≈ 15.70 cm

Model It

You can make a graph to look at the relationship between circumference and diameter for each circle.

The *x*-axis shows the diameter. The *y*-axis shows the approximate circumference.

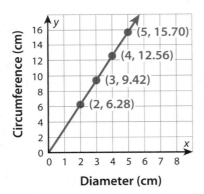

(5, 15.70)
(4, 12.56)
(3, 9.42)
(2, 6.28)

Model It

You can look for a constant of proportionality in the relationship between the approximate circumference of each circle and the diameter.

Divide the circumference of each circle by its diameter.

$\frac{6.28}{2} = 3.14$ $\frac{9.42}{3} = 3.14$ $\frac{12.56}{4} = 3.14$ $\frac{15.70}{5} = 3.14$

$r = 2.5$ cm, so $d = 5$ cm.

The constant of proportionality is 3.14.

➤ **Use the problem from the previous page to help you understand how to find the circumference of a circle.**

1 Each circumference is given using the ≈ symbol. What does that mean about the circumferences? What is the approximate circumference of a circle with diameter 1 cm?

2 Look at the first **Model It**. Why is the point (5, 15.70) on the graph?

3 Look at the second **Model It**. What does the constant of proportionality tell you about the relationship between the circumference and diameter of a circle?

4 The quotient $\frac{circumference}{diameter}$ is called **pi (π)**. π represents a decimal that goes on forever without repeating. Use π to write a formula for the circumference of a circle, C, when you know the diameter, d.

5 An exact circumference uses π. To find an approximate circumference you can use 3.14 or $\frac{22}{7}$ as a value for π. What is the exact circumference for a circle with diameter 6 cm? What is the approximate circumference?

6 **Reflect** Think about all the models and strategies you have discussed today. Describe how one of them helped you better understand how to find the circumference of a circle.

Apply It

➤ **Use what you learned to solve these problems.**

7 The circumference of a circle is 12π feet. What is the diameter? Show your work.

SOLUTION _____

8 What is the circumference of the circle? Write your answer using π. Show your work.

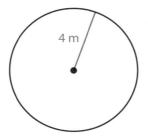

4 m

SOLUTION _____

9 The diameter of a gong is 20 inches. Find the approximate circumference of the gong, using 3.14 for π. Then find the exact circumference of the gong. Show your work.

SOLUTION _____

_____

Practice Using the Relationship Between a Circle's Circumference and Diameter

➤ **Study the Example showing how to find the circumference of a circle. Then solve problems 1–5.**

Example

A model of a circular pool is shown. What is the exact circumference of the pool?

You can use a formula to find the circumference of a circle.

The diagram shows that the diameter of the pool is **9 ft**.

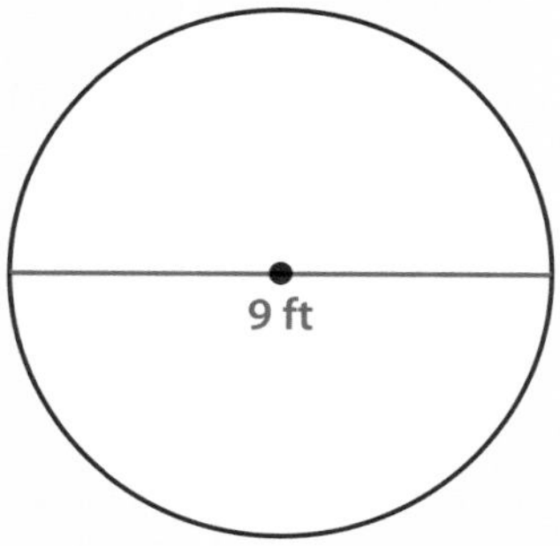

$C = \pi d$

$\quad = \pi \cdot 9$

$\quad = 9\pi$

9 ft

Using π gives an exact circumference. The circumference of the pool is 9π ft.

1 **a.** A circular dining room table top has a radius of 22 inches. What is the diameter of the table top?

   b. What is the circumference of the table top? Write your answer using π. Show your work.

   SOLUTION _____

2 A circular coin has circumference 32π millimeters. Will the coin fit through a slot that is 35 millimeters long? Explain.

Vocabulary

circumference
the distance around the outside of a circle.

diameter
the distance across a circle through the center.

pi (π)
in a circle, the quotient $\frac{\text{circumference}}{\text{diameter}}$.
Common approximations are 3.14 and $\frac{22}{7}$.

radius (of a circle)
the distance from the center of a circle to any point on the circle.

3 Destiny draws a circle with radius 14 centimeters.

    a. What is the circumference of Destiny's circle? Write your answer using π. Show your work.

    SOLUTION _____

    b. Is 85 centimeters a reasonable estimate for the circumference of Destiny's circle? Explain.

4 The diameter of a basketball rim is 18 inches. What is the circumference of the rim? Write your answer using π. Show your work.

18 in.

    SOLUTION _____

5 A circular mirror has a circumference of 50π inches. What is the radius of the mirror? Show your work.

    SOLUTION _____

Develop Finding the Area of a Circle

➤ **Read and try to solve the problem below.**

What is the approximate area of a circle with radius 2 units?

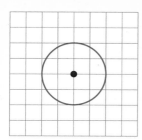

  Math Toolkit grid paper, tracing paper

DISCUSS IT

Ask: What did you do first to find the area of the circle?

Share: First, I . . .

LESSON 6 Solve Area and Circumference Problems Involving Circles   **109**

➤ **Explore different ways to find the area of a circle.**

What is the approximate area of a circle with radius 2 units?

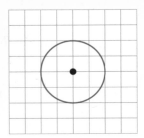

Model It

You can decompose a circle.

Divide a circle into equal parts. Then compose the parts into a figure that looks like a parallelogram.

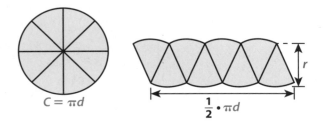

$C = \pi d$

$\frac{1}{2} \cdot \pi d$

A formula for the area of the circle is $A = \frac{1}{2}C \cdot r$ or $\frac{1}{2} \cdot \pi d \cdot r$.

Picture It

You can visualize "unrolling" a circle into a triangle.

Think of a circle as made of rings. Slice the rings along a radius. Then unroll the rings to make a triangular shape.

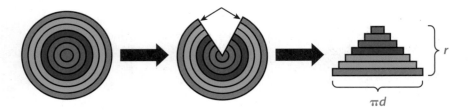

πd

The formula for the area of a triangle is $A = \frac{1}{2}bh$. The length of the base of the triangle is the circumference of the circle, πd. The height of the triangle is r.

So, a formula for the area of a circle is $A = \frac{1}{2} \cdot \pi d \cdot r$.

➤ **Use the problem from the previous page to help you understand how to find the area of a circle.**

1 Look at **Model It**. Why is the base of the parallelogram $\frac{1}{2}$ the circumference of the circle?

2 Look at **Picture It**. Why is the base of the triangle the same as the circumference of the circle?

3 **Model It** and **Picture It** both show the area of a circle using the formula $A = \frac{1}{2} \cdot \pi \cdot d \cdot r$. What is a formula for the area of a circle that only uses r?

4 The formula for the area of a circle contains π. That means you can find both an exact and an approximate area of a circle. What is the approximate area of a circle with radius 2 cm? Why might you want to find an approximate area of a circle?

5 The formula for circumference uses diameter. The formula for area uses radius. Explain how you can find the area of a circle if you know the circumference.

6 **Reflect** Think about all the models and strategies you have discussed today. Describe how one of them helped you better understand how to solve the **Try It** problem.

Apply It

➤ **Use what you learned to solve these problems.**

7 Gaspar draws a circle in the coordinate plane with the center at (6, 5). What is the area of Gaspar's circle? Write your answer using π. Show your work.

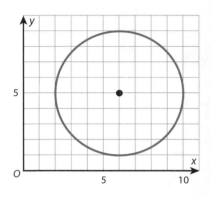

SOLUTION _____

8 The diameter of a circular dartboard is 18 inches. What is the area of the dartboard? Write your answer using π. Show your work.

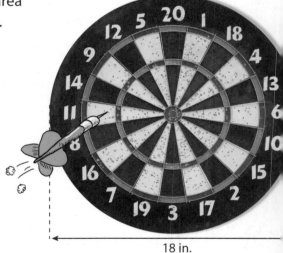

18 in.

SOLUTION _____

9 The radius of a circle is 10 cm. What is the approximate area of the circle? What is the exact area of the circle? Show your work.

SOLUTION _____

_____

Practice Finding the Area of a Circle

➤ **Study the Example showing how to find the area of a circle. Then solve problems 1–5.**

Example

What is the exact area of the circle?

To find the radius, count the number of units from the center of the circle to the edge. The radius is 6 units.

Then find the area of the circle.

$$A = \pi r^2$$
$$= \pi(6)^2$$
$$= 36\pi$$

To find the exact area, use π.

The area of the circle is 36π units^2.

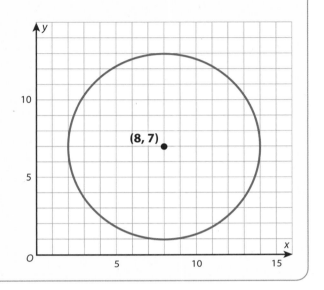

(8, 7)

---

1 A round tablecloth has a diameter of 30 inches.

   a. What is the radius of the tablecloth?

   b. What is the area of the tablecloth? Write your answer using π. Show your work.

   SOLUTION _____

2 A circular garden has a radius of 3 meters. What is the area of the garden? Write your answer using π. Show your work.

   SOLUTION _____

Vocabulary

area
the amount of space inside a closed two-dimensional figure. Area is measured in square units.

diameter
a line segment that goes through the center of a circle and has endpoints on the circle. Also, the distance across a circle through the center.

radius (of a circle)
a line segment from the center of a circle and to any point on the circle. Also, the distance from the center of a circle to any point on the circle.

3 The diameter of a Canadian penny is 19 millimeters. The diameter of a Canadian nickel is 21 millimeters. How much greater is the area of a Canadian nickel than the area of a Canadian penny? Show your work.

19 mm

21 mm

SOLUTION _____

4 A circle has radius 12 millimeters. What is its area? Use 3.14 for π. Show your work.

SOLUTION _____

5 What is the exact area of the circle below? Show your work.

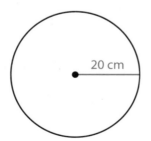

20 cm

SOLUTION _____

Refine Solving Circumference and Area Problems Involving Circles

➤ **Complete the Example below. Then solve problems 1–11.**

Example

Four identical circles are drawn within a square. What is the total area of the circles?

Look at how you could use the formula for the area of a circle.

The diameter of each circle is $\frac{5}{2}$ in.

The radius of each circle is $\frac{5}{2} \div 2 = \frac{5}{4}$ in.

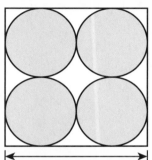

5 in.

Total shaded area is 4 times the area of one circle.

Area of one circle = πr^2

$$= \pi \cdot \left(\frac{5}{4}\right)^2$$

$$= \pi \cdot \frac{25}{16}$$

SOLUTION _____

Apply It

1 A circle with radius 3 centimeters is cut from a square piece of felt. The sides of the felt square are 8 centimeters long. How much felt is left over? Use 3.14 for π. Show your work.

SOLUTION _____

2 A middle school has an oval track with the dimensions shown. What is the distance around the track? Use 3.14 for π. Show your work.

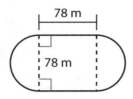

CONSIDER THIS . . .
You can think of the track as a square with half circles on the right and left sides.

PAIR/SHARE
Why might you want to find an approximate distance?

SOLUTION _____

3 Mr. Aba builds a circular patio with a diameter of 12 feet. He covers the patio with paving stones. The cost of the paving stones is $10.50 per square foot. To the nearest dollar, how much do the paving stones cost?

A $126

B $378

C $1,187

D $4,748

Jacob chose D as the correct answer. How might he have gotten that answer?

CONSIDER THIS . . .
Multiply the number of square feet by the cost per square foot to find the total cost.

PAIR/SHARE
How could you estimate the area to check that your answer makes sense?

4 The stained glass window shown is a half circle. What is the perimeter of the window? Use 3.14 for π. Show your work.

26 in.

SOLUTION _____

5 Erin wants to find the circumference of a circle with radius 7 cm. Which of the following can she use to find the circumference of the circle? Select all that apply.

A $2 \cdot 7 \cdot \pi$

B $2 \cdot 14 \cdot \pi$

C $\frac{7}{2} \cdot \pi$

D $14 \cdot \pi$

E $49 \cdot \pi$

6 Is there a proportional relationship between the area and radius of a circle? Explain.

7 The area of a circle is 25π ft². What is the circumference of the circle? Explain.

8 A box holds three circular flower pots, each with the same diameter. What is the exact area of the base of one pot? Show your work.

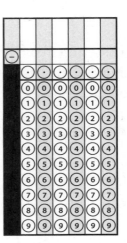

15 in.

SOLUTION _____

9 The quotient of a circle's circumference divided by its diameter is _____ .

10 The radius of the wheel of a unicycle is 14 inches. What is the distance, in inches, that the unicycle covers after 10 full rotations of the wheel? Use 3.14 for π.

11 **Math Journal** Draw a circle and give its radius or diameter. Then find the circumference and the area of the circle. Write your answers using π.

✓ **End of Lesson Checklist**

☐ **INTERACTIVE GLOSSARY** Find the entries for *circumference* and *pi* (π). Rewrite the definitions in your own words.

☐ **SELF CHECK** Go back to the Unit 1 Opener and see what you can check off.

SMP 1 Make sense of problems and persevere in solving them.

Study an Example Problem and Solution

➤ **Read this problem involving ratios and proportions. Then look at one student's solution to this problem on the following pages.**

Student ID Cards

Agustin's art club is designing new student ID cards. Read an email from the school's principal and help Agustin come up with a design.

Delete   Archive   Reply   Reply All   Forward

To: Art Club
Subject: Help Design Student ID Cards

Dear Art Club Members,

I would like your help designing the new student ID cards. These are the requirements:

- Each card will show the student's name and photo, and the school name and mascot.

- Each card is $3\frac{3}{8}$ inches by $2\frac{1}{8}$ inches. ID cards can be oriented in either direction.

- The ratio of width to height for the student photo is 3 : 4.

- The space for the school name must be at least $1\frac{3}{4}$ inches by $\frac{1}{2}$ inch.

- The space for the student name must be at least $1\frac{1}{2}$ inches by $\frac{1}{4}$ inch.

I took this photo of our mascot, Sammie, and included the dimensions. I hope it helps!

Please reply to this email with your sketch of a design for the new student ID cards. Include dimensions of the student photo and school mascot on your sketch.

Thanks!

Mr. Ramírez

The term *mascot* is believed to come from the French word *mascotte*, which means good luck charm.

One Student's Solution

> **NOTICE THAT . . .**
> You can cut out rectangles the size of the student name and school name and move them around as you plan your design.

> **NOTICE THAT . . .**
> The space was $2\frac{1}{2}$ inches tall, but the photo will only be $1\frac{1}{2}$ inches tall. This will allow for space between the different elements of the ID card.

First, I need to decide which direction to orient the ID card.

I will orient the card vertically. I know the minimum dimensions for the spaces for the student name and school name. I can arrange the school name and student name spaces like this.

School Name
Student Name

Next, I will decide how big to make the student photo.

I measure $2\frac{1}{2}$ inches from the bottom of the student name space to the bottom of the ID card. I need to leave room for the mascot, so I will make the student photo $1\frac{1}{2}$ inches tall.

The ratio of width to height for the photo must be 3 : 4. I can model the proportional relationship between width, w, and height, h, with the equation $w = \frac{3}{4}h$. Now, I can find the width of the photo.

$$w = \frac{3}{4}h$$

$$w = \frac{3}{4}\left(1\frac{1}{2}\right)$$

$$w = 1\frac{1}{8}$$

The width is $1\frac{1}{8}$ inches. The photo will be $1\frac{1}{2}$ inches tall and $1\frac{1}{8}$ inches wide.

> ☑ **Problem-Solving Checklist**
> - ☐ Tell what is known.
> - ☐ Tell what the problem is asking.
> - ☐ Show all your work.
> - ☐ Show that the solution works.

ratio of width to height is 3 : 4

$1\frac{1}{2}$ in.

$1\frac{1}{8}$ in.

Then, I will measure the remaining space for the mascot.

The mascot will be a scale drawing of the original. I want to leave space around the mascot, so I will make the length that corresponds to AB be $\frac{5}{8}$ inch. I can use a scale factor to find the other dimensions.

Because AB is 5 feet, I can find the scale factor from the original mascot to the scale drawing on the card by dividing $\frac{5}{8}$ by 5.

$$\frac{\frac{5}{8}}{5} = \frac{5}{8} \cdot \frac{1}{5}$$

$$= \frac{1}{8}$$

> **NOTICE THAT . . .**
> The scale factor is a unit rate. It tells you how many inches on the drawing there are for each foot on the original figure.

The scale factor is $\frac{1}{8}$. To find the other lengths on the card, I can multiply each original length by $\frac{1}{8}$.

BC on card: $\frac{1}{8} \cdot 7\frac{3}{4} = \frac{31}{32}$

CD on card: $\frac{1}{8} \cdot 7\frac{1}{2} = \frac{15}{16}$

AD on card: $\frac{1}{8} \cdot 7\frac{1}{3} = \frac{11}{12}$

On the card, AB is $\frac{5}{8}$ inches, BC is $\frac{31}{32}$ inches, CD is $\frac{15}{16}$ inches, and AD is $\frac{11}{12}$ inches.

> **NOTICE THAT . . .**
> The dimensions of the original mascot photo are given in feet, and the dimensions of the scale drawing on the ID card should be expressed in inches.

Finally, I will draw all of the elements, as precisely as I can, on an ID card.

All the elements fit on the card. The design meets all the requirements in Mr. Ramírez's email.

Try Another Approach

➤ **There are many ways to solve problems. Think about how you might solve the Student ID Cards problem in a different way.**

Student ID Cards

Agustin's art club is designing new student ID cards. Read an email from the school's principal and help Agustin come up with a design.

🗑 Delete   🗄 Archive | ✉ Reply   ✉ Reply All   ✉ Forward

To: Art Club
Subject: Help Design Student ID Cards

Dear Art Club Members,

I would like your help designing the new student ID cards. These are the requirements:

- Each card will show the student's name and photo, and the school name and mascot.

- Each card is $3\frac{3}{8}$ inches by $2\frac{1}{8}$ inches. ID cards can be oriented in either direction.

- The ratio of width to height for the student photo is 3 : 4.

- The space for the school name must be at least $1\frac{3}{4}$ inches by $\frac{1}{2}$ inch.

- The space for the student name must be at least $1\frac{1}{2}$ inches by $\frac{1}{4}$ inch.

I took this photo of our mascot, Sammie, and included the dimensions. I hope it helps!

Please reply to this email with your sketch of a design for the new student ID cards. Include dimensions of the student photo and school mascot on your sketch.

Thanks!

Mr. Ramírez

Plan It

➤ **Answer these questions to help you start thinking about a plan.**

   a. If the card is oriented horizontally, how tall can the student photo be? How tall can the mascot be?

   b. Should the scale factor for the mascot be greater than 1 or less than 1?

Solve It

➤ **Find a different solution for the Student ID Cards problem. Show all your work on a separate sheet of paper. You may want to use the Problem-Solving Tips to get started.**

PROBLEM-SOLVING TIPS

Math Toolkit ruler, grid paper

Key Terms

scale factor	dimensions	scale drawing
proportion	trapezoid	

Sentence Starters

- The dimensions for the student picture . . .

- The scale factor from the orginal mascot to my design . . .

Reflect

Use Mathematical Practices As you work through the problem, discuss these questions with a partner.

- **Use Tools** Would grid paper be helpful for this problem? Explain how it can help, or explain why it would not be helpful.

- **Make an Argument** Which element(s) should you arrange on the card first? Why?

Discuss Models and Strategies

➤ **Read the problem. Write a solution on a separate sheet of paper. Remember, there can be lots of ways to solve a problem.**

Painting the Art Room

The art club is planning to paint the art room. Read Agustin's notes about the club's plan, and help him come up with a solution:

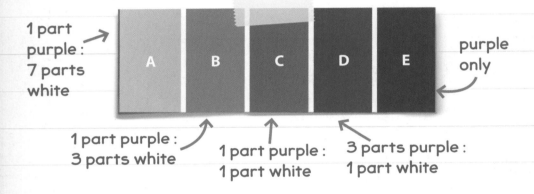

Art Room Paint Job

1 part purple : 7 parts white → A

1 part purple : 3 parts white → B

1 part purple : 1 part white → C

3 parts purple : 1 part white → D

E ← purple only

- We have $1\frac{1}{2}$ gallons of white paint to mix with purple paint to make different shades.

- We will use three of the shades above.

  - One shade will cover three walls (525 square feet).

  - Another shade will cover the fourth wall (175 square feet).

  - A third shade will cover all the trim ($131\frac{1}{4}$ square feet).

- One gallon of paint covers approximately 350 square feet. Try not to have too much leftover paint.

WHAT WE NEED TO FIGURE OUT:

- Which shades of purple should we use for the three walls, the fourth wall, and the trim?

- Purple paint is sold by the gallon. How many gallons will we need to buy?

Plan It and Solve It

➤ **Find a solution to the Painting the Art Room problem.**

Write a detailed plan and support your answer. Be sure to include:

- your recommendation for which shades to use for the three walls, the fourth wall, and the trim.

- the amount of purple paint the art club will need to buy.

- how much purple paint and white paint will be left over.

PROBLEM-SOLVING TIPS

 Math Toolkit double number lines, grid paper, ruler

Key Terms

| unit rate | proportional relationship | ratio |
| graph | double number line | table |

Models You may want to use . . .

- double number lines to find the amounts of different shades needed.

- graphs or tables to show how the amount of purple paint needed is related to the total amount of paint for each shade.

- a table to organize your work.

Reflect

Use Mathematical Practices As you work through the problem, discuss these questions with a partner.

- **Persevere** Why might you try different paint combinations before deciding on a final answer?

- **Make an Argument** Did you round the amount of purple paint up or down to determine how many gallons the art club will need to buy? Why?

The ancient Phoenicians were known for the purple dye they manufactured. The dye, known as Tyrian purple, was very expensive and was seen as a symbol of authority and status.

Persevere On Your Own

➤ **Read the problem. Write a solution on a separate sheet of paper.**

Painting a Mural

The art club is planning to paint a circular mural using light blue and green paint. Read the email from Agustin, and help come up with a response to the email.

Delete　Archive　　Reply　Reply All　Forward

To: Art Club
Subject: Circular Mural – Test painting complete!

Hi Everybody,

I finished the test painting for our mural. It should help us figure out how much paint we need.

- The test painting has a circumference of 0.2π meters. The diameter of the mural should be between 2 and 4 meters.

- I used 3 parts green paint for every 2 parts light blue paint.

- I used a total of $2\frac{1}{2}$ oz paint in the test painting.

- I mixed cobalt and white to make the light blue.

These are the paints I used. We have $1,000 to spend on paint.

| white 8 oz. $7.28 | cobalt 16 oz. $31.04 | green 16 oz. $16.80 |

PLEASE TELL ME:

- the diameter that you suggest for the mural.

- a ratio of cobalt to white we could use to make light blue.

- the amount of each color paint we will need to buy.

- the total cost of all the paint.

Thanks!

Agustin

Solve It

➤ **Find a solution to the Painting a Mural problem.**

- Suggest a diameter for the mural.

- Suggest a ratio of cobalt paint to white paint that the art club could use to mix the light blue paint.

- Determine how much green, cobalt, and white paint the art club will need.

- Calculate the total cost of all the paint.

Reflect

Use Mathematical Practices After you complete the problem, choose one of these questions to discuss with a partner.

- **Reason Mathematically** How many times larger is the area of the mural than the area of the test painting?

- **Be Precise** Did you use π or an approximation of π in your calculations? Why?

It would take around 14.6 trillion gallons of paint to cover Earth.

In this unit you learned to . . .

Skill	Lesson
Find actual distance given a scale drawing.	1
Find actual area given a scale drawing.	1
Draw a scale drawing at a different scale.	1
Find unit rates with complex fractions.	2
Identify proportional relationships and the constant of proportionality.	3, 4, 5
Write an equation to represent a proportional relationship.	3, 4, 5
Interpret graphs of proportional relationships.	4
Find the circumference and area of circles.	6
Make connections between representations of proportional relationships by explaining how they are similar and different.	3, 4, 5

Think about what you have learned.

➤ **Use words, numbers, and drawings.**

1 The math I could use in my everyday life is _____ because . . .

2 Something I know well is . . .

3 One thing I still need to work on is . . .

➤ **Review the unit vocabulary. Put a check mark by items you can use in speaking and writing. Look up the meaning of any terms you do not know.**

Math Vocabulary | **Academic Vocabulary**

☐ center (of a circle)
☐ circumference
☐ complex fraction
☐ constant of proportionality

☐ diameter
☐ pi (π)
☐ proportional relationship
☐ radius (of a circle)

☐ approximate (adjective)
☐ constant
☐ exact
☐ illustrate

➤ **Use the unit vocabulary to complete the problems.**

1 Make a labeled diagram that illustrates at least four math or academic vocabulary terms that relate to circles.

2 Use at least two math or academic vocabulary terms to explain what 3.14 and $\frac{22}{7}$ represent. Underline each term you use.

3 Write an expression that gives the exact value of the area of a circle with radius 4 cm. Then write an expression that gives an approximate value of the area.

4 Give an example of a proportional relationship and identify the constant of proportionality.

➤ **Use what you have learned to complete these problems.**

1 Anna is on a road trip. She uses $\frac{3}{4}$ of a tank of gas every $\frac{9}{2}$ hours. How many tanks of gas will Anna use after 12 hours? Show your work.

SOLUTION _____

2 Water leaks through a roof and collects in a bucket. The table shows how many cups of water collect in the bucket for different numbers of hours. What is the constant of proportionality for hours to cups of water?

Time (hours)	2	4	6	8	10	12
Water (cups)	6	12	18	24	30	36

A $\frac{1}{6}$ **B** $\frac{1}{3}$

C 3 **D** 6

3 The graph models the proportional relationship between the amount of money Tessa earns and the hours she works. Decide if each statement is true or false.

Choose *True* or *False* for each statement.

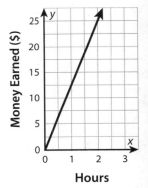

Hours

	True	False
a. The point (1, 12.5) means Tessa makes $1.00 in 12.5 hours.	○	○
b. The point (1, 12.5) identifies the constant of proportionality.	○	○
c. The point (0, 0) means the constant of proportionality is 0.	○	○
d. The point (0.5, 6.25) means that Tessa earns $6.25 every half hour.	○	○

4 Companies A and B produce phone chargers. Company A makes 15 phone chargers when Company B makes 20 phone chargers. When Company A makes 30 phone chargers, how many phone chargers does Company B make? Write your answers in the blanks.

$$\frac{15}{20} = \frac{30}{x}$$ Since $30 = 15 \cdot 2$, $x =$ _____ $\cdot 2$

$$x = \text{_____}$$

5 A circular rug has a diameter of 18 ft. What is the area of the rug? Use 3.14 for π. Record your answer on the grid. Then fill in the bubbles.

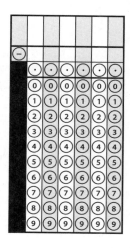

6 Emerson pays $227.25 for 3 new windows. Write an equation that represents the cost, c, for w windows. Show your work.

SOLUTION _____

7 The scale from a square tabletop to a drawing of the tabletop is 6 in. to 1 cm. The actual tabletop has an area of 1,296 in.^{2}. What is the area of the drawing of the tabletop? Show your work.

SOLUTION _____

Unit Review

Performance Task

➤ **Answer the questions and show all your work on separate paper.**

Janice wants to have the interior of her house and office painted. The total area she needs painted is 3,840 ft^2. She wants to choose one company to paint 2,880 ft^2 at her house and a second company to paint 960 ft^2 at her office. Janice finds pricing information from four different painting companies, shown below:

- Primary Painters provides this pricing table.

Primary Painters					
Area (square feet)	0	50	100	150	200
Cost (in dollars)	0	137.50	275.00	412.50	550.00

- Hardy's Handy Helpers charges $47.00 for every 20 ft^2.

- Roll It On charges $2.80 per square foot.

- Perfection Painting provides three examples of an area in square feet and the corresponding cost in dollars: (30, 81.00), (60, 162.00), and (80, 216.00).

Write an equation to represent each company's cost per square foot. Then decide which two companies Janice should choose for the lowest total cost. Finally, calculate Janice's total cost for having her house and office painted.

Reflect

Use Mathematical Practices After you complete the task, choose one of the following questions to answer.

- **Use Reasoning** How is the information from each company related to the equations you wrote?

- **Be Precise** How do you know the two painting companies you chose have the lowest total cost?

Unit 2

Numbers and Operations

Add and Subtract Rational Numbers

✓ **Self Check**	Before starting this unit, check off the skills you know below. As you complete each lesson, see how many more skills you can check off!

I can . . .	Before	After
Add positive and negative integers.	☐	☐
Add positive and negative fractions and decimals.	☐	☐
Subtract positive and negative integers.	☐	☐
Subtract positive and negative fractions and decimals.	☐	☐
Justify solutions to problems about adding and subtracting rational numbers by telling what I noticed and what I decided to do as a result.	☐	☐

Prepare for Adding and Subtracting Rational Numbers

➤ **Use what you know to estimate the value of each expression below. Plot your estimates on the number line. Label each estimate with its letter.**

a. $1\frac{5}{8} - \frac{3}{4}$ **d.** $4\frac{3}{8} - 2\frac{1}{2}$ **g.** -4.5

b. $1\frac{3}{5} + 1\frac{1}{2}$ **e.** $2\frac{8}{9} + \frac{2}{3}$ **h.** $2.6 + 1.65$

c. $-1\frac{3}{4}$ **f.** $4.25 - 1.75$ **i.** -4.0

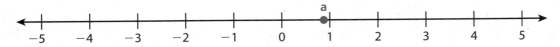

Meet with a partner and compare responses. Discuss any estimates or labels that you do not agree about. You may revise or add to your work as needed. With your partner, write two more expressions and label them on the number line.

Dear Family,

This week your student is exploring addition with integers. The set of integers includes all whole numbers and their opposites. They can be positive, negative, or zero.

Integers: 1, −4, 0, 107, −200   **Not Integers:** $-\frac{1}{3}$, 2.35, −0.75, $\frac{7}{5}$

Here are some examples of situations in which you might need to add integers:

- It is −8°F and the temperature increases by 15°F. What is the new temperature?
- A hiking trail starts at 150 feet below sea level and increases by 600 feet in elevation. What is the ending elevation?

You can add integers just like you can add whole numbers. If you add an integer to its opposite, the sum is 0. The integers −4 and 4 are opposites.

$$4 + (-4) = 0 \qquad (-4) + 4 = 0$$

Opposites, like 4 and −4, form **zero pairs** because their sum is 0.

Your student will be modeling addition problems like the one below.

What is 4 + (−7)?

➤ **ONE WAY** to model addition with negative integers is with integer chips.

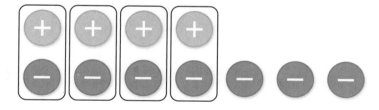

➤ **ANOTHER WAY** is to use a number line. Move left to add a negative number.

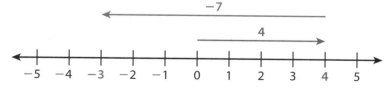

Both models show that 4 + (−7) = −3.

 Use the next page to start a conversation about addition with negative integers.

Activity Thinking About Positive and Negative Numbers Around You

➤ **Do this activity together to investigate positive and negative numbers in the real world.**

Have you ever played a team sport and wondered how you impacted the game? Basketball has a statistic used to measure this called plus-minus.

To find a player's plus-minus, find how many points that player's team scored while the player was in the game. Then find how many points the other team scored during that same time, and write that as a negative number. Then add the two numbers.

So, if your team scores 10 points while you are in the game and the other team scores fewer than 10, your plus-minus is positive. But if the other team scores more than 10 points, your plus-minus is negative.

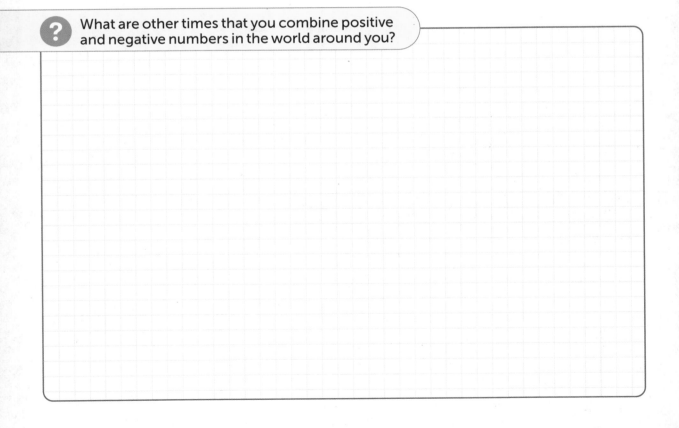

? What are other times that you combine positive and negative numbers in the world around you?

Explore Addition with Negative Integers

Model It

➤ **Complete the problems about adding opposites with integer chips.**

1 Neva plays a video game. On her first turn, she gets 3 points. On her second turn, she loses 3 points. The expression $3 + (-3)$ represents her score after the two turns. You can use integer chips to find the sum of 3 and -3.

a. The sum of any number and its opposite is 0. Another term for opposites is *additive inverses*. Since the sum of 1 and -1 is 0, 1 and -1 form a **zero pair**. Circle the zero pairs in the model.

b. How many points does Neva have after her second turn?

c. What is $3 + (-3)$?

2 Neva starts the game over. The integer chips represent the number of points she has after her first turn. Then she earns 5 points on her second turn.

a. How many points does Neva have after her first turn?

b. Draw chips to show the points Neva earns on her second turn. Then circle the zero pairs.

c. How many points does Neva have after her second turn?

d. What is $(-5) + 5$?

> **DISCUSS IT**
>
> **Ask:** Why do you circle both a positive chip and a negative chip?
>
> **Share:** The value of a zero pair is . . . because . . .

◎ **Learning Targets** SMP 2, SMP 3, SMP 7
Apply and extend previous understandings of addition and subtraction to add and subtract rational numbers; represent addition and subtraction on a horizontal or vertical number line diagram.
• Describe situations in which opposite quantities combine to make 0.
• Understand $p + q$ as the number located a distance $|q|$ from p, in the positive or negative direction. Show that a number and its opposite have a sum of 0. Interpret sums of rational numbers.

Model It

➤ **Complete the problems about adding opposites with a number line.**

3 The numbers 5 and −5 are opposites. Explain why 5 and −5 have the same absolute value.

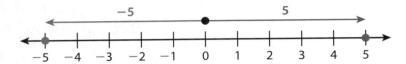

4 Use the number line to explain why 5 + (−5) = 0.

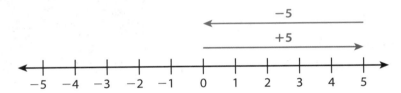

5 **Reflect** Give an example of two integers that make a zero pair. Explain how they are additive inverses.

Prepare for Addition with Negative Integers

1 Think about what you know about negative numbers. Fill in each box. Use words, numbers, and pictures. Show as many ideas as you can.

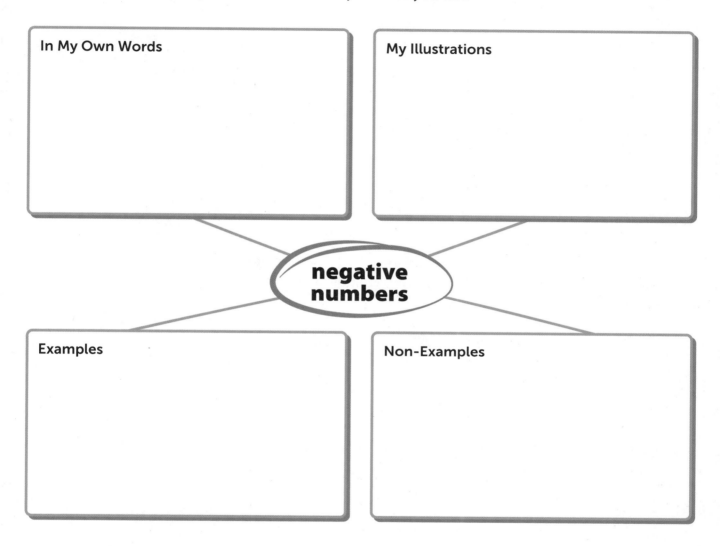

In My Own Words

My Illustrations

negative numbers

Examples

Non-Examples

2 What is one way the numbers −10 and 10 are similar? What is one way they are different?

➤ **Complete problems 3–5.**

3 Andrew plays a card game. In the first round, he gets 4 points. In the second round, he loses 4 points. The expression $4 + (-4)$ represents his score after the two rounds.

a. Circle the zero pairs in the model.

b. How many points does Andrew have after the second round?

c. What is $4 + (-4)$?

4 Kiara plays the card game with Andrew. The integer chips below represent the number of points she has after the first round. Then she earns 7 points in the second round.

a. How many points does Kiara have after the first round?

b. Draw chips to show the points Kiara earns in the second round. Then circle the zero pairs.

c. How many points does Kiara have after the second round?

d. What is $-7 + 7$?

5 The number line shows adding 2 and -2. Use the number line to explain why $2 + (-2) = 0$.

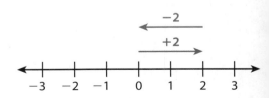

Develop Understanding of Addition with Negative Integers

Model It: Adding a Positive and a Negative Integer

➤ **Try these two problems involving adding a positive and a negative integer.**

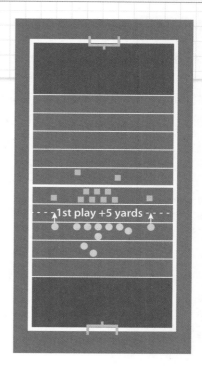

1 On the first play, Angel's football team gains 5 yards from its starting position. On the second play, the team loses 7 yards. To find where the team is relative to its starting position, add 5 and −7.

   a. You can use integer chips to model $5 + (-7)$. Circle all the zero pairs.

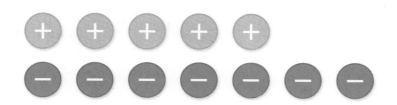

   b. What is the value of the remaining chips?

   c. $5 + (-7) =$

   d. After the second play, where is Angel's team relative to its starting position?

2 You can also use a number line to find $5 + (-7)$.

   a. Draw and label arrows to show −7 added to 5.

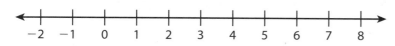

   b. What number do you end at?

   c. $5 + (-7) =$

DISCUSS IT

Ask: How do you know if you should draw an arrow to the right or the left on the number line?

Share: First, I . . . because . . .

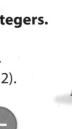

Model It: Adding Two Negative Integers

➤ **Try these two problems about adding two negative integers.**

3 The football team loses 5 yards from its starting position.
Then it loses another 2 yards. The model shows $-5 + (-2)$.

a. Why are there no zero pairs to circle?

b. What is the value of the chips? What does the sum mean in this situation?

4 Complete the model to find $-5 + (-2)$.

$-5 + (-2) =$ _____

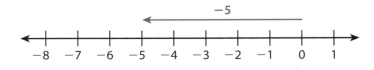

CONNECT IT

➤ **Complete the problems below.**

5 How is finding the sum $2 + (-3)$ using integer chips similar to finding the sum $2 + (-3)$ using a number line? How is it different?

6 A football team loses 6 yards on its first play. It gains 8 yards on the next play. Use a model to find the sum $-6 + 8$. What does the sum mean in this situation?

Name: _____

Practice Understanding of Addition with Negative Integers

➤ **Study how the Example shows adding with negative numbers. Then solve problems 1–5.**

Example

Aisha owes her brother $3. Then she borrows $5 more from her brother. The expression $-3 + (-5)$ represents the amount Aisha owes her brother in all. How much does Aisha owe her brother?

You can model this situation using integer chips.

There are 0 positive chips and 8 negative chips in all. That means $(-3) + (-5) = -8$.

Aisha owes her brother $8.

1 Use number line models to add the same values as the Example.

a. Complete the model to find $-3 + (-5)$.

$-3 + (-5) =$ _____

b. Complete the model to find $-5 + (-3)$.

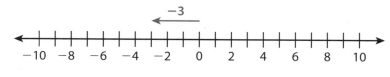

$-5 + (-3) =$ _____

c. Does the order in which you add -3 and -5 matter? Explain.

2 Akio is playing a board game. He starts with 0 points. On his first turn, Akio earns 8 points. On his second turn, he loses 3 points. The expression $8 + (-3)$ represents this situation.

a. Use a model to find $8 + (-3)$.

b. What is Akio's score after his second turn?

3 Complete the model to find $2 + (-6)$.

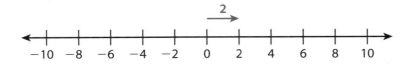

$$2 + (-6) =$$

4 Alec says the sum of two numbers can never be less than either number. Use a model to explain why Alec is incorrect.

5 Suppose the sum of two integers is negative. Must both integers be negative? Explain.

Refine Ideas About Addition with Negative Integers

Apply It **Math Toolkit** integer chips, number lines

➤ **Complete problems 1–5.**

1 **Construct** What two addition equations does the number line show? Describe a situation involving temperature that one of the equations could represent.

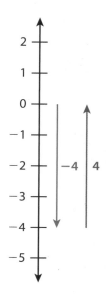

2 **Analyze** Cheryl says that when you add two negative numbers, the sum is always negative. Is Cheryl's statement *true* or *false*? Explain.

3 **Describe** The expression $2 + x$ represents a number. This number can be located on a number line.

a. When is $2 + x$ located to the right of 2? When is it located to the left of 2?

b. What is the distance between $2 + x$ and 2? Why is the distance the same when x is positive or negative?

4 An orca is swimming at an elevation of −6 m relative to sea level. Several seconds later the orca's elevation increases by 7 m.

PART A Write an addition expression for the orca's new elevation relative to sea level. Draw a model to represent your expression.

PART B Describe the orca's new elevation. Explain how your model represents the orca's new elevation.

5 **Math Journal** How is adding 3 + (−5) similar to adding 3 + 5? How is it different? Use words and models in your explanation.

✓ End of Lesson Checklist

☐ **INTERACTIVE GLOSSARY** Find the entry for *zero pair*. Give 3 examples of zero pairs.

Dear Family,

This week your student is learning about adding positive and negative numbers. Previously, your student explored representing sums involving integers on a number line.

You can also use a number line to add fractions and decimals.

$$-\frac{3}{10} + \frac{4}{10} = \frac{1}{10}$$

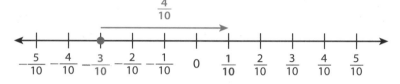

Your student will be solving problems like the one below.

> Winona searches for valuables in a lake bed. She stands on a dock 1 yd above the lake's surface. She dives and changes her elevation by -4 yd to reach the lake bed. Where is the lake bed relative to the surface of the lake? This problem can be represented by the expression $1 + (-4)$.

➤ **ONE WAY** to find $1 + (-4)$ is to use a number line.

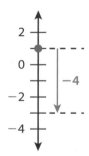

➤ **ANOTHER WAY** is to break apart, or decompose, numbers to form zero pairs.

Think of -4 as $(-1) + (-3)$.

$$1 + (-4) = 1 + [(-1) + (-3)]$$
$$= [1 + (-1)] + (-3)$$
$$= 0 + (-3)$$
$$= -3$$

Both methods show that the lake bed is -3 yd from the surface of the lake.

 Use the next page to start a conversation about positive and negative numbers.

Activity Thinking About Positive and Negative Numbers Around You

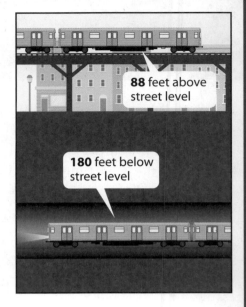

88 feet above street level

180 feet below street level

➤ **Do this activity together to investigate positive and negative numbers in the real world.**

Have you ever ridden on a subway? Some subway stations are underground, and some are above ground.

In New York City, the deepest subway station is in Manhattan. It is 180 ft below street level. The highest subway station is in Brooklyn. It is 88 ft above street level.

This means that if you travel on the subway from the station in Manhattan to the station in Brooklyn, your elevation compared to street level will increase by 268 ft, since $-180 + 268 = 88$.

? What else extends both below ground and above ground in the world around you?

Explore Adding with Negative Numbers

Previously, you learned how to add positive and negative integers. In this lesson, you will learn about adding positive and negative rational numbers.

➤ **Use what you know to try to solve the problem below.**

> The temperature at a mountain weather station is −3°F at sunrise.
> Then the temperature rises 5°F. What is the new temperature?

 TRY IT

 Math Toolkit grid paper, integer chips, number lines

DISCUSS IT

Ask: What did you do first to find the new temperature? Why?

Share: I knew . . .
so I . . .

◎ **Learning Targets** SMP 1, SMP 2, SMP 3, SMP 4, SMP 5, SMP 6, SMP 7
Apply and extend previous understandings of addition and subtraction to add and subtract rational numbers; represent addition and subtraction on a horizontal or vertical number line diagram.
• Apply properties of operations as strategies to add and subtract rational numbers.

CONNECT IT

1 Look Back What is the new temperature at the weather station? How do you know?

2 Look Ahead To find the new temperature, you found the sum of a positive and a negative integer. You can use a number line to help you think about adding positive and negative numbers.

a. During the day, the temperature at another weather station is 4°C. Overnight, it changes by −9°C. Enrico models the situation on the number line below. Hasina says she can model it with one arrow. How can she model the situation with just one arrow?

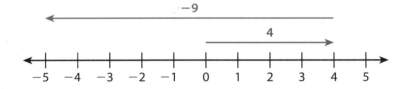

b. What is the sum of 4 and −9? What does that tell you about the temperature at the weather station?

c. How much would the temperature need to change the next day to be 0°C?

3 Reflect What addition expression does the number line below model? Explain.

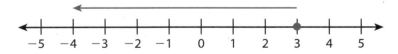

Prepare for Adding with Negative Numbers

1 Think about what you know about integers. Fill in each box. Use words, numbers, and pictures. Show as many ideas as you can.

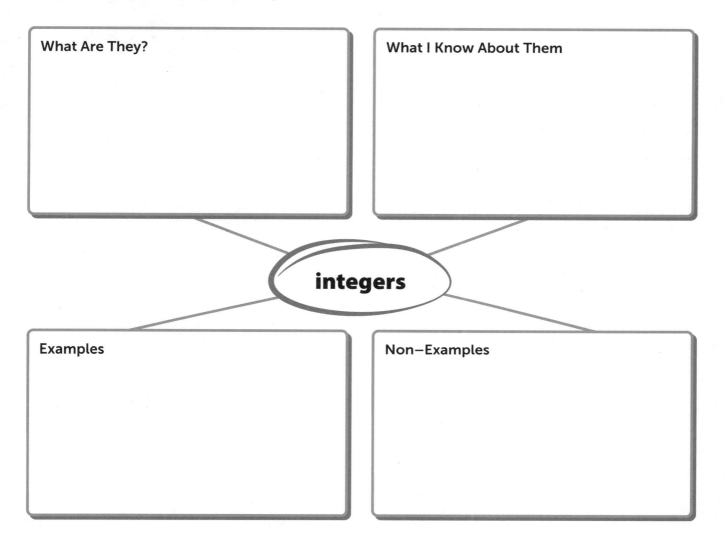

What Are They?

What I Know About Them

integers

Examples

Non–Examples

2 Amata says that 12.00 is not an integer because it has a decimal point. Is Amata correct? Explain.

3 When Ria goes to school, the temperature is $-5°F$. During the school day, the temperature rises 15°F.

a. What is the temperature when Ria leaves school? Show your work.

Morning: $-5°F$

SOLUTION _____

b. Check your answer to problem 3a. Show your work.

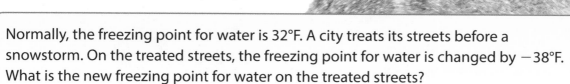

Develop Adding Positive and Negative Integers

➤ **Read and try to solve the problem below.**

Normally, the freezing point for water is 32°F. A city treats its streets before a snowstorm. On the treated streets, the freezing point for water is changed by −38°F. What is the new freezing point for water on the treated streets?

 TRY IT

 Math Toolkit grid paper, integer chips, number lines

DISCUSS IT

Ask: In your own words, what is the problem asking?

Share: The problem is asking . . .

➤ **Explore different ways to add with negative numbers.**

Normally, the freezing point for water is 32°F. A city treats its streets before a snowstorm. On the treated streets, the freezing point for water is changed by −38°F. What is the new freezing point for water on the treated streets?

Model It

You can use a number line to find a sum.

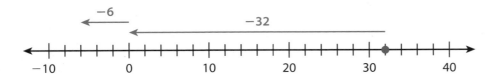

Model It

You can represent the situation with an addition expression.

32 + (−38)

32 + [(−32) + (−6)]

[32 + (−32)] + (−6)

zero pair

➤ **Use the problem from the previous page to help you understand how to add with negative integers.**

1 Look at the first **Model It**. What is the new freezing point? How does the number line show the new freezing point?

2 How do both **Model Its** use zero pairs?

3 Explain how you can find $38 + (-32)$.

4 Without finding the sum, how do you know $-32 + (-38)$ is negative?

5 The sum of two integers can be positive, negative, or zero. Why?

6 **Reflect** Think about all the models and strategies you have discussed today. Describe how one of them helped you better understand adding negative integers.

Apply It

➤ **Use what you learned to solve these problems.**

7 A dragonfish is swimming at -900 m relative to sea level. It rises 250 m. What is the dragonfish's new depth relative to sea level? Show your work.

Dragonfish

SOLUTION _____

8 What is $79 + (-26)$?

A -105

B -53

C 53

D 105

9 Find $-18 + (-67)$. Show your work.

SOLUTION _____

Practice Adding Positive and Negative Integers

➤ **Study the Example showing addition of positive and negative integers. Then solve problems 1–6.**

Example

Which is greater: −38 + (−24) or 26 + (−90)?

One way to find a sum is to use a number line.

−38 + (−24) = −62

One way to add a positive and a negative number is to make a zero pair.

26 + (−90) = 26 + (−26) + (−64)

$$= 0 + (−64)$$

$$= −64$$

Since −62 > −64, −38 + (−24) is greater than 26 + (−90).

1 In the Example, how can you tell −38 + (−24) will be negative before finding the sum?

2 Which is less: −54 + 17 or 35 + (−61)? Show your work.

SOLUTION _____

③ What is the sum of −21 and −49?

A 70

B −28

C 28

D −70

④ Find 15 + (−72). Show your work.

SOLUTION _____

⑤ Which sums are equal to −8 + 17? Select all that apply.

A −(8 + 17)

B 17 + (−8)

C −8 + 8 + 9

D 8 + (−17)

E −8 + (−17)

⑥ The temperature at Wonder Lake is 12°F. During a storm, the temperature changes by −26°F. What is the temperature after the storm? Show your work.

SOLUTION _____

Develop Adding Positive and Negative Fractions and Decimals

➤ **Read and try to solve the problem below.**

On a cave dive in Oahu, a scuba diver swims at an elevation of $-20\frac{3}{4}$ ft relative to sea level. She notices a sea turtle above her and rises 6 ft to take its picture. At what elevation does the diver take the picture?

TRY IT **Math Toolkit** grid paper, number lines

83

$$20\frac{3}{4} + 6$$

DISCUSS IT

Ask: Why did you use that strategy to find the elevation of the diver?

Share: I used this strategy because . . .

➤ **Explore different ways to add positive and negative fractions and decimals.**

On a cave dive in Oahu, a scuba diver swims at an elevation of $-20\frac{3}{4}$ ft relative to sea level. She notices a sea turtle above her and rises 6 ft to take its picture. At what elevation does the diver take the picture?

Picture It

You can make a drawing to make sense of the problem.

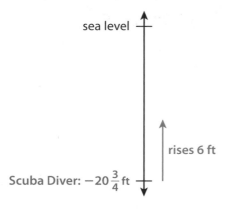

sea level

rises 6 ft

Scuba Diver: $-20\frac{3}{4}$ ft

Model It

You can break apart a mixed number.

$$-20\frac{3}{4} + 6 = -20 + \left(-\frac{3}{4}\right) + 6$$
$$= -20 + 6 + \left(-\frac{3}{4}\right)$$
$$= -14 + \left(-\frac{3}{4}\right)$$

➤ **Use the problem from the previous page to help you understand how to add positive and negative fractions and decimals.**

1 Look at **Picture It**. At what elevation does the diver take the picture? How does the picture help you understand that the elevation is negative?

2 Look at **Model It**. Suppose the problem used -20.75 instead of $-20\frac{3}{4}$. How could you use this strategy?

3 The sum of $-20\frac{3}{4}$ and $-12\frac{1}{4}$ is -33. How can you break apart the mixed numbers to find the sum?

$$-20 + \left(-\frac{3}{4}\right) +$$

4 How is adding positive and negative fractions or decimals similar to adding positive and negative integers? How is it different?

5 **Reflect** Think about all the models and strategies you have discussed today. Describe how one of them helped you better understand how to solve the **Try It** problem.

Apply It

➤ **Use what you learned to solve these problems.**

6 A chemist has a mixture with a temperature of 3.5°C. Then the chemist cools the mixture. The temperature changes by −14.2°C. What is the temperature of the mixture after it cools? Show your work.

SOLUTION _____

7 What is $-12\frac{3}{4} + \left(-5\frac{1}{2}\right)$? Show your work.

$$\frac{51}{4} \qquad -\frac{11}{2}$$

SOLUTION _____

8 What is $-2.75 + 8.25$? Show your work.

SOLUTION _____

Practice Adding Positive and Negative Fractions and Decimals

➤ **Study the Example showing addition of positive and negative decimals. Then solve problems 1–5.**

Example

Oren is conducting a chemistry experiment. The starting temperature of a mixture is −14.8°C. The temperature of the mixture rises by 8.5°C. What is the new temperature of the mixture?

To find the new temperature, add the change to the starting temperature.

$$-14.8 + 8.5 = -14 + (-0.8) + 8 + 0.5$$
$$= -14 + 8 + (-0.8) + 0.5$$
$$= -6 + (-0.8) + 0.5$$
$$= -6 + (-0.3)$$
$$= -6.3$$

The new temperature of the solution is −6.3°C.

---

1. The next day, the temperature of the mixture in the Example rises by another 7.2°C. What is the new temperature? Show your work.

SOLUTION _____

2. Write two addition equations that each have a sum of −21.5.

$$10.5 + 11$$
$$5 + 16.5$$

---

3 What is the sum of 13.75 and -11.25? Show your work.

SOLUTION _____

4 Find $1\frac{2}{3} + \left(-2\frac{1}{2}\right)$. Show your work.

SOLUTION _____

5 A submarine travels at an elevation of $-75\frac{3}{4}$ ft relative to sea level. Then its elevation changes by $-16\frac{3}{8}$ ft. What is the new elevation of the submarine? Show your work.

SOLUTION _____

Dear Family,

This week your student is exploring subtraction with negative integers.

Your student has already seen that subtracting a number and adding the opposite of that number have the same result.

Subtraction problem: $7 - 3 = 4$

Addition problem: $7 + (-3) = 4$

same result

Now your student will see how to use this fact to subtract negative integers. The opposite of a negative integer is a positive integer. So, subtracting a negative number and adding a positive number have the same result.

Subtraction problem: $7 - (-3) = 10$

Addition problem: $7 + 3 = 10$

same result

Your student will be modeling subtraction problems with negative integers.

What is $(-4) - (-1)$?

➤ **ONE WAY** to model subtraction with negative integers is with integer chips.

➤ **ANOTHER WAY** is to use a number line. To show adding a negative number on a number line, draw an arrow to the left. To show subtracting a negative number on a number line, draw an arrow to the right.

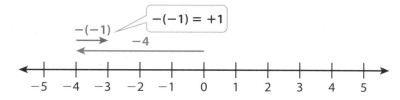

Both models show that $(-4) - (-1) = -3$.

 Use the next page to start a conversation about subtraction with negative integers.

Activity Exploring Subtraction with Negative Integers

➤ **Do this activity together to explore subtraction with negative integers.**

What do you notice about the two equations in each set?
How are the equations alike? How are they different?

SET 1

$(-6) - (-1) = -5$

$(-1) - (-6) = 5$

SET 2

$(-7) - 3 = -10$

$(-7) + (-3) = -10$

SET 3

$(-4) - (-12) = 8$

$(-12) + 8 = -4$

? Do you notice anything that is the same in two of the sets? In all of the sets?

Explore Subtraction with Negative Integers

Model It

➤ **Complete the problems about adding and subtracting integers.**

1 Sierra has $5. She plans to spend $2 on a notepad. She can use the expression 5 − 2 to find how much money she will have left after buying the notepad.

a. Cross out integer chips to model 5 − 2.

b. How much money will Sierra have left after buying the notepad? How does the model show this?

Price $2.00

2 Another way to represent spending $2 is with the integer −2. So, you can also use the expression 5 + (−2) to find how much money Querida will have left.

The integer chips below model finding 5 + (−2). Why are two positive chips and two negative chips crossed out?

DISCUSS IT

Ask: How are the two models similar? How are they different?

Share: I think the two models show the same value because . . .

◎ **Learning Target**   SMP 2, SMP 3, SMP 7
Understand subtraction of rational numbers as adding the additive inverse, $p − q = p + (−q)$.
Show that the distance between two rational numbers on the number line is the absolute value of their difference, and apply this principle in real-world contexts.

Model It

➤ **Complete the problems about adding and subtracting with negative integers.**

3 You can also subtract negative numbers.

a. You can use integer chips to find $-5 - (-2)$. Subtracting -2 means taking away -2. Cross out integer chips to show taking away -2.

b. What is $-5 - (-2)$? How can you tell?

4 The integer chips below model the expression $-5 + 2$.

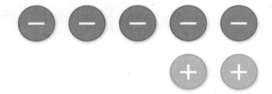

What is $-5 + 2$?

5 Compare the models in problems 3 and 4. How do they show that $-5 - (-2)$ is the same as $-5 + 2$?

6 **Reflect** When you subtract a number, you get the same result as when you add the opposite of that number. Why?

Prepare for Subtraction with Negative Integers

1 Think about what you know about integers and opposites. Fill in each box.
Use words, numbers, and pictures. Show as many ideas as you can.

In My Own Words	My Illustrations

opposite numbers

Examples	Non-Examples

2 What is the opposite of *k*? How do you know?

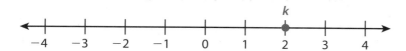

$$k$$

$$-4 \quad -3 \quad -2 \quad -1 \quad 0 \quad 1 \quad 2 \quad 3 \quad 4$$

➤ **Complete problems 3–6.**

3 Michael has 6 dimes. He plans to give 5 dimes to his cousin. He can use the expression $6 - 5$ to find how many dimes he will have left. Cross out integer chips to model $6 - 5$.

4 Michael can also represent giving away 5 dimes with the integer -5. The model below shows $6 + (-5)$. What is $6 + (-5)$?

How do the models in problems 3 and 4 show that $6 + (-5)$ is the same as $6 - 5$?

5 Cross out integer chips to find $-6 - (-5)$. What is $-6 - (-5)$?

6 How do the models below and in problem 5 show that $-6 - (-5)$ is the same as $-6 + 5$?

Develop Understanding of Subtraction with Negative Integers

Model It: Adding Opposites on a Number Line

➤ **Try these two problems involving subtracting integers by adding its opposite.**

1 **a.** Complete the number line to show finding $-6 + 2$.

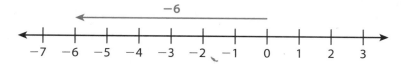

b. Why does $-6 - (-2)$ have the same result as $-6 + 2$?

c. What is $-6 - (-2)$? Explain how you know.

2 **a.** Complete the number line to show finding $4 + (+2)$.

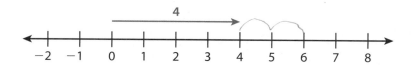

b. How does the number line in problem 2a also show the addition problem $4 + 2$?

$$4 + 2 = 6$$

c. What is $4 + (+2)$?

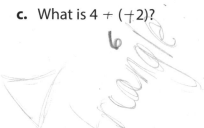

DISCUSS IT

Ask: Why might you want to rewrite a subtraction problem as an addition problem?

Share: I think that you draw an arrow to the right when you subtract a negative number because . . .

Model It: Finding Distances on a Number Line

➤ **Try this problem about absolute value.**

3 A number's absolute value is its distance from 0. You can also use absolute value to talk about the distance between any two numbers.

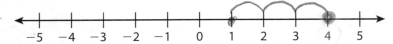

a. On a number line, what is the distance between 4 and 1?

b. One way to express the distance between 4 and 1 is to write $|1 - 4|$. Why do you use absolute value notation to express the distance between two numbers?

c. To find the distance between 4 and 1, does it matter whether you find $|1 - 4|$ or $|4 - 1|$? Explain.

DISCUSS IT

Ask: Why can you write the distance between two numbers as a difference?

Share: Another way I could find $1 - 4$ is to . . .

CONNECT IT

➤ **Complete the problems below.**

4 What is $-2 - 5$? Explain how you can use the distance between -2 and 5 to check your answer.

−7   the distance between 2 and 5 is 7. then you turn it into a negative

5 Use a model of your choice to find $-1 - (-6)$.

Practice Understanding Subtraction with Negative Integers

➤ **Study how the Example shows two ways to find the distance between two numbers. Then solve problems 1–4.**

Example

What is the distance between an elevation of −8 ft and −3 ft?

One way you can find the distance is to subtract: −3 − (−8).

Subtracting an integer is the same as adding its opposite. The opposite of −8 is 8. So, you can find −3 − (−8) by finding −3 + 8.

You can also use a number line to find −3 − (−8).

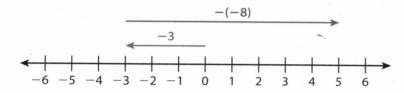

Either way, −3 − (−8) = 5. The distance between −8 ft and −3 ft is 5 ft.

1 **a.** Complete the model to find −7 + 4.

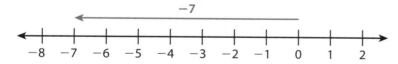

b. Why does −7 − (−4) have the same result as −7 + 4?

c. What is −7 − (−4)? Explain how you know.

2 Soledad has −3 points in a trivia contest. In the next round, she loses 6 points.

a. Complete the model to find −3 − 6.

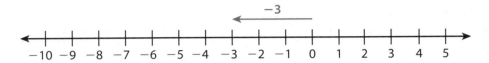

−3

−10 −9 −8 −7 −6 −5 −4 −3 −2 −1 0 1 2 3 4 5

b. How does the model in problem 2a also show the addition problem −3 + (−6)?

c. What is −3 − 6? What does that tell you about how many points Soledad has after the next round?

3 How is the value of 2 − 3 like the value of 3 − 2? How is it different?

4 **a.** On a number line, what is the distance between −9 and −5?

b. One way to express the distance between −9 and −5 is |−5 − (−9)|. Why do you use absolute value notation to express the distance between two numbers?

c. To find the distance between −9 and −5, does it matter whether you find |−5 − (−9)| or |−9 − (−5)|? Explain.

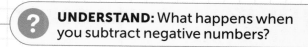
Refine Ideas About Subtraction with Negative Integers

Apply It **Math Toolkit** integer chips, number lines

➤ **Complete problems 1–5.**

1 **Conclude** Mr. Lin writes the expressions $-20 - 8$ and $8 - (-20)$ on the board. He asks his class which result is greater. How can his class decide without finding the value of each difference?

2 **Critique** Patrick thinks that when a is a negative integer and b is a positive integer, each of the following statements is always true. Read the statements below and decide whether they are true or false. For statements that are true, give an example to support Patrick's claim. For statements that are false, give a counterexample.

a. $a - b$ is positive.

b. $b - a$ is positive.

c. $a - (-b)$ is negative.

3 **Interpret** The current temperature is $-8°F$. By how many degrees does the temperature need to change to reach $7°F$? Write two subtraction problems that model the distance on the thermometer between $-8°F$ and $7°F$.

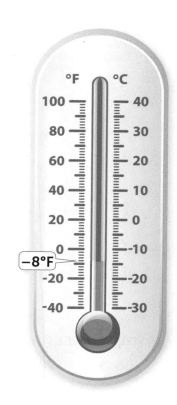

4 Anica's teacher writes the expression $a - b$ on the board.

PART A Anica says you can rewrite any subtraction problem as an addition problem. Is Anica correct? Explain.

PART B Rewrite $a - b$ as an addition problem. Then choose negative integers as values for a and b and find $a - b$.

5 **Math Journal** How is finding $-15 - (-6)$ similar to finding $15 - 6$? How is it different?

✓ **End of Lesson Checklist**

☐ **INTERACTIVE GLOSSARY** Write a new entry for *counterexample*. Tell what you do when you give a *counterexample* to a math argument.

Dear Family,

This week your student is learning about adding and subtracting positive and negative decimals and fractions.

Your student has already learned to add and subtract integers. The strategies for adding and subtracting positive and negative decimals and fractions are similar to those for adding and subtracting integers.

Addition

$-0.2 + 0.6 = 0.4$

Subtraction

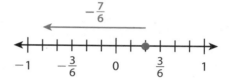

$\frac{2}{6} - \frac{7}{6} = -\frac{5}{6}$

Your student will be solving problems like the one below.

> A manatee is swimming at -5.6 feet relative to sea level. It swims down 3.8 feet. What is the manatee's new elevation?

➤ **ONE WAY** to find the manatee's new elevation is to use a number line.

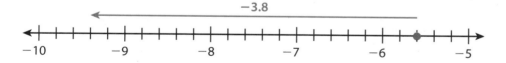

➤ **ANOTHER WAY** is to rewrite a subtraction problem as an addition problem.

$$-5.6 - 3.8 = -5.6 + (-3.8)$$
$$= [-5 + (-3)] + [-0.6 + (-0.8)]$$
$$= -8 + (-1.4)$$
$$= -9.4$$

Both ways show that the manatee's new elevation is -9.4 feet.

 Use the next page to start a conversation about positive and negative numbers.

Activity Thinking About Positive and Negative Numbers Around You

➤ **Do this activity together to investigate positive and negative numbers in the real world.**

The hottest temperature recorded in the United States was in California in 1913. It was 134.1°F!

In 1971, a settlement in Alaska reached −79.8°F. That is the coldest temperature recorded in the United States.

The difference between the hottest and coldest temperatures is 134.1 − (−79.8), or 213.9°F!

? Where else do you see positive and negative fractions and decimals around you?

Explore Adding and Subtracting with Integers

10 m above water's surface

Previously, you learned how to add positive and negative numbers. In this lesson, you will learn about subtracting positive and negative fractions and decimals.

➤ **Use what you know to try to solve the problem below.**

A pool's diving platform is 10 m above the water's surface. The bottom of the pool is at −5 m, relative to the surface of the water. What is the distance between the diving platform and the bottom of the pool?

 TRY IT

 Math Toolkit grid paper, integer chips, number lines

DISCUSS IT

Ask: How does your work represent the surface of the water?

Share: In my work . . . represents . . .

◎ **Learning Targets** SMP 1, SMP 2, SMP 3, SMP 4, SMP 5, SMP 6, SMP 7
Apply and extend previous understandings of addition and subtraction to add and subtract rational numbers; represent addition and subtraction on a horizontal or vertical number line diagram.
• Apply properties of operations as strategies to add and subtract rational numbers.

CONNECT IT

1 **Look Back** What is the distance between the diving platform and the bottom of the pool? How do you know?

2 **Look Ahead** In the **Try It**, you found the distance between two elevations represented by integers. You can also find the distance between non-integers.

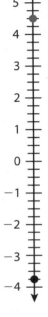

a. Explain how you can use the number line to find the distance between 4.5 and −3.75.

b. You can use both the expression $|4.5 - (-3.75)|$ and the expression $|-3.75 - 4.5|$ to find the distance between 4.5 and −3.75. Why?

c. You can subtract to find the difference between 4.5 and −3.75. Explain why −3.75 − 4.5 is the opposite of 4.5 − (−3.75).

3 **Reflect** How is finding the distance between two numbers on the number line like finding the difference between two numbers? How is it different?

Name:

Prepare for Subtracting Positive and Negative Numbers

1 Think about what you know about numbers and absolute value. Fill in each box. Use words, numbers, and pictures. Show as many ideas as you can.

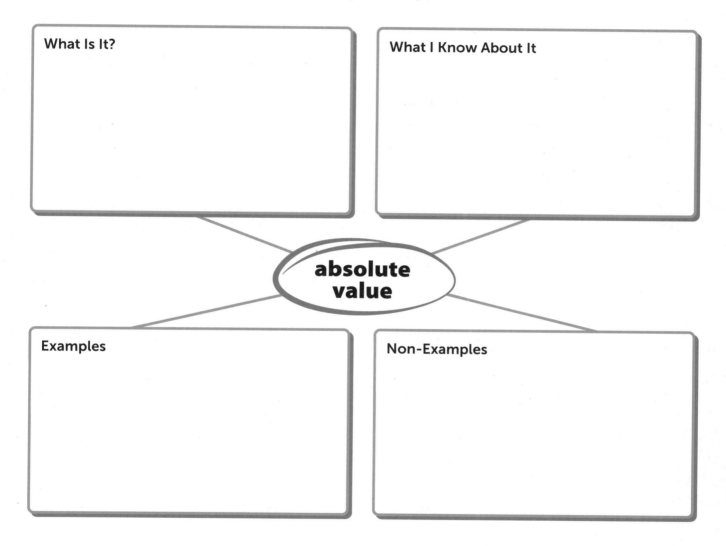

What Is It?

What I Know About It

absolute value

Examples

Non-Examples

2 Is -4 the absolute value of $3 - 7$? Explain.

3 The top of a molehill is 4 in. above ground level.
The bottom of a mole's burrow is at −9 in. relative to ground level.

a. What is the distance between the top of the molehill and the burrow? Show your work.

SOLUTION _____

_____

b. Check your answer to problem 3a. Show your work.

Develop Subtracting Positive and Negative Fractions and Decimals

➤ **Read and try to solve the problem below.**

During December, the average daily temperature in a town is −1.7°C. The average daily temperature in the same town is 3.2°C lower in January. What is the average daily temperature in January?

TRY IT

 Math Toolkit grid paper, number lines, place-value charts

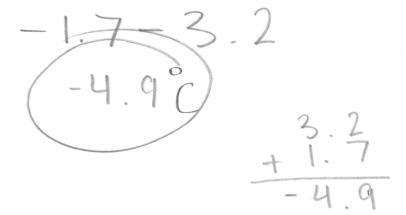

$-1.7 - 3.2$

$-4.9°C$

$$\begin{array}{r} 3.2 \\ + 1.7 \\ \hline -4.9 \end{array}$$

DISCUSS IT

Ask: What did you do first to find the temperature in January?

Share: I started by . . .

➤ **Explore different ways to understand adding or subtracting negative decimals.**

During December, the average daily temperature in a town is −1.7°C. The average daily temperature in the same town is 3.2°C lower in January. What is the average daily temperature in January?

Model It

You can write an expression to represent the situation.

You can write a **subtraction** expression:

−1.7 − 3.2

You can also write an **addition** expression:

−1.7 + (−3.2)

Model It

You can use a number line to add or subtract negative decimals.

The average temperature in January was **3.2°C lower** than in **December**.

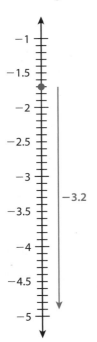

CONNECT IT

➤ **Use the problem from the previous page to help you understand how to subtract with negative decimals and fractions.**

1 Look at the first **Model It**. Why can you write both an addition expression and a subtraction expression for the situation?

2 Look at the second **Model It**. How does the number line represent both the addition expression and the subtraction expression?

3 What is the average temperature in January?

4 How is adding two negative decimals like adding two positive decimals? How is it different?

5 How is subtracting a negative decimal like subtracting a negative integer?

6 **Reflect** Think about all the models and strategies you have discussed today. Describe how one of them helped you better understand how to subtract negative decimals.

Apply It

➤ **Use what you learned to solve these problems.**

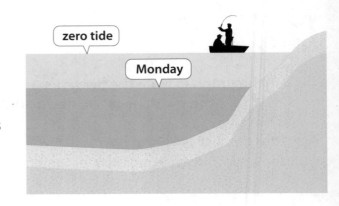

zero tide

Monday

7 On Monday, the low tide at Cook Inlet, Alaska, is $-1\frac{1}{2}$ ft. On Tuesday, the low tide is $-1\frac{1}{3}$ ft. How does the low tide on Tuesday compare to the low tide on Monday? Show your work.

$$-1\frac{1}{2} \quad \downarrow \quad \frac{3}{2}$$

$$-1\frac{1}{3} \quad \downarrow \quad \frac{4}{3}$$

$$\frac{3}{2} \times \frac{3}{3} = \frac{9}{6}$$

$$\frac{4}{3} \times \frac{2}{2} = \frac{8}{6}$$

$$= \frac{1}{6}$$

SOLUTION _____

8 Find $3\frac{1}{4} - 4\frac{1}{2}$. Show your work.

SOLUTION _____

9 Find $5.4 - 7.1$. Show your work.

SOLUTION _____

Practice Subtracting Positive and Negative Fractions and Decimals

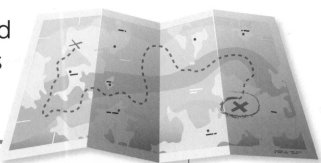

➤ **Study the Example showing how to subtract negative fractions. Then solve problems 1–5.**

Example

A path from a dry lake bed starts at an elevation of $-12\frac{1}{2}$ ft relative to sea level. The path ends at an elevation of $60\frac{1}{3}$ ft above sea level. What number represents the change in elevation from the start to the end of the path?

You can subtract to find the change in elevation.

$$60\frac{1}{3} - \left(-12\frac{1}{2}\right) = 60\frac{1}{3} + 12\frac{1}{2}$$

$$= 60\frac{2}{6} + 12\frac{3}{6}$$

$$= 72\frac{5}{6}$$

The number that represents the change in elevation is $72\frac{5}{6}$.

1 You can also find $-12\frac{1}{2} - 60\frac{1}{3} = -72\frac{5}{6}$. What information does that give you about the path in the Example?

2 The lowest point of the dry lake bed in the Example has an elevation of $-18\frac{3}{4}$ ft. What number represents the change in elevation from the start of the path to the lowest point in the dry lake bed? Show your work.

SOLUTION _____

3 What is 2.6 − 7.3? Show your work.

SOLUTION _____

4 When Daria gets to school, the temperature is 5.7°F. The temperature changes by −9.5°F by the time she goes to bed. What is the temperature when Daria goes to bed? Show your work.

SOLUTION _____

5 An otter is swimming at −4.2 yd relative to the surface of the water. It dives 8.6 yd deeper. After the dive, what is the otter's elevation relative to the surface of the water?

A −12.8 yd

B −4.4 yd

C 4.4 yd

D 12.8 yd

Develop Adding and Subtracting Positive and Negative Fractions and Decimals

rises
913.9 m

➤ **Read and try to solve the problem below.**

Mei releases a lantern for the Lantern Festival. She stands in a field that is 0.5 m below sea level. The lantern rises 913.9 m. Then the candle in the lantern goes out. The lantern comes down 925.2 m to land on the surface of a lake. What is the elevation of the lake relative to sea level?

  Math Toolkit grid paper, number lines, place-value charts

DISCUSS IT

Ask: What did you do first to find the elevation of the lake?

Share: The first thing I did to find the elevation was . . .

LESSON 10 Add and Subtract Positive and Negative Numbers   **193**

➤ **Explore different ways to understand adding and subtracting positive and negative numbers.**

Mei releases a lantern for the Lantern Festival. She stands in a field that is 0.5 m below sea level. The lantern rises 913.9 m. Then the candle in the lantern goes out. The lantern comes down 925.2 m to land on the surface of a lake. What is the elevation of the lake relative to sea level?

Picture It

You can draw a diagram to model the lantern's movement.

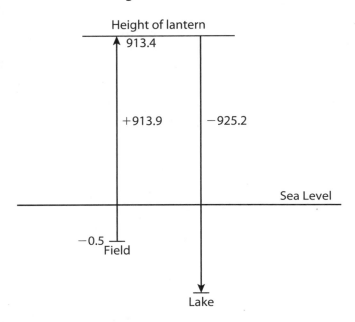

Model It

You can add and subtract from left to right to simplify.

$$-0.5 + 913.9 - 925.2 = -0.5 + 913.9 - 925.2$$
$$= 913.4 - 925.2$$

Model It

You can reorder the terms before simplifying.

$$-0.5 + 913.9 - 925.2 = -0.5 + 913.9 + (-925.2)$$
$$= -0.5 + (-925.2) + 913.9$$
$$= -925.7 + 913.9$$

➤ **Use the problem from the previous page to help you understand how to add and subtract positive and negative numbers.**

1 Look at **Picture It**. Does the lantern end up lower or higher than its starting point? How do the arrows show the lantern's movement?

2 Look at the first **Model It**. What is the value of the expression $-0.5 + 913.9 - 925.2$? How does the expression show the movement of the lantern?

3 Look at the second **Model It**. Why can you change the order of the terms?

4 How does changing the order of the terms change the way you find the sum?

5 Consider the expression $1\frac{5}{6} - 2\frac{1}{3} - 1\frac{1}{6}$. To find the value, which two terms might you combine first? Why?

6 **Reflect** Think about all the models and strategies you have discussed today. Describe how one of them helped you better understand how to solve the **Try It** problem.

Apply It

➤ **Use what you learned to solve these problems.**

7 A helicopter is 19.25 meters above the top of a canyon wall. It goes down 27.60 meters, passing into the canyon. Then it goes up 5.25 meters. What is the new position of the helicopter relative to the top of the canyon wall?

A −52.1 m

B −3.1 m

C 3.1 m

D 52.1 m

8 The temperature during the day is 5.4°C. After sunset, the temperature falls 7.5°C. Wind chill makes the temperature after sunset feel 6.3°C colder. What temperature does it feel like after sunset? Show your work.

SOLUTION _____

9 What is $-5\frac{1}{2} - 9\frac{1}{4} + 2\frac{3}{4}$? Show your work.

SOLUTION _____

Name:

Practice Adding and Subtracting Positive and Negative Fractions and Decimals

➤ **Study the Example showing adding and subtracting positive and negative fractions. Then solve problems 1–4.**

Example

Hummingbirds sip $2\frac{1}{2}$ fl oz of the liquid food in a feeder.

Then $1\frac{1}{2}$ fl oz of food is added to the feeder. Last, hummingbirds

sip another $3\frac{1}{4}$ fl oz of food. What is the overall change in the

amount of food in the feeder?

You can write an expression to represent the situation.

$$-2\frac{1}{2} + 1\frac{1}{2} - 3\frac{1}{4}$$

You can begin simplifying the expression by reordering the terms.

$$-2\frac{1}{2} + 1\frac{1}{2} - 3\frac{1}{4} = -2\frac{1}{2} - 3\frac{1}{4} + 1\frac{1}{2}$$

$$= -5\frac{3}{4} + 1\frac{1}{2}$$

$$= -4\frac{1}{4}$$

The overall change in the amount of food in the feeder is $-4\frac{1}{4}$ fl oz.

1️⃣ The feeder in the Example had 16 fl oz of food in it to start. How much food does it have now? Show your work.

SOLUTION _____

2 Is each expression equivalent to $-2.7 + (-3.1)$?

	Yes	No
a. $-2.7 - 3.1$	○	○
b. $-2.7 + (-3) + (-0.1)$	○	○
c. $-2 + (-0.7) + (-3) + (-0.1)$	○	○
d. $-2 + 0.7 + (-3.1)$	○	○

3 Reth is playing a game. First, he loses 4.8 points. Then he gains 2.5 points. Finally, he loses another 7.8 points. What is the overall change in Reth's score? Show your work.

SOLUTION _____

4 An autonomous underwater vehicle (AUV) is at an elevation of -8.25 ft. It dives down $6\frac{2}{3}$ ft to collect a specimen. Then the AUV dives another $15\frac{3}{4}$ ft. What is the final elevation of the AUV? Show your work.

AUV: autonomous underwater vehicle

SOLUTION _____

Refine Adding and Subtracting Positive and Negative Numbers

➤ **Complete the Example below. Then solve problems 1–10.**

Example

What is 2.5 − 4.3?

Look at how you could use absolute value to find the difference.

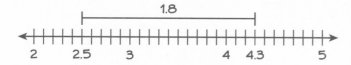

On a number line, 2.5 and 4.3 are 1.8 units apart. The distance between two numbers is the same as the absolute value of their difference. So, |2.5 − 4.3| = 1.8.

Since 2.5 − 4.3 has a negative result, the difference is a negative number with an absolute value of 1.8.

SOLUTION _____

CONSIDER THIS . . .
Distance on a number line is never negative.

PAIR/SHARE
Does the method in the Example work for subtracting negative numbers?

Apply It

1 Cece's dog loses $1\frac{1}{4}$ lb. Then her dog loses another $1\frac{1}{8}$ lb. Finally, it gains $\frac{3}{8}$ lb. What is the total change in her dog's weight? Show your work.

CONSIDER THIS . . .
The result would be the same if Cece's dog lost weight, then gained weight, then lost weight.

PAIR/SHARE
Suppose Cece's dog weighs 38 pounds to start. Does that change your answer? Why?

SOLUTION _____

2 What is $-8.3 - (-5.4)$? Show your work.

CONSIDER THIS...
The inverse of subtraction is addition.

PAIR/SHARE
How can you check that your answer makes sense?

SOLUTION _____

3 Which value of x makes the following statement true?

$-0.5 - x =$ a positive number

CONSIDER THIS...
Zero is not a positive or a negative number.

A $x = 1.5$

B $x = 0.5$

C $x = -0.5$

D $x = -1.5$

Lulu chose A as the correct answer. How might she have gotten that answer?

PAIR/SHARE
What is another value that makes this statement true?

4 A submarine 50.2 m below the surface of the ocean goes up 15.6 m. Then it goes down 35.7 m. What is the submarine's new position relative to the surface of the ocean? Show your work.

50.2 m
below surface

SOLUTION _____

5 Which situation could the expression $-8 - 10$ represent?

A An elevator stops at the 8th floor. Then it stops at the 10th floor.

B Gabe earned $8. Then he spent $10 on a new book.

C At a bus stop, 8 people got off and 10 people got on.

D The temperature dropped 8°F. Then it dropped another 10°F.

6 Without calculating, explain how you can tell if the value of the expression $-9.45 - (-1.72) - 2.53$ is *positive* or *negative*.

7 The value of $-4\frac{5}{8} - x$ is positive. What are two possible values of x? Show your work.

SOLUTION _____

_____

8 Is $a - b$ a *positive number* or a *negative number*? How do you know?

9 Esteban stands on a dock 1.25 yd above the water. A fish swims below Esteban at −4.61 yd from the surface of the water. How many yards apart are Esteban and the fish?

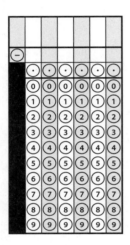

10 **Math Journal** Write a subtraction problem involving two negative decimal numbers. At least one decimal must include hundredths. Explain how to solve your problem.

✓ **End of Lesson Checklist**

☐ **INTERACTIVE GLOSSARY** Write a new entry for *represent*. Write at least one synonym for *represent*.

☐ **SELF CHECK** Go back to the Unit 2 Opener and see what you can check off.

Study an Example Problem and Solution

SMP 1 Make sense of problems and persevere in solving them.

➤ **Read this problem involving addition and subtraction with integers. Then look at one student's solution to this problem on the following pages.**

Planning a Route

Chantel and Keith are scientists who are part of a team that explores caves. They study bacteria that live in extreme conditions. They are planning an expedition to collect samples of bacteria that live in pools of water deep within a cave. The expedition will last several days. The caving team will camp inside the cave. Read this email from Chantel and help Keith respond.

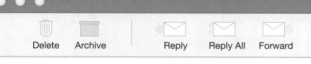

Delete   Archive   Reply   Reply All   Forward

To: Keith
Subject: Pools for sample collections

Hi Keith,

I spoke to the caving team today. We decided to collect samples from four pools. The table lists the pools we can visit and their elevations relative to ground level. The cave entrance is at ground level, so its elevation is 0 m.

HOW YOU CAN HELP:

• Select the four pools we should visit.

• Decide on the order in which we will visit the pools.

• Determine the change in elevation for each stage of our expedition.

  • **Stage 1:** Cave entrance to first pool

  • **Stage 2:** First pool to second pool

  • **Stage 3:** Second pool to third pool

  • **Stage 4:** Third pool to fourth pool

  • **Stage 5:** Fourth pool to cave entrance

Thanks!

Chantel

Pool Name	Elevation (m)
Castle Keep Pool	−221
Flower Garden Pool	−439
Glowing Pool	−277
Murky Pool	−130
Orange Dot Pool	−55
Pink Giants Pool	−319
Hawke Bay Pool	−307

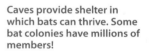

Caves provide shelter in which bats can thrive. Some bat colonies have millions of members!

One Student's Solution

☐ Tell what is known.

☐ Tell what the
problem is asking.

☐ Show all your work.

☐ Show that the
solution works.

First, I have to choose four pools for the scientists to visit.

I will pick Castle Keep, Glowing, Murky, and Pink Giants Pools.

Now, I need to decide on an order
for the scientists to visit the pools.

I think they should start with the pool that
is farthest from the cave entrance and
then move back up toward the surface. I
will make a vertical number line to model
the locations of the pools.

The first pool the scientists will visit will be
Pink Giants Pool, because it is the farthest
from the cave entrance. Next will be
Glowing Pool, then Castle Keep Pool, and
last will be Murky Pool.

Then, I can determine the change in elevation for Stage 1,
from the cave entrance to Pink Giants Pool.

To find the change in elevation, I will subtract the **starting** elevation
from the **ending** elevation.

elevation of **Pink Giants Pool** − elevation of **cave entrance** =

$$-319 \qquad - \qquad 0 \qquad = -319$$

NOTICE THAT . . .
Because any number
minus 0 is equal to the
number, you know
that $-319 - 0$ is
equal to -319.

The change in elevation for Stage 1 is -319 m.

Next, I can find the change in elevation for Stage 2,
from Pink Giants Pool to Glowing Pool.

Again, I will subtract the starting elevation from the ending elevation.

elevation of Glowing Pool − elevation of Pink Giants Pool =

$$-277 \qquad - \qquad (-319) \qquad =$$
$$-277 \qquad + \qquad 319 \qquad = 42$$

NOTICE THAT . . .
You can rewrite the
subtraction problem as
an addition problem.

The change in elevation for Stage 2 is 42 m.

Now, I will use the same steps to find the change in elevation for Stages 3, 4, and 5.

Stage 3: elevation of Castle Keep Pool − elevation of Glowing Pool =

| −221 | − | (−277) | = |
| −221 | + | 277 | = 56 |

Stage 4: elevation of Murky Pool − elevation of Castle Keep Pool =

| −130 | − | (−221) | = |
| −130 | + | 221 | = 91 |

Stage 5: elevation of cave entrance − elevation of Murky Pool =

| 0 | − | (−130) | = |
| 0 | + | 130 | = 130 |

NOTICE THAT...
The changes in elevation are positive for stages in which the scientists move upward.

Next, I can check that my calculations are reasonable.

The expedition starts and ends at the same place, so the total change in elevation should be 0 m. I can add the changes in elevation for the five stages to check that the sum is 0.

$$-319 + 42 + 56 + 91 + 130 =$$
$$-319 + 319 = 0$$

The sum is 0, so my calculations are reasonable.

NOTICE THAT...
You can simplify the addition by adding all of the positive numbers first.

Finally, I will present my plan for the expedition in a table.

Stage	Description	Elevation Change (m)
1	Cave entrance to Pink Giants Pool	−319
2	Pink Giants Pool to Glowing Pool	42
3	Glowing Pool to Castle Keep Pool	56
4	Castle Keep Pool to Murky Pool	91
5	Murky Pool to cave entrance	130

Try Another Approach

➤ **There are many ways to solve problems. Think about how you might solve the Planning a Route problem in a different way.**

Planning a Route

Chantel and Keith are scientists who are part of a team that explores caves. They study bacteria that live in extreme conditions. They are planning an expedition to collect samples of bacteria that live in pools of water deep within a cave. The expedition will last several days. The caving team will camp inside the cave. Read this email from Chantel and help Keith respond.

Delete   Archive | Reply   Reply All   Forward

To: Keith
Subject: Pools for sample collections

Hi Keith,

I spoke to the caving team today. We decided to collect samples from four pools. The table lists the pools we can visit and their elevations relative to ground level. The cave entrance is at ground level, so its elevation is 0 m.

HOW YOU CAN HELP:

- Select the four pools we should visit.
- Decide on the order in which we will visit the pools.
- Determine the change in elevation for each stage of our expedition.
  - **Stage 1:** Cave entrance to first pool
  - **Stage 2:** First pool to second pool
  - **Stage 3:** Second pool to third pool
  - **Stage 4:** Third pool to fourth pool
  - **Stage 5:** Fourth pool to cave entrance

Thanks!

Chantel

Pool Name	Elevation (m)
Castle Keep Pool	−221
Flower Garden Pool	−439
Glowing Pool	−277
Murky Pool	−130
Orange Dot Pool	−55
Pink Giants Pool	−319
Hawke Bay Pool	−307

Plan It

➤ **Answer these questions to help you start thinking about a plan.**

a. Which four pools will you select for the scientists to visit?

b. In what order will you have the scientists visit the pools?

Solve It

➤ **Find a different solution for the Planning a Route problem. Show all your work on a separate sheet of paper. You may want to use the Problem-Solving Tips to get started.**

PROBLEM-SOLVING TIPS

 Math Toolkit grid paper, integer chips, number lines

Key Terms

addend	difference	integers
inverse operations	negative numbers	opposite numbers
positive numbers	sum	zero pair

Sentence Starters

• To find the change in elevation for Stage 1, I will . . .

• I know that the change in elevation for Stage 1 will be negative because . . .

Reflect

Use Mathematical Practices As you work through the problem, discuss these questions with a partner.

• **Reason Mathematically** How can you tell, without doing any calculations, whether a change in elevation will be positive or negative?

• **Make an Argument** If you change the order in which the scientists visit the four pools you chose, will this affect the total change in elevation for the expedition? Why or why not?

The Waitomo Caves in New Zealand are known for their glowworms. You can explore these caves by walking, taking a boat tour, or even floating on a rubber tube.

Discuss Models and Strategies

➤ **Read the problem. Write a solution on a separate sheet of paper. Remember, there can be lots of ways to solve a problem.**

Budgeting for Caving Equipment

A cave expedition group is arranging for several experienced cavers to go with Chantel and Keith on their expedition. The group is planning to buy some new equipment for the cavers. Look at the information about the group's budget and the equipment price list.

Select at least five pieces of equipment for the group to buy. Then determine the value that should be entered in the equipment row of the budget. Show that the group can afford the equipment you selected.

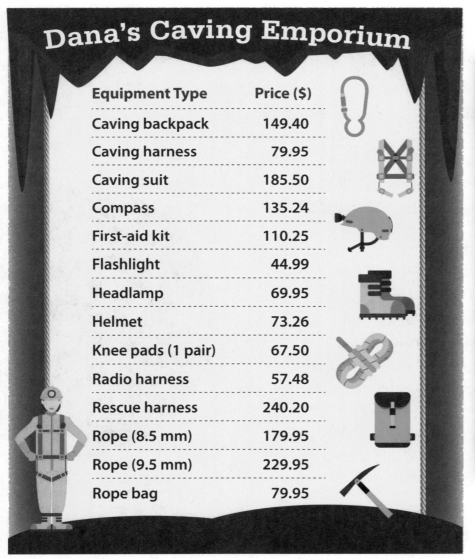

Dana's Caving Emporium

Equipment Type	Price ($)
Caving backpack	149.40
Caving harness	79.95
Caving suit	185.50
Compass	135.24
First-aid kit	110.25
Flashlight	44.99
Headlamp	69.95
Helmet	73.26
Knee pads (1 pair)	67.50
Radio harness	57.48
Rescue harness	240.20
Rope (8.5 mm)	179.95
Rope (9.5 mm)	229.95
Rope bag	79.95

MY BUDGETS

Cave Expedition Group

Category	Amount
Membership dues	$4,715
Other revenue	$7,410
Professional fees	−$6,975
Insurance	−$1,286
Equipment	?
Other expenses	−$3,035

* Positive numbers represent revenue (money the group takes in).

* Negative numbers represent expenses (money the group spends).

Plan It and Solve It

➤ **Find a solution to the Budgeting for Caving Equipment problem.**

Write a detailed plan and support your answer. Be sure to include:

- a list of at least five pieces of equipment you selected for the group to buy.
- the value that should be entered in the equipment row of the budget.
- work showing that the group can afford the equipment you selected by showing that the sum of the numbers in the budget is not a negative amount.

PROBLEM-SOLVING TIPS

 Math Toolkit grid paper, integer chips, number lines, place-value charts

Key Terms

integers	inverse operations	negative numbers
opposite numbers	positive numbers	zero pair

Questions

- What is the total amount the cave expedition group will spend on equipment?
- How do you know what sign to use for the value in the equipment row of the budget?

Reflect

Use Mathematical Practices As you work through the problem, discuss these questions with a partner.

- **Use Models** How could a number line help you solve this problem?

- **Reason Mathematically** What is the greatest amount the cave expedition group can spend on equipment if the sum of the numbers in the budget cannot be negative? How do you know?

A caving team may spend several days underground, not returning to the surface until its expedition is over.

Persevere On Your Own

➤ **Read the problem. Write a solution on a separate sheet of paper.**

Deciding Whether to Delay an Expedition

Chantel and Keith have planned an expedition to a different cave. The expedition is scheduled to start on May 8. However, heavy rains have been falling near the cave and local rivers are flooding. Read this email from Keith and help Chantel respond.

To: Chantel
Subject: Possible flooding

Hi Chantel,

There are three river monitoring stations near the cave. If the gauge height at any of the stations is above flood stage by the start date, we will need to postpone the expedition due to the risk of flooding in the cave. Station PR3311 has a flood stage of 34 ft. Station FR3145 has a flood stage of 28 ft. Station BR3103 has a flood stage of 18 ft.

Station ID	Gauge Height on May 1 (ft)	Change in Gauge Height from Previous Day (ft)					
		May 2	May 3	May 4	May 5	May 6	May 7
PR3311	$27\frac{1}{2}$	$+18\frac{1}{2}$	$+6$	-1	$-5\frac{1}{4}$	-11	$-8\frac{1}{4}$
FR3145	5	$+8$	$+22\frac{1}{4}$	$+6\frac{3}{4}$	-9	$-10\frac{1}{2}$	$-6\frac{1}{4}$
BR3103	$2\frac{1}{4}$	$+2\frac{1}{2}$	$+15\frac{1}{4}$	$+7\frac{1}{4}$	$-13\frac{1}{4}$	-6	$-1\frac{1}{2}$

River Monitoring Stations Near Cave

HERE'S WHAT I NEED FROM YOU:

• Choose one of the three monitoring stations and determine its gauge height on May 7. I will do the two stations you do not pick.

• The expedition should be postponed if the gauge height on May 7 for the station you selected is greater than the flood stage height. Based on your calculations, recommend whether the expedition should be postponed.

Thanks!

Keith

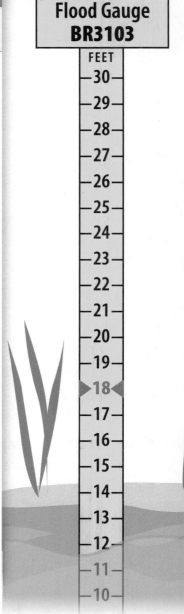

Flood Gauge BR3103

FEET
30
29
28
27
26
25
24
23
22
21
20
19
▶18◀
17
16
15
14
13
12
11
10

Solve It

➤ **Find a solution to the Deciding Whether to Delay an Expedition problem.**

- Choose one of the three monitoring stations and determine the gauge height at that station on May 7.

- Make a recommendation about whether the expedition should be delayed based on the station you picked. The expedition should be delayed if the gauge height on May 7 is greater than the flood stage height for that station.

Reflect

Use Mathematical Practices After you complete the problem, choose one of these questions to discuss with a partner.

- **Use Structure** What strategy did you use to determine the gauge height on May 7? Why did you choose that strategy?

- **Critique Reasoning** Look at your partner's solution to the problem. Do you agree with your partner's recommendation about whether the expedition should be delayed? Explain.

Most caves are formed by water. They are usually located where there is an abundance of limestone.

In this unit you learned to . . .

Skill	Lesson
Add positive and negative integers.	**7, 8**
Add positive and negative fractions and decimals.	**8**
Subtract positive and negative integers.	**9, 10**
Subtract positive and negative fractions and decimals.	**10**
Justify solutions to problems about adding and subtracting rational numbers by telling what you noticed and what you decided to do as a result.	**7, 8, 9, 10**

Think about what you have learned.

➤ **Use words, numbers, and drawings.**

1 The most important topic I learned is _____ because . . .

2 A mistake I made that helped me learn was . . .

3 One thing I could do better is . . .

➤ **Review the unit vocabulary. Put a check mark by items you can use in speaking and writing. Look up the meaning of any terms you do not know.**

Math Vocabulary		Academic Vocabulary
☐ absolute value	☐ opposite numbers	☐ claim
☐ integers	☐ positive numbers	☐ counterexample
☐ negative numbers	☐ zero pair	☐ notation
		☐ relative to
		☐ represent

➤ **Use the unit vocabulary to complete the problems.**

1 How are opposite numbers and zero pairs related?

2 How are integers and rational numbers the same and different?

3 Give an example of a pair of integers that form a zero pair and explain why they do. Then give an example of a pair of integers that do not form a zero pair and explain why they do not.

4 Think about the meaning of *relative to*. Then rephrase this sentence in your own words: The altitude of the bird is 4 feet relative to the rooftop.

➤ **Use what you have learned to complete these problems.**

1 Todd's team starts a football game. On the first play, they gain 6 yards. On the second play, they lose 12 yards. The expression $6 + (-12)$ represents this situation.

Use a model to find $6 + (-12)$. Show your work.

SOLUTION _____

2 What is the sum of -18 and -27?

A -45

B -9

C 9

D 45

3 What is $\left(-3\frac{3}{4}\right) - \left(-2\frac{1}{4}\right)$? Show your work.

SOLUTION _____

4 Which expression is equivalent to $a - b$?

A $a + b$

B $(-a) + b$

C $a + (-b)$

D $(-a) + (-b)$

5 Which sums are equal to $-9 + 21$? Choose all the correct answers.

A $21 + (-9)$

B $9 + (-21)$

C $(-9) + 9 + 12$

D $-(9 + 21)$

E $(-9) + (-21)$

6 A bird flies 8.64 meters above a pond. A fish swims below the bird at -1.78 meters from the surface of the water. How many meters apart are the bird and the fish? Record your answer on the grid. Then fill in the bubbles.

7 What addition equation does this number line show? Write and solve a word problem about elevation that matches the addition equation. Show your work.

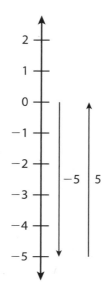

SOLUTION _____

_____

_____

_____

_____

Performance Task

➤ **Answer the questions and show all your work on separate paper.**

A smartphone company asks you to compare battery life on its two newest models. You created the table below to show the percent of battery life remaining after users complete each activity.

- Find the change in battery life after each activity. Record each change as a positive or negative integer.

- Decide which phone has a better battery life. Explain your reasoning.

Activity	Slim-XL	Slim-XL Change	Mindtouch	Mindtouch Change	Difference of Slim-XL Change and Mindtouch Change
Starting charge	100%		100%		
Watch an exercise video for 1 hour	93%	93% − 100% = −7%	90%	90% − 100% = −10%	−7% − (−10%) = 3%
Play a math game for 1 hour	84%		76%		
Charge for 1 hour	100%		95%		
Make science videos for 1 hour	57%		49%		
Sit idle for 2 hours	47%		37%		
Charge for 2 hours	99%		95%		
	Overall Change:		Overall Change:		

Reflect

Use Mathematical Practices After you complete the task, choose one of the following questions to answer.

- **Use Reasoning** How can the positive or negative signs on the differences of changes in battery life help show which phone performs better after that activity?

- **Argue and Critique** How did you prove that one phone has a better battery life than the other?

Unit 3

Numbers and Operations

Multiply and Divide Rational Numbers

☑ **Self Check** | Before starting this unit, check off the skills you know below.
As you complete each lesson, see how many more skills you can check off!

I can . . .	Before	After
Multiply positive and negative integers.	☐	☐
Divide positive and negative integers.	☐	☐
Multiply positive and negative fractions and decimals.	☐	☐
Divide positive and negative fractions and decimals.	☐	☐
Express rational numbers as terminating or repeating decimals.	☐	☐
Solve word problems with rational numbers.	☐	☐
Use math vocabulary and precise language to explain problems with rational numbers.	☐	☐

Prepare for Multiplying and Dividing Rational Numbers

➤ **Think about what you know about working with positive and negative numbers. Find the value of each expression. Then write the expression in the correct part of the Venn diagram.**

$3 - 5$ $-3 + (-1)$ $-2 + (-2) + (-2)$

$-4.5 + 5$ $-6 - (-7)$ $-1 + (-1) + (-1) + 3\frac{1}{2}$

$4 - (-1)$ $4 + (-3.5)$

$-5 + (-5) + (-5)$ $5\frac{1}{2} + \left(-4\frac{1}{4}\right)$

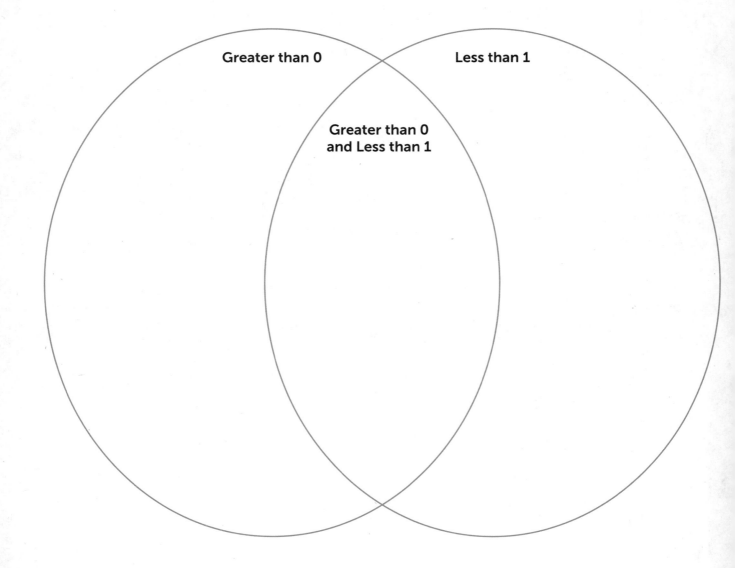

Greater than 0

Less than 1

Greater than 0
and Less than 1

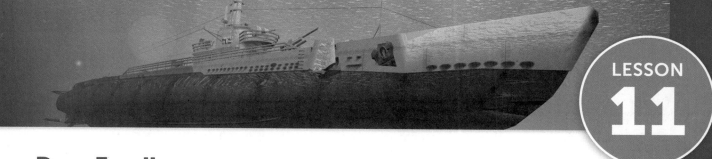

Dear Family,

This week your student is exploring multiplication with negative integers. Below are some examples of multiplying positive and negative integers that you may be familiar with.

- You can pay a bill by having the payment taken out of your bank account each month. To find the change in your account over several months, you can multiply the amount of the payment (negative) by the number of months (positive).

- A submarine's rate of change in elevation can be measured in feet per second. When it dives deeper, this rate is negative. You can multiply the rate (negative) by the amount of time it moves (positive) to find its change in elevation.

Your student will be modeling multiplication problems with negative integers like the one below.

What is $5 \cdot (-3)$?

➤ **ONE WAY** to model multiplication with negative integers is with repeated addition.

Think of $5 \cdot (-3)$ as finding the sum of 5 groups of -3.

$$(-3) + (-3) + (-3) + (-3) + (-3) = -15$$

➤ **ANOTHER WAY** is to use a number line.

Each arrow represents adding one group of -3.

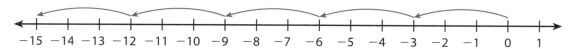

Both models show that $5 \cdot (-3) = -15$.

 Use the next page to start a conversation about multiplication with negative integers.

Activity Seeing Patterns in Multiplication with Negative Integers

➤ **Do this activity together to look for patterns in multiplying negative integers.**

What do you notice about the factors and products in each set?
How are the equations alike? How are they different?

SET 1

$5 \cdot 7 = 35$

$5 \cdot (-7) = -35$

$-5 \cdot 7 = -35$

$-5 \cdot (-7) = 35$

SET 2

$9 \cdot (-3) = -27$

$-3 \cdot 9 = -27$

SET 3

$4 \cdot 2 = 8$

$4 \cdot 1 = 4$

$4 \cdot 0 = 0$

$4 \cdot (-1) = -4$

$4 \cdot (-2) = -8$

 Do you notice any similarities between two of the sets? Between all three?

Explore Multiplication with Negative Integers

Model It

➤ **Complete the problems about multiplying integers.**

1 The jumps on the number line show $(-2) + (-2) + (-2)$.

a. What is $(-2) + (-2) + (-2)$?

b. What is $3(-2)$?

2 **a.** What is $(-2) + (-2) + (-2) + (-2)$?

b. Draw jumps on the number line to show $4(-2)$.

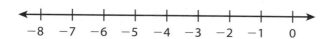

c. What is $4(-2)$?

d. The temperature changes by $-2°F$ every hour for 4 hours. What is the total temperature change in 4 hours? How does the number line in problem 2b show this?

3 How can you use what you know about $5(2)$ to find $5(-2)$?

> **DISCUSS IT**
>
> *Ask:* How can you represent repeated addition?
>
> *Share:* I can describe $(5)(-2)$ as . . .

◎ **Learning Targets** SMP 2, SMP 3, SMP 7

Apply and extend previous understandings of multiplication and division and of fractions to multiply and divide rational numbers.
- Understand that multiplication is extended from fractions to rational numbers by requiring that operations continue to satisfy the properties of operations, particularly the distributive property, leading to products such as $(-1)(-1) = 1$ and the rules for multiplying signed numbers. Interpret products of rational numbers by describing real–world contexts.

Model It

➤ **Complete the problems to think about multiplying integers another way.**

4 Complete each set of equations.

a.

$3 \cdot 2 = \underline{6}$

$2 \cdot \underline{2} = 4$

$\underline{1} \cdot 2 = 2$

$0 \cdot 2 = \underline{0}$

$-1 \cdot 2 = -2$

$-2 \cdot 2 = -4$

$-3 \cdot 2 = -6$

b.

$3 \cdot \underline{3} = 9$

$2 \cdot 3 = \underline{6}$

$\underline{1} \cdot 3 = 3$

$\underline{0} \cdot 3 = 0$

$\underline{-1} \cdot 3 = -3$

$-2 \cdot 3 = \underline{-6}$

$-3 \cdot \underline{3} = -9$

c.

$3 \cdot 4 = 12$

$2 \cdot 4 = 8$

$1 \cdot 4 = 4$

$0 \cdot 4 = 0$

$-1 \cdot 4 = \underline{-4}$

$-2 \cdot \underline{4} = -8$

$\underline{-3} \cdot 4 = -12$

5 **a.** $-4(2) = \underline{-8}$

b. $2(-4) = \underline{-8}$

c. Does the order of the factors change the product when multiplying negative integers? Justify your answer.

> **DISCUSS IT**
>
> *Ask:* What patterns do you notice?
>
> *Share:* I found the missing numbers by . . .

6 **Reflect** You have explored how to multiply two integers when one is positive and the other is negative. Is the product of a positive integer and a negative integer always *positive* or *negative*? Explain.

Prepare for Multiplication with Negative Integers

1 Think about what you know about operations with numbers and the distributive property. Fill in each box. Use words, numbers, and pictures. Show as many ideas as you can.

In My Own Words	My Illustrations

distributive property

Examples	Non-Examples

2 Jada says she used the distributive property to find 8 · (4 + 4). Did she use the distributive property correctly? Explain.

$$8(4 + 4) = (8 \cdot 4) + (8 \cdot 4)$$
$$= 32 + 32$$
$$= 64$$

➤ **Complete problems 3–5.**

3 **a.** What is $(-4) + (-4) + (-4)$?

b. Draw jumps on the number line to show $3(-4)$.

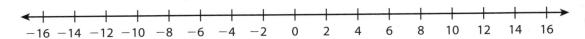

c. What is $3(-4)$?

d. The temperature changes by $-4°F$ every hour for 3 hours. What is the total temperature change in 3 hours? How does the number line above show this?

4 Complete each set of equations.

a.
$$3 \cdot 5 = 15$$
$$2 \cdot 5 = 10$$
$$1 \cdot 5 = 5$$
$$0 \cdot 5 = 0$$
$$-1 \cdot 5 = -5$$
$$-2 \cdot 5 = -10$$
$$-3 \cdot 5 = -15$$

b.
$$3 \cdot 6 = 18$$
$$2 \cdot 6 = 12$$
$$1 \cdot 6 = 6$$
$$0 \cdot 6 = 0$$
$$-1 \cdot 6 = -6$$
$$-2 \cdot 6 = -12$$
$$-3 \cdot 6 = -18$$

5 **a.** $-4(5) = -20$

b. $5(-4) = -20$

Develop Understanding of Multiplication with Negative Integers

Model It: Patterns

➤ **Try these two problems involving multiplying negative numbers.**

1 Complete each set of equations.

a. $3 \cdot (-1) = \underline{\hspace{1cm}}$ **b.** $3 \cdot (\underline{\hspace{1cm}}) = -6$ **c.** $3 \cdot (-5) = -15$

$2 \cdot (\underline{\hspace{1cm}}) = -2$ $\qquad$ $2 \cdot (-2) = \underline{\hspace{1cm}}$ $\qquad$ $2 \cdot (-5) = -10$

$\underline{\hspace{1cm}} \cdot (-1) = -1$ $\qquad$ $\underline{\hspace{1cm}} \cdot (-2) = -2$ $\qquad$ $1 \cdot (-5) = -5$

$0 \cdot (-1) = \underline{\hspace{1cm}}$ $\qquad$ $\underline{\hspace{1cm}} \cdot (-2) = 0$ $\qquad$ $0 \cdot (-5) = 0$

$-1 \cdot (-1) = 1$ $\qquad$ $\underline{\hspace{1cm}} \cdot (-2) = 2$ $\qquad$ $-1 \cdot (-5) = \underline{\hspace{1cm}}$

$-2 \cdot (-1) = 2$ $\qquad$ $-2 \cdot (-2) = \underline{\hspace{1cm}}$ $\qquad$ $-2 \cdot (\underline{\hspace{1cm}}) = 10$

$-3 \cdot (-1) = 3$ $\qquad$ $-3 \cdot (\underline{\hspace{1cm}}) = 6$ $\qquad$ $\underline{\hspace{1cm}} \cdot (-5) = 15$

2 Use what you know about multiplying a negative number by a positive number and what you did in problem 1 to complete each set of equations.

a. $3 \cdot 2 = \underline{\hspace{1cm}}$

$3 \cdot 0 = \underline{\hspace{1cm}}$

$3 \cdot (-2) = \underline{\hspace{1cm}}$

b. positive · positive $= \underline{\hspace{2cm}}$

positive · zero $= \underline{\hspace{2cm}}$

positive · negative $= \underline{\hspace{2cm}}$

c. $-2 \cdot (-3) = \underline{\hspace{1cm}}$

$-2 \cdot 0 = \underline{\hspace{1cm}}$

$-2 \cdot 3 = \underline{\hspace{1cm}}$

d. negative · negative $= \underline{\hspace{2cm}}$

negative · zero $= \underline{\hspace{2cm}}$

negative · positive $= \underline{\hspace{2cm}}$

DISCUSS IT

Ask: What is true about all the equations with a positive result?

Share: I notice that when I multiply a positive or negative number by zero . . .

Model It: Equations

➤ **Try these two problems about finding the product of two negative numbers.**

3 You can use the distributive property to understand why the product of two negative numbers must be a positive number. Complete each step to show that $-5(-2) = 10$.

$$-5(2) + (-5)(-2) = -5[2 + (-2)]$$

$$-5(2) + (-5)(-2) = -5(\underline{\hspace{1cm}})$$

$$-5(2) + (-5)(-2) = \underline{\hspace{1cm}}$$

$$\underline{\hspace{1cm}} + (-5)(-2) = \underline{\hspace{1cm}}$$

$$-5(-2) = \underline{\hspace{1cm}}$$

4 Complete each step to show another way to understand why the product of two negative numbers must be a positive number.

$$-3(1) + (-3)(-1) = \underline{\hspace{1cm}} [\underline{\hspace{1cm}} + (\underline{\hspace{1cm}})]$$

$$-3(1) + (-3)(-1) = -3[0]$$

$$-3(1) + (-3)(-1) = \underline{\hspace{1cm}}$$

$$\underline{\hspace{1cm}} + (-3)(-1) = \underline{\hspace{1cm}}$$

$$\underline{\hspace{1cm}} + \underline{\hspace{1cm}} = \underline{\hspace{1cm}}$$

DISCUSS IT

Ask: Why is $(-5)(-2) + (-5)(2)$ equal to 0?

Share: You can use the distributive property to see that . . .

CONNECT IT

➤ **Complete the problems below.**

5 How are the products of $-3(1)$ and $-3(-1)$ the same? How are they different?

6 Explain why $-6(3) = -18$.

Name:

Practice Multiplying with Negative Integers

➤ **Study how the Example shows multiplying negative integers. Then solve problems 1–6.**

Example

Issay plays a game with a spinner. For each turn, he spins twice and finds the product of the two numbers.

On his first turn, he spins −3 and 8.

On his next turn, he spins 3 and −8.

Finally, he spins −3 and −8.

He says all three products are −24. Is Issay correct?

The product of 3 and 8 is 24.

Since the product of a positive number and a negative number is a negative number, −3(8) and 3(−8) are both −24.

Since the product of a negative number and a negative number is a positive number, −3(−8) = 24.

Issay is not correct.

1 In the Example, the expressions −3(8) and 3(−8) have a value of −24. Write three different multiplication expressions using two integers that also have a value of −24.

2 Without solving, tell whether the value of −3(−8)(9)(10) is *positive* or *negative*. Justify your answer.

Vocabulary

integers
the set of whole numbers and their opposites.

LESSON 11 Understand Multiplication with Negative Integers   **227**

3 Claudia draws four cards with integers on them. She must choose two of the integers to multiply.

    a. Which cards can Claudia choose to make the greatest product?

    b. Which cards can Claudia choose to make the least product?

    c. Compare the product of $-3(-2)$ to the product of $-2(-3)$.

4 Complete each statement about multiplying positive and negative integers using the word *positive* or *negative*. Then provide an example for each statement.

    a. positive · positive = _____

    b. positive · negative = _____

    c. negative · negative = _____

5 **a.** Adrian says that $4(-9) = 36$. Why is Adrian incorrect?

    b. What is one change you can make to Adrian's equation to make it correct?

6 The product of three integers is -40. What could the three integers be? Explain your thinking.

Refine Ideas About Multiplication with Negative Integers

Apply It

➤ **Complete problems 1–5.**

1 **Compare** Dawn says $-2(-3)(4)$ is equal to $6(4)$. Javier says $-2(-3)(4)$ is equal to $-2(-12)$. Who is right? Explain.

2 **Analyze** Complete the equations. What do you notice about the products?

$(-1)(-1) = (-1)^2$ $(-1)^2 = -2$

$(-1)(-1)(-1) = (-1)^3$ $(-1)^3 = -3$

$(-1)(-1)(-1)(-1) = (-1)^4$ $(-1)^4 = -4$

$(-1)(-1)(-1)(-1)(-1) = (-1)^5$ $(-1)^5 = -5$

3 **Justify** Keiko says that when n is any positive integer, 1^n always equals 1 and $(-1)^n$ always equals -1. Is Keiko correct? Justify your answer.

④ James is solving a number puzzle that involves three integers, *a*, *b*, and *c*, where *c* is a positive integer. The product of *a* and *b* is 6. The product of *a* and *c* is −4. The product of *b* and *c* is −6.

PART A What are the values of *a*, *b*, and *c*? Justify your answer.

PART B Suppose *c* is a negative integer. How does that change the values of *a*, *b*, and *c*? Justify your answer.

⑤ **Math Journal** Think about multiplying two integers. When will the product be less than 0? When will the product be greater than 0?

✓ **End of Lesson Checklist**

☐ **INTERACTIVE GLOSSARY** Write a new entry for *justify*. Tell what you do when you *justify* your answer to a problem.

Dear Family,

This week your student is learning about multiplying and dividing negative rational numbers.

Your student has already learned to multiply and divide integers and positive **rational numbers**. Now your student will multiply and divide with all types of rational numbers, including negative fractions and decimals.

Every rational number can be written in the form $\frac{a}{b}$, where a and b are integers and b is not 0. Multiplying or dividing rational numbers is similar to multiplying or dividing integers.

- The **product of two positive numbers** is always **positive**.
- The **product of two negative numbers** is always **positive**.
- The **product of a positive number and a negative number** is always **negative**.

Your student will be solving problems like the one below.

> The shoreline at a local beach is receding by the same amount each year. Over 5 years, the width of the beach changes by $-12\frac{1}{4}$ ft. What is the yearly change in the shoreline?

➤ **ONE WAY** to find the yearly change in the shoreline is to divide fractions.

$$-12\frac{1}{4} \div 5 = -\frac{49}{4} \div \frac{5}{1}$$
$$= -\frac{49}{4} \cdot \frac{1}{5}$$
$$= -\frac{49}{20}$$
$$= -2\frac{9}{20}$$

➤ **ANOTHER WAY** is to divide decimals.

$$-12\frac{1}{4} \div 5 = -12.25 \div 5$$
$$= -2.45$$

Both methods show that the yearly change in the shoreline is $-2\frac{9}{20}$, or -2.45, ft. This means the shore is receding by an average of 2.45 ft each year.

 Use the next page to start a conversation about rational numbers.

Activity Thinking About Multiplication and Division with Rational Numbers

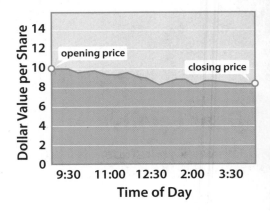

➤ **Do this activity together to investigate multiplying and dividing rational numbers.**

Have you ever wanted to own a piece of your favorite company? Stocks let you own a piece, or a share, of a company.

Each day, the prices of stocks change depending on how the companies are doing. Suppose you own 6 shares of a company. On a given day, the change in the value of a share is -1.64. That means the change in the value of what you own is $6(-1.64) = -9.84$. So, your share of the company is worth $9.84 less.

? Where else might you multiply or divide with rational numbers in the world around you?

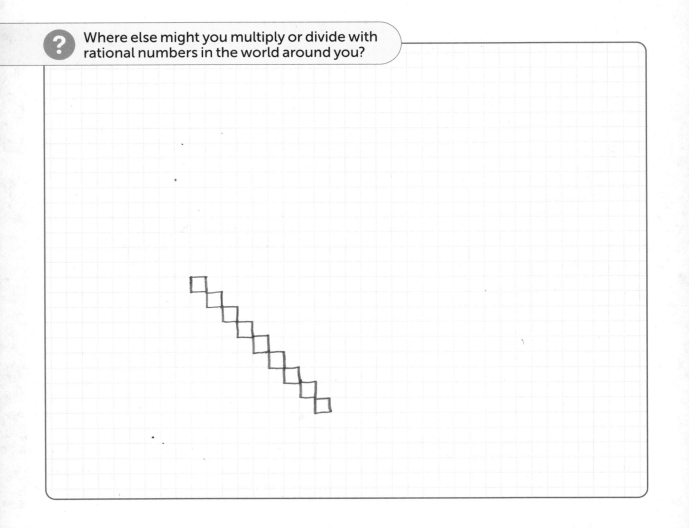

Explore Multiplying and Dividing with Negative Numbers

Previously, you learned about multiplying integers. In this lesson, you will learn about multiplying and dividing with rational numbers.

➤ **Use what you know to try to solve the problem below.**

Ryan is washing windows on a skyscraper. He lowers himself six times, going down an equal distance each time. In all, Ryan lowers himself 48 ft. What integer represents the change in Ryan's position each time he lowers himself? What does this integer tell you?

TRY IT

  Math Toolkit grid paper, integer chips, number lines

DISCUSS IT

Ask: How would you explain what the problem is asking in your own words?

Share: The problem is asking . . .

◎ **Learning Targets** SMP 1, SMP 2, SMP 3, SMP 4, SMP 5, SMP 6, SMP 8
• Understand that integers can be divided, provided that the divisor is not zero, and every quotient of integers (with non-zero divisor) is a rational number. If p and q are integers, then $-\left(\frac{p}{q}\right) = \frac{(-p)}{q} = \frac{p}{(-q)}$. Interpret quotients of rational numbers by describing real-world contexts.
• Apply properties of operations as strategies to multiply and divide rational numbers.

CONNECT IT

1 **Look Back** What integer represents the change in Ryan's position each time he lowers himself? How does the integer show that Ryan is going lower?

2 **Look Ahead** One way to find the rational number that represents Ryan's change in position each time he lowers himself is to divide. An integer can be divided by any integer except 0. Any **rational number** can be written as the quotient of two integers, where the divisor is not 0. That means every rational number can be written in the form $\frac{a}{b}$, where a and b are integers and $b \neq 0$.

a. Another way to think of a rational number is as the fraction $\frac{a}{b}$. Explain why it makes sense that a can equal 0, but b cannot.

b. How can you write 0.07 in the form $\frac{a}{b}$? How can you write 1.07 in the form $\frac{a}{b}$?

c. When a rational number is negative, you can express it as a fraction in three different forms. For example, you can write -4 as $\frac{-4}{1}$, $\frac{4}{-1}$, and $-\frac{4}{1}$.

Express each fraction above as an expression using the division symbol ($\div$). How does this show that the fractions are equivalent?

3 **Reflect** Why is $\frac{-3}{4}$ a rational number?

Name:

Prepare for Multiplying and Dividing with Negative Numbers

1 Think about what you know about fractions and negative numbers. Fill in each box. Use words, numbers, and pictures. Show as many ideas as you can.

Word	In My Own Words	Examples
fraction		
opposite numbers		
reciprocal		

2 Doug says that the opposite of $\frac{-2}{5}$ is $\frac{5}{-2}$. Is Doug correct? Explain.

3 Tameka pilots a hot air balloon. She lowers the balloon five times, going down an equal distance each time. In all, Tameka lowers the balloon 75 m.

a. What integer represents the change in the hot air balloon's elevation each time Tameka lowers it? What does this integer tell you? Show your work.

SOLUTION _____

b. Check your answer to problem 3a. Show your work.

Develop Multiplying Negative Rational Numbers

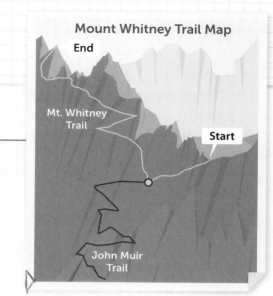

Mount Whitney Trail Map

> **Read and try to solve the problem below.**

Mount Whitney Trail starts at an elevation of 8,350 ft above sea level and ends at an elevation of 14,500 ft above sea level. The temperature changes by −5.4°F for every thousand feet gained in elevation. What is the change in temperature from the starting elevation to the ending elevation of Mount Whitney Trail?

 TRY IT

 Math Toolkit grid paper, number lines

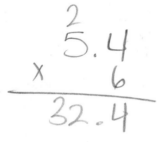

$$\begin{array}{r} \overset{2}{5}.4 \\ \times \quad 6 \\ \hline 32.4 \end{array}$$

$$\begin{array}{r} \overset{1}{-3}\overset{13}{2}.40 \\ .81 \\ \hline \boxed{-33.21} \end{array}$$

Alysha

Starts at 8,350 | Ends at 14,500

Difference: 6,150

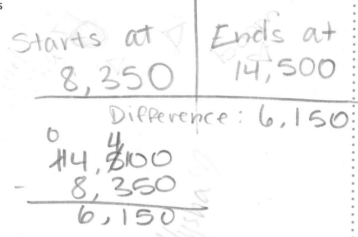

$$\begin{array}{r} {}^{0}{}^{4}\\ \cancel{1}4,\cancel{5}00 \\ -\quad 8,350 \\ \hline 6,150 \end{array}$$

Alysha

$$\begin{array}{r} \overset{2}{5}.4 \\ \times \ .15 \\ \hline 270 \\ +\ 540 \\ \hline .810 \end{array}$$

DISCUSS IT

Ask: How do you know your answer is reasonable?

Share: My answer is reasonable because . . .

➤ **Explore different ways to multiply positive and negative rational numbers.**

Mount Whitney Trail starts at an elevation of 8,350 ft above sea level and ends at an elevation of 14,500 ft above sea level. The temperature changes by −5.4°F for every thousand feet gained in elevation. What is the change in temperature from the starting elevation to the ending elevation of Mount Whitney Trail?

Picture It

You can use a diagram to understand the relationship.

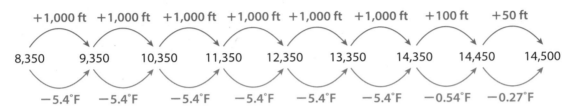

Model It

You can multiply to find the change in temperature.

The change in elevation is $14,500 - 8,350 = \textbf{6,150}$ ft.

The temperature decreases 5.4°F every 1,000 ft. That is a rate of $\frac{-5.4}{1,000}$°F per foot.

change in temperature = rate of temperature change × change in elevation

$$= \frac{-5.4}{1,000}(6,150)$$

$$= \frac{-5.4 \times 6,150}{1,000}$$

$$= -5.4\left(\frac{6,150}{1,000}\right)$$

$$= -5.4(6.15)$$

➤ **Use the problem from the previous page to help you understand how to multiply positive and negative rational numbers.**

1 How does the **Picture It** model $-5.4(6.15)$?

2 What is the temperature change from the beginning to the ending of the trail? What does this number mean in the context of the problem?

3 Why does $-5.4(6.15)$ have the same product as $-\dfrac{54}{10} \cdot \dfrac{615}{100}$?

4 You can start solving the problem by finding -5.4×6. How is this similar to finding 5.4×6? How is this different from finding 5.4×6?

5 How is multiplying negative rational numbers like multiplying negative integers?

6 **Reflect** Think about all the models and strategies you have discussed today. Describe how one of them helped you better understand how to multiply rational numbers.

LESSON 12 Multiply and Divide with Negative Numbers   **239**

Apply It

➤ **Use what you learned to solve these problems.**

7 A peregrine falcon dives for prey. Its elevation changes by an average of −11.5 meters every second. The dive lasts for 3.2 seconds. What is the change in the falcon's elevation? What does this mean in the context of the problem? Show your work.

Dives **−11.5** meters per second
Dives for **3.2** seconds

SOLUTION _____

8 Find $-\frac{1}{9}(-27)$. Show your work.

$$-\frac{1}{9}\left(-27\right)$$

$$\frac{1}{9} \quad \frac{27}{1}$$

$$\overset{6}{\underset{27}{}}$$
$$\times \quad 9$$
$$\overline{3}$$

$$\frac{1}{9} \times \frac{1}{1} = \frac{1}{9}$$

$$\frac{27}{1} \times \frac{9}{9} = \frac{9}{9}$$

SOLUTION _____

9 A freezer in a lab is set so that the temperature changes at a rate of −1.6°C every hour. What is the change in the temperature after $4\frac{1}{4}$ h? Show your work.

SOLUTION _____

Practice Multiplying Negative Rational Numbers

➤ **Study the Example showing how to multiply negative rational numbers. Then solve problems 1–5.**

Example

What is $-6\left(-8\frac{1}{2}\right)$**?**

$$-8\frac{1}{2} = -\frac{17}{2}$$

The product of two negative rational numbers is positive.

$$-6\left(-8\frac{1}{2}\right) = -\frac{6}{1}\left(-\frac{17}{2}\right)$$

$$= 51$$

---

1 a. Show how to solve the problem in the Example by multiplying decimals.

b. Is your answer to problem 1a *greater than*, *less than*, or *equal to* the answer in the Example? Why?

2 Find $-\frac{3}{5}\left(-1\frac{1}{3}\right)$. Show your work.

SOLUTION _____

3 **a.** Find $-0.2(4.75)$. Show your work.

SOLUTION _____

b. Explain how you can use your answer to problem 3a to find $-0.2(-4.75)$.

4 Amare drops a probe into a lake. The elevation of the probe changes by $-1\frac{1}{2}$ feet every second. The probe takes 50 seconds to reach the bottom of the lake. How deep is the lake? Show your work.

Elevation changes by $-1\frac{1}{2}$ ft every second.

SOLUTION _____

5 Salvador drives 6.5 miles to his aunt's house. For every mile Salvador drives, the amount of gas in the car's gas tank changes by -0.04 gallon. What is the total change in the gallons of gas in the car's tank? Show your work.

SOLUTION _____

Develop Dividing Negative Rational Numbers

SMITH CREEK FLOOD 2013

➤ **Read and try to solve the problem below.**

After a flood, a creek's water level changes by $-2\frac{4}{5}$ ft in $3\frac{1}{2}$ h.

What is the average change in the creek's water level each hour?

TRY IT

  Math Toolkit grid paper, number lines

DISCUSS IT

Ask: What did you do first to find the change in the water level?

Share: First, I . . .

➤ **Explore different ways to divide negative rational numbers.**

After a flood, a creek's water level changes by $-2\frac{4}{5}$ ft in $3\frac{1}{2}$ h. What is the average change in the creek's water level each hour?

Picture It

You can use a picture to make sense of the problem.

Water Level (ft)   Time (h)

Model It

You can divide fractions.

Divide the total change in the level of the water by the number of hours to get the average change in the level each hour.

$$-2\frac{4}{5} \div 3\frac{1}{2} = -\frac{14}{5} \div \frac{7}{2}$$
$$= -\frac{14}{5} \cdot \frac{2}{7}$$

Model It

You can divide decimals.

$$-2\frac{4}{5} = -2\frac{8}{10} \qquad 3\frac{1}{2} = 3\frac{5}{10}$$
$$= -2.8 \qquad\qquad = 3.5 \qquad -2.8 \div 3.5$$

➤ **Use the problem from the previous page to help you understand how to divide positive and negative rational numbers.**

1 Look at the second **Model It**. Without doing any calculations, explain how you can use $2.8 \div 3.5$ to find $-2.8 \div 3.5$.

2 What is the average change in the creek's height each hour? How does each **Model It** help you see if the average change in the creek's height each hour is positive or negative?

3 The product of a positive number and a negative number is negative. Explain why the quotient of a negative number and a positive number is negative.

4 How is dividing with negative rational numbers like dividing with positive rational numbers? How is it different?

5 **Reflect** Think about all the models and strategies you have discussed today. Describe how one of them helped you better understand dividing with negative numbers.

Apply It

➤ **Use what you learned to solve these problems.**

6. What is $16.8 \div (-3.5)$? Show your work.

SOLUTION _____

7. What is $-\dfrac{3}{8} \div \left(-\dfrac{1}{2}\right)$?

A $-\dfrac{3}{4}$

B $-\dfrac{3}{16}$

C $\dfrac{3}{16}$

D $\dfrac{3}{4}$

8. A helicopter's altitude changes by $-28\dfrac{1}{8}$ ft in $3\dfrac{3}{4}$ s. What is the average change in the helicopter's altitude each second? Show your work.

Altitude change: $-28\dfrac{1}{8}$ feet in $3\dfrac{3}{4}$ seconds

SOLUTION _____

_____

Practice Dividing Negative Rational Numbers

➤ **Study the Example showing how to divide with negative rational numbers. Then solve problems 1–5.**

Example

On a winter day, the temperature changes by $-12.6°F$ in $2\frac{1}{4}$ h.

What rational number represents the average change in the

temperature each hour?

The total change in the temperature is $-12.6°F$.

The amount of time is $2\frac{1}{4}$, or 2.25, h.

$-12.6 \div 2.25 = -5.6$

The number -5.6 represents the average hourly temperature change.

1 Explain how to use the Example to find the quotient of -12.6 and -2.25.

2 What is $-6\frac{4}{5} \div \left(-\frac{2}{5}\right)$? Show your work.

SOLUTION _____

3 Paula is scuba diving. Her elevation changes by $-37\frac{4}{5}$ m in 4.5 min.

a. What rational number represents the average change in Paula's elevation each minute? Show your work.

> $-37\frac{4}{5}$ m change in elevation in 4.5 min

SOLUTION _____

b. Is Paula going deeper in the water or back toward the surface? How do you know?

4 What is $57.2 \div (-10,000)$? Show your work.

SOLUTION _____

5 A full bathtub drains at a constant rate. The amount of water in the bathtub changes by $-4\frac{1}{2}$ gallons in $\frac{3}{4}$ minute. What is the rate, in gallons per minute, at which the amount of water in the bathtub changes? Show your work.

SOLUTION _____

Refine Multiplying and Dividing with Negative Numbers

➤ **Complete the Example below. Then solve problems 1–10.**

Example

What is the product of $-\frac{3}{8}$, $-\frac{2}{3}$, **and** $-\frac{5}{2}$?

Look at how you could show your work using multiplication.

$$-\frac{3}{8} \cdot \left(-\frac{2}{3}\right) \cdot \left(-\frac{5}{2}\right) = \left(-\frac{3}{8} \cdot -\frac{2}{3}\right) \cdot \left(-\frac{5}{2}\right)$$

$$= \frac{6}{24} \cdot \left(-\frac{5}{2}\right)$$

$$= \frac{1}{4} \cdot \left(-\frac{5}{2}\right)$$

SOLUTION _____

CONSIDER THIS . . .
You can multiply in any order.

PAIR/SHARE
How would the answer change if $-\frac{3}{8}$ were $\frac{3}{8}$?

Apply It

1 Noor, Layla, and Diego play a trivia game. Noor's score is -2. Layla's score is $\frac{3}{4}$ of Noor's score. Diego's score is $\frac{2}{3}$ of Layla's score. What is Diego's score? Show your work.

CONSIDER THIS . . .
You can multiply to find $\frac{3}{4}$ of a quantity.

PAIR/SHARE
How can you find Diego's score another way?

SOLUTION _____

2 Yolanda measures the depth of the water in a reservoir. In one week, the depth changes from 2,366.74 ft to 2,354.63 ft. What rational number represents the average change in depth each day? Show your work.

CONSIDER THIS . . .
Is the change in depth positive or negative?

PAIR/SHARE
What does the rational number you found mean in the context of the problem?

SOLUTION _____

3 What is $4.8(-2.5) \div (-0.1)$?

A 1.2

B −120

C 120

D 1,200

Maria chose D as the correct answer. How might she have gotten that answer?

CONSIDER THIS . . .
Dividing by a number is the same as multiplying by its reciprocal.

PAIR/SHARE
How would the answer be different if you divided by −0.01 instead of −0.1?

4 What is $-79.2 \div (-16.5)$? Show your work.

SOLUTION _____

5 Without doing any calculations, is $\left(-\dfrac{1}{2}\right)^{50}$ *positive* or *negative*? Explain how you know.

6 Write three different division expressions that each have a negative quotient. Use at least two of the rational numbers $-\dfrac{1}{2}$, $\dfrac{4}{5}$, and -3 in each expression.

7 The quotient of a and b is positive. Which of the following could be true about a and b? Select all that apply.

A The product ab is negative.

B The quotient $b \div a$ is negative.

C Both a and b are negative.

D The quotient $-b \div a$ is negative.

E Both a and b are positive.

8 Kwame fills a bird feeder with seeds. As birds visit the feeder, the height of the seeds changes from 13.6 cm to 11.1 cm over a period of $6\frac{1}{4}$ h. What is the average change in the height of the seeds each hour? Show your work.

----,13.6 cm

----11.1 cm

SOLUTION _____

_____

9 What is $-0.3(0.2)(12)$?

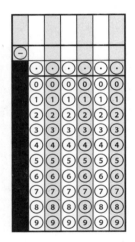

10 **Math Journal** Write a division expression that results in $-\frac{3}{8}$.

Explain your thinking.

✓ **End of Lesson Checklist**

☐ **INTERACTIVE GLOSSARY** Find the entry for *rational number*. Add two important things you learned about rational numbers in this lesson.

☐ **SELF CHECK** Go back to the Unit 3 Opener and see what you can check off.

Dear Family,

This week your student is learning about expressing fractions as decimals.

Every rational number can be written as a fraction. You can divide the numerator by the denominator to find the decimal form of a fraction.

$\frac{3}{4}$ means $3 \div 4$.

$\frac{2}{3}$ means $2 \div 3$.

```
      0.75
  4)3.00
   - 2 8↓
      20
   -  20
       0
```

```
      0.66 . . .
  3)2.00
   - 1 8↓
      20
   -  18
       2
```

A **terminating decimal** like 0.75 ends. A **repeating decimal** like 0.66 . . . never ends. It repeats the same digit or group of digits over and over. Another way to write a repeating decimal is to put a bar over the digits that repeat. So, 0.66 . . . can be written as $0.\overline{6}$. Your student will be solving problems like the one below.

A label on an orange says it weighs 6 oz, or $\frac{3}{8}$ lb. A scale says that the

orange weighs 0.375 lb. Is the orange labeled accurately?

➤ **ONE WAY** to express $\frac{3}{8}$ as a decimal is to use equivalent fractions.

$\frac{3}{8} = 3 \times \frac{1}{8}$

$= 3 \times \frac{1}{2} \times \frac{1}{4}$

$= 3 \times 0.5 \times 0.25$

$= 0.375$

➤ **ANOTHER WAY** is to divide.

```
        0.375
   8)3.000
    - 2 4
        60
     -  56
        40
      - 40
         0
```

Both methods show that the fraction $\frac{3}{8}$ is equivalent to the decimal 0.375. The orange is labeled accurately.

 Use the next page to start a conversation about fractions and decimals.

Activity Thinking About Decimals and Fractions

➤ **Do this activity together to investigate using fractions and their decimal forms.**

You might use both fractions and their decimal equivalents in a given situation. Have you ever lost a button and needed to sew on a new one? First, you need to find a button that fits the buttonhole.

You might measure the buttonhole and find that it is $\frac{3}{4}$ in. wide. Then you might measure a button with digital calipers and see that it is 0.63 in. wide.

You can express $\frac{3}{4}$ as 0.75. Since 0.75 is greater than 0.63, the button is small enough to fit through the buttonhole.

? Where else might you use both fractions and decimals in the world around you?

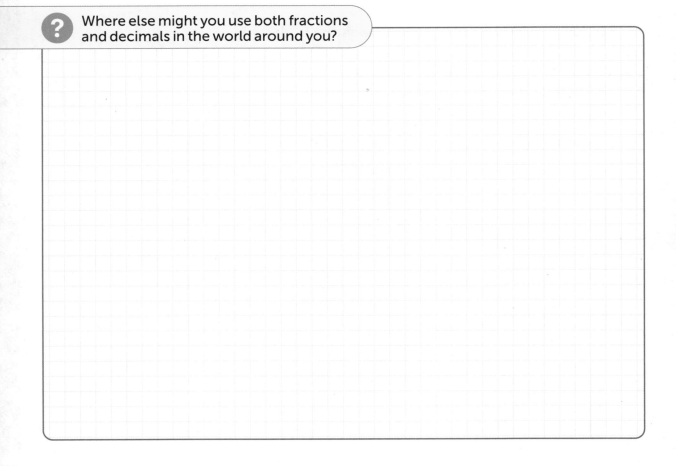

Explore Terminating or Repeating Decimals

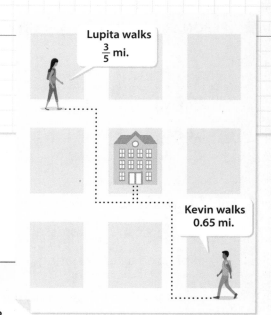

Lupita walks
$\frac{3}{5}$ mi.

Kevin walks
0.65 mi.

Previously, you learned how to divide integers and express rational numbers as fractions. In this lesson, you will learn about expressing fractions as decimals.

➤ **Use what you know to try to solve the problem below.**

Lupita and Kevin walk to school. Lupita walks $\frac{3}{5}$ mi. Kevin walks 0.65 mi. Who walks a greater distance to school? How much greater?

TRY IT

 Math Toolkit base-ten blocks, fraction bars, hundredths grids, number lines, place-value charts

$$\frac{3}{5} \times \frac{20}{20} = \frac{}{100}$$

$$\frac{6}{10}$$

$$\frac{65}{60}$$

0.05 mi

DISCUSS IT

Ask: What did you do first to compare the distances?

Share: First, I . . .

⊚ **Learning Targets** SMP 1, SMP 2, SMP 3, SMP 4, SMP 5, SMP 6, SMP 7, SMP 8
• Convert a rational number to a decimal using long division; know that the decimal form of a rational number terminates in 0s or eventually repeats.
• Solve multi-step real-life and mathematical problems posed with positive and negative rational numbers in any form. Apply properties of operations to calculate with numbers in any form; convert between forms as appropriate.

CONNECT IT

1 **Look Back** Does Lupita or Kevin walk farther to school? How much farther?

2 **Look Ahead** The numbers $\frac{3}{5}$ and 0.65 are both rational numbers. All rational numbers can be expressed as a fraction or a decimal. All rational numbers can be expressed as terminating or repeating decimals.

a. A **terminating decimal** has a decimal form that ends, or ends in 0s. The rational number $\frac{3}{5}$ can be expressed as the terminating decimal 0.6. Why is it not necessary to show the 0s after the 6?

b. A **repeating decimal** has a decimal form that repeats the same digit or group of digits without end. You can use . . ., or ellipses, to show that a pattern of digits continues on without end. What is the repeating digit or group of digits for each repeating decimal below?

0.333 . . . _____ $0.\overline{3}$

0.121212 . . . _____ $0.\overline{12}$

0.0555 . . . _____ $0.0\overline{5}$

c. You can also write repeating decimals with a bar over the repeating digit or digits. Write each repeating decimal below using a bar.

0.4444 . . . _____ $0.\overline{4}$

0.502502502 . . . _____ $0.\overline{502}$

3.333 . . . _____ $3.\overline{3}$

0.422 . . . _____ $0.4\overline{2}$

3 **Reflect** Is the decimal 0.101010. . . a *terminating decimal* or a *repeating decimal*? How do you know?

Prepare for Expressing Rational Numbers as Terminating or Repeating Decimals

1 Think about what you know about quotients. Fill in each box. Use words, numbers, and pictures. Show as many ideas as you can.

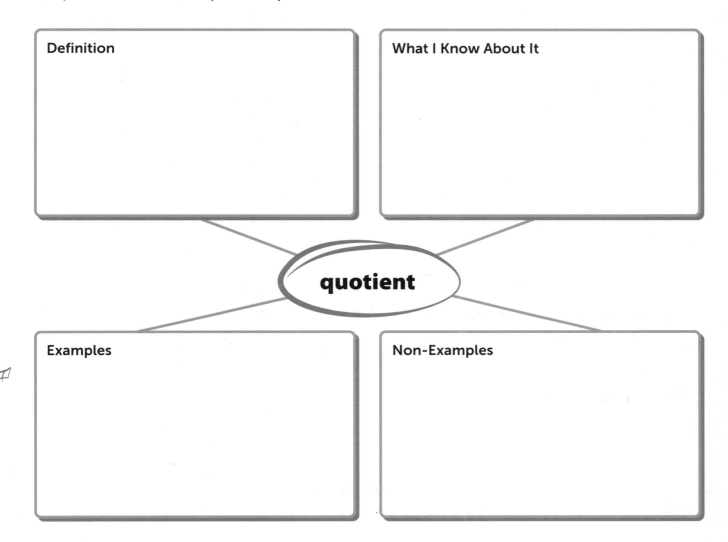

Definition

What I Know About It

quotient

Examples

Non-Examples

2 Darius says that $\frac{1}{4}$ is a division expression and is not a quotient. Badru says that $\frac{1}{4}$ is a division expression and is also the quotient of $1 \div 4$. Who is correct? Explain.

3 Adoncia lives $\frac{4}{5}$ mi from the library. Miyako lives 0.72 mi from the library.

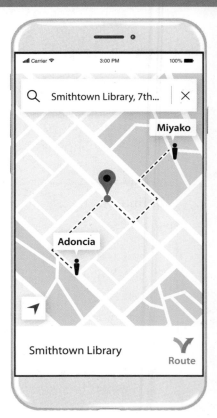

a. Who lives farther from the library? How much farther? Show your work.

SOLUTION _____

b. Check your answer to problem 3a. Show your work.

Develop Writing Rational Numbers as Terminating Decimals

➤ **Read and try to solve the problem below.**

There are 20 blocks per mile in Tara's city. Tara walks 13 blocks. Her fitness tracker says she walked 0.71 mile. Show if her fitness tracker is accurate.

Math Toolkit base-ten blocks, fraction bars, hundredths grids, number lines, place-value charts

20|13.0

base ten block

fraction bar

hundreth grid

number line

1   3   5   7   10

DISCUSS IT

Ask: How did you get started comparing the distances?

Share: I knew . . . so I . . .

➤ **Explore different ways to express a fraction as a terminating decimal.**

There are 20 blocks per mile in Tara's city. Tara walks 13 blocks. Her fitness tracker says she walked 0.71 mile. Show if her fitness tracker is accurate.

Model It

You can use equivalent fractions to express a fraction as a decimal.

You can think of $\frac{13}{20}$ as $13 \times \frac{1}{20}$.

$$\frac{1}{20} = \frac{1}{2} \times \frac{1}{10}$$
$$= 0.5 \times 0.1$$
$$= 0.05$$

$$\frac{13}{20} = 13 \times 0.05$$

Model It

You can use long division to express a fraction as a decimal.

$$
\begin{array}{r}
0.65 \\
20\overline{)13.00} \\
-\ 12\ 0 \\
\hline
100 \\
-\ 100 \\
\hline
\end{array}
$$

➤ **Use the problem from the previous page to help you understand how to express a fraction as a terminating decimal.**

1 Look at the first **Model It**. After Tara walks 13 blocks, what decimal should her fitness tracker show? How can finding a decimal equivalent to $\frac{1}{20}$ help you?

2 Look at the second **Model It**. Suppose 13.00 were written as 13.0000 instead. Would the value of the quotient change? Explain.

3 When you divide to express a rational number as a decimal, how do you know it is a terminating decimal?

4 When you divide to express a fraction as a decimal, when can you stop writing the dividend with more zeros after the decimal point? Why?

5 **Reflect** Think about all the models and strategies you have discussed today. Describe how one of them helped you better understand how to express a fraction as a decimal.

Apply It

➤ **Use what you learned to solve these problems.**

6 Alyssa plans to run $\frac{7}{8}$ mile on a trail. At one point, she sees that she is at mile marker 0.3. How much farther does she have to run? Show your work.

0.875

0.575 mi

Plan: run $\frac{7}{8}$ mi

SOLUTION _____

7 Express $-\frac{5}{16}$ as a decimal. Show your work.

8 Is $\frac{27}{40}$ equal to 0.675? Show your work.

SOLUTION _____

SOLUTION _____

Name:

Practice Writing Rational Numbers as Terminating Decimals

➤ **Study the Example showing how to work with fractions and terminating decimals. Then solve problems 1–5.**

Example

What is the decimal form of $-\dfrac{11}{8}$ **?**

You can use long division to express a fraction as a decimal. Since $-\dfrac{11}{8}$ is the opposite of $\dfrac{11}{8}$, find the decimal form of $\dfrac{11}{8}$.

```
      1.375
   8)11.000
     − 8
      ‾‾‾
       3 0
     − 2 4
      ‾‾‾
        60
      − 56
       ‾‾‾
        40
      − 40
       ‾‾
         0
```

Since $-\dfrac{11}{8}$ is the opposite of $\dfrac{11}{8}$, that means $-\dfrac{11}{8}$ is the opposite of 1.375.

So, the decimal form of $-\dfrac{11}{8}$ is -1.375.

1. Is $-\dfrac{11}{8}$ *greater than* or *less than* -1.37? Show your work.

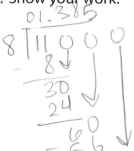

SOLUTION _____

2. Ellema knows that $\dfrac{1}{5}$ written as a decimal is 0.2. How can Ellema use this information to find the decimal form of $\dfrac{9}{5}$ without dividing 9 by 5?

3 A puzzle book weighs $\frac{3}{5}$ lb. A comic book weighs 0.35 lb. How much more does the puzzle book weigh than the comic book? Show your work.

Brain Teasing PUZZLES
Weight: $\frac{3}{5}$ pound

the Courageous **CATMAN**
Weight: 0.35 pound

SOLUTION _____

4 What is $-\frac{11}{40} - 0.278$ in decimal form? Show your work.

SOLUTION _____

5 Is $\frac{-17}{-40}$ equal to -0.425? Show your work.

SOLUTION _____

Develop Writing Rational Numbers as Repeating Decimals

➤ **Read and try to solve the problem below.**

Robert wants to make a small batch of japchae. He needs $4\frac{1}{6}$ oz of noodles. His scale shows he has 4.18 oz of noodles. Does Robert have enough noodles? How do you know?

TRY IT

Math Toolkit fraction bars, hundredths grids, number lines, place-value charts

DISCUSS IT

Ask: Why did you choose that strategy to compare the weights?

Share: I chose that strategy because . . .

➤ **Explore different ways to express a fraction as a repeating decimal.**

Robert wants to make a small batch of japchae. He needs $4\frac{1}{6}$ oz of noodles. His scale shows he has 4.18 oz of noodles. Does Robert have enough noodles? How do you know?

Model It

You can think of a mixed number as the sum of an integer and a fraction.

Then find the decimal form of the fraction.

$$4\frac{1}{6} = 4 + \frac{1}{6}$$

$$\begin{array}{r} 0.166\ldots \\ 6\overline{)1.000} \\ -6 \\ \hline 40 \\ -36 \\ \hline 40 \\ -36 \\ \hline 4 \end{array}$$

Then add 4 to 0.166 . . . .

Model It

You can rewrite a mixed number as a fraction greater than 1.

Then find the decimal form of the fraction.

$$4\frac{1}{6} = \frac{25}{6}$$

$$\begin{array}{r} 4.166\ldots \\ 6\overline{)25.000} \\ -24 \\ \hline 1\,0 \\ -6 \\ \hline 40 \\ -36 \\ \hline 40 \\ -36 \\ \hline 4 \end{array}$$

CONNECT IT

➤ **Use the problem from the previous page to help you understand how to express a fraction as a repeating decimal.**

1. How many ounces of noodles does Robert need? Does he have enough noodles for the recipe?

2. Look at the second **Model It**. Does rewriting the mixed number as a fraction before dividing change its decimal form? Explain.

3. Look at the long division in the **Model Its**. If you keep dividing, will you ever be able to get a remainder of 0? Why or why not?

4. When the remainder of 4 starts to repeat, what happens in the quotient?

5. When you divide to find the decimal form of a rational number, how can you tell when it is a repeating decimal?

6. You can use long division to find the decimal form of any rational number. What is similar when the result is a repeating decimal instead of a terminating decimal? What is different?

7. **Reflect** Think about all the models and strategies you have discussed today. Describe how one of them helped you better understand how to solve the **Try It** problem.

Apply It

➤ **Use what you learned to solve these problems.**

8 Is $-3\frac{2}{11} + 3.18$ *positive* or *negative*? Show your work.

SOLUTION _____

9 Cody sells sourdough bread by weight. He cuts a 1-lb loaf into 12 equal slices. What is the weight of one slice of Cody's bread?

A $0.\overline{083}$ lb

B $0.0\overline{83}$ lb

C $0.08\overline{3}$ lb

D 0.083 lb

1 lb

10 What is $1\frac{50}{99}$ expressed as a decimal? Show your work.

SOLUTION _____

Name:

Practice Writing Rational Numbers as Repeating Decimals

➤ **Study the Example showing how to work with fractions and repeating decimals. Then solve problems 1–5.**

Example

Is $\frac{8}{11}$ *less than* or *greater than* 0.723?

You can divide to express $\frac{8}{11}$ as a decimal.

The pattern of alternating remainders of **8** and **3** will continue forever. So, the pattern of 7272 ... will continue forever in the quotient.

You can use a bar to show the repeating decimal as $0.\overline{72}$.

Since $0.\overline{72}$ is greater than 0.723, that means $\frac{8}{11}$ is greater than 0.723.

$$
\begin{array}{r}
0.7272\ldots \\
11\overline{)8.0000} \\
-7\,7 \\
\hline
30 \\
-22 \\
\hline
80 \\
-77 \\
\hline
30 \\
-22 \\
\hline
8
\end{array}
$$

1. There are 11 students running a relay race that is 2 mi long. Each student runs approximately $\frac{2}{11}$ mi. The course has a marker every 0.1 mi. Between which two markers does the second student finish? Show your work.

SOLUTION _____

2 David says $\frac{333}{1,000}$ is the same as $0.\overline{3}$. Is David correct? Explain.

3 The decimal form of $\frac{1}{3}$ is a repeating decimal. Are all the multiples of $\frac{1}{3}$ also repeating decimals? Explain.

4 On the number line, is $-3\frac{8}{9}$ or -3.89 farther from 0? Explain.

5 An underwater robot takes pictures at an elevation of $-8\frac{5}{12}$ m relative to sea level. What is the robot's elevation expressed as a decimal? Show your work.

SOLUTION _____

An underwater robot takes pictures in the sea.

Refine Expressing Rational Numbers as Terminating or Repeating Decimals

➤ **Complete the Example below. Then solve problems 1–9.**

Example

Express $\dfrac{\frac{15}{8}}{3}$ as a decimal.

Look at how you could show your work using division.

$$\dfrac{\frac{15}{8}}{3} = \dfrac{15}{8} \div \dfrac{3}{1}$$

$$= \dfrac{15}{8} \cdot \dfrac{1}{3}$$

$$= \dfrac{5}{8}$$

$$
\begin{array}{r}
0.625 \\
8{\overline{\smash{\big)}\,5.000}} \\
\underline{-48} \\
20 \\
\underline{-16} \\
40 \\
\underline{-40} \\
0
\end{array}
$$

SOLUTION _____

CONSIDER THIS...

In the fraction $\dfrac{\frac{15}{8}}{3}$, $\dfrac{15}{8}$ is the numerator and 3 is the denominator.

PAIR/SHARE

How can you tell that $\dfrac{\frac{15}{8}}{3}$ is a rational number?

Apply It

1 Are $4\dfrac{7}{9}$ and $4.\overline{7}$ equal? Show your work.

CONSIDER THIS...
The decimal expansion of all rational numbers will either repeat or end.

PAIR/SHARE
How can you use the decimal form of $\dfrac{1}{9}$ to check your answer?

SOLUTION _____

2   Carmen places the cards below in order from least to greatest. How does Carmen organize the cards? Show your work.

SOLUTION _____

3   What is the decimal form of $-1\frac{1}{12}$?

   A $-1.08\overline{3}$

   B $-1.0\overline{83}$

   C $-1.\overline{083}$

   D -1.083

Greg chose C as the correct answer. How might he have gotten that answer?

4 A digital scale shows weight in decimal form. A bag of pinto beans weighs $\frac{9}{16}$ lb. What weight, in pounds, will the scale show?

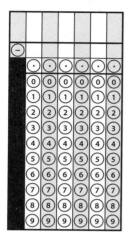

5 Express the fraction $\frac{\frac{5}{9}}{\frac{1}{3}}$ as a decimal. Show your work.

SOLUTION _____

6 Which fractions can be expressed as a terminating decimal? Select all that apply.

A $\frac{4}{3}$

B $\frac{11}{12}$

C $\frac{9}{15}$

D $\frac{10}{18}$

E $\frac{\frac{7}{12}}{\frac{1}{9}}$

7 Are $6.\overline{4}$ and $6.\overline{40}$ equal? Explain.

8 Isabel divides to find the decimal form of $\frac{1}{7}$. Her work is shown below. Isabel says that $\frac{1}{7}$ is not a rational number because the decimal form neither terminates nor repeats. Is Isabel correct? Explain.

```
      0.142857
   7)1.000000
    − 7
      30
    − 28
      20
     − 14
       60
      − 56
        40
       − 35
         50
        − 49
          1
```

9 **Math Journal** Express $-\frac{7}{8}$ and $\frac{10}{3}$ as decimals. Explain whether each is a terminating or a repeating decimal.

$-\frac{7}{8}$ -12.5

$\frac{10}{3} \rightarrow 3.\overline{1}$

```
    3.1
  3)100
   −9
    10
    −9
     1
```

```
   12.5
 8)100 0
   8
   20
  −16
   40
  −40
    0 0
```

✅ **End of Lesson Checklist**

📗 **INTERACTIVE GLOSSARY** Find the entries for *terminating decimals* and *repeating decimals*. Give an example of each.

☐ **SELF CHECK** Go back to the Unit 3 Opener and see what you can check off.

Dear Family,

This week your student is learning about using approximations to show that their answers to problems involving operations with rational numbers are reasonable.

Your student has already learned to add, subtract, multiply, and divide rational numbers. In this lesson, your student will focus on using estimation to approximate the results of calculations. Finding an approximation can be a useful tool to make sense of a problem. Approximating an answer first can also help to determine whether an answer is reasonable.

One way you can make an approximation is by rounding rational numbers to the nearest integer.

Your student will be solving problems like the one below.

> Ms. Seda deposits $41.60 into her bank account on Wednesday.
> On Thursday, she pays two bills for $17.15 and $26.85 from the account.
> Does Ms. Seda have more or less money in the account after the withdrawals than she did before the deposit?

➤ **ONE WAY** to find the answer is to approximate.

$41.60 − $17.15 − $26.85

Round each amount to the nearest $1.

$42 − 17 − 27 = −2$

➤ **ANOTHER WAY** is to find the exact answer.

$41.60 − 17.15 − 26.85 = −2.40$

Both the estimate and the exact answer show that Ms. Seda has less money in the account after the withdrawals than she did before the deposit. Since the exact answer is close to the approximation, you know the answer is reasonable.

 Use the next page to start a conversation about rational numbers.

Activity Thinking About Rational Numbers Around You

Ticket Sales

Cost of Movie

➤ **Do this activity together to investigate rational numbers in the real world.**

Most movies cost many millions of dollars to produce. How do movie studios make a profit? One way is from ticket sales. A movie studio's ticket sale profit can be represented by the following expression:

Ticket Price × Number of Tickets Sold − Cost to Make Movie

So, if the total money from ticket sales is more than the cost to make the movie, then the movie studio's profit is positive. But if the total money from ticket sales is less than the cost to make the movie, the movie studio's profit is negative. Movie studios approximate their costs and sales to decide whether or not a movie is worth making.

? What are other situations where you use rational numbers?

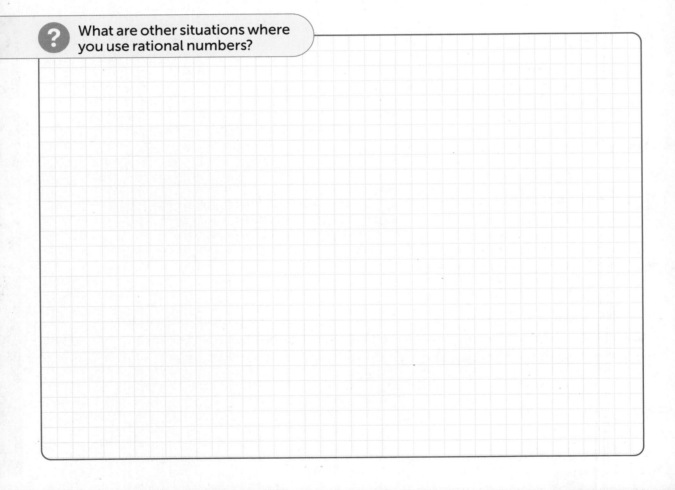

Explore Using the Four Operations with Negative Numbers

Previously, you learned about adding, subtracting, multiplying, and dividing with rational numbers. In this lesson, you will use all four operations to solve problems.

➤ **Use what you know to try to solve the problem below.**

Notah lives in Minnesota. He records the lowest temperature each day for one week. What is the mean of the temperatures?

−7.3°F, −11.2°F, 2.2°F, 0°F, −1.7°F, 3.3°F, 0°F

 TRY IT

 Math Toolkit grid paper, integer chips, number lines

DISCUSS IT

Ask: What did you do first to find the mean? Why?

Share: I started by . . . because . . .

 Learning Targets SMP 1, SMP 2, SMP 3, SMP 4, SMP 5, SMP 6
- Solve real-world and mathematical problems involving the four operations with rational numbers.
- Solve multi-step real-life and mathematical problems posed with rational numbers in any form, using tools strategically. Assess the reasonableness of answers using mental computation and estimation strategies.

LESSON 14 Use the Four Operations with Negative Numbers   **277**

CONNECT IT

1 Look Back What is the mean of the temperatures? Explain how you know.

2 Look Ahead You can find the mean by writing and simplifying an expression with rational numbers. When you solve a problem involving rational numbers, it can sometimes be hard to get a sense of how large or small the solution should be or even whether it should be positive or negative. Starting by approximating the solution can help you understand the problem and decide whether your solution is reasonable.

a. One way you can approximate the sum $-24\frac{3}{4} + 15\frac{1}{4}$ is by rounding each fraction to the nearest integer. What is the approximate value of $-24\frac{3}{4} + 15\frac{1}{4}$ if you round to the nearest integer?

b. Imani says $-24\frac{3}{4} + 15\frac{1}{4}$ is equal to -40. Is her statement reasonable? Explain why or why not.

c. Approximate the value of $-28.3(-47.9)$ by rounding each factor to the nearest ten.

d. Erik calculates $-28.3(-47.9)$ and gets 1,355.57. Is his answer reasonable? Explain.

3 Reflect Why is it useful to approximate the solution to a problem involving rational numbers?

Name:

Prepare for Using the Four Operations with Negative Numbers

1 Think about what you know about rounding numbers. Fill in each box. Use words, numbers, and pictures. Show as many ideas as you can.

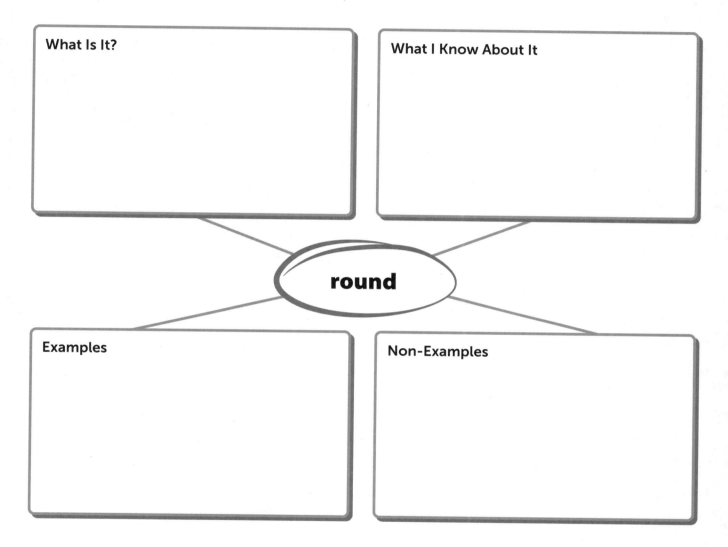

What Is It?

What I Know About It

round

Examples

Non-Examples

2 Enrique says that to round a decimal to the nearest integer, you can just ignore the decimal part. Is Enrique correct? Explain.

BEAUTIFUL
DEATH VALLEY
CALIFORNIA

3 Mei is a park ranger at Death Valley National Park in California. She records the elevation relative to sea level at different points in the park.

Elevation (m)	−32.6	24.7	−8.3	19.1	−8.4

a. What is the mean of the elevations? Show your work.

SOLUTION _____

b. Check your answer to problem 3a. Show your work.

Develop Solving Problems Using the Four Operations with Negative Numbers

➤ **Read and try to solve the problem below.**

Elena repairs pinball machines. She orders a part that costs $44.50. She also returns parts that cost $26.30 and $21.40. Is the cost of Elena's order more or less than her return? How much more or less?

TRY IT

Math Toolkit grid paper, integer chips, number lines

➤ **Explore different ways to solve problems involving negative numbers.**

Elena repairs pinball machines. She orders a part that costs $44.50. She also returns parts that cost $26.30 and $21.40. Is the cost of Elena's order more or less than her return? How much more or less?

Model It

You can approximate the answer by rounding each value to the nearest $5 or to the nearest $1.

Actual Amount	Rounded to the Nearest $5	Rounded to the Nearest $1
44.50	45	45
−26.30	−25	−26
−21.40	−20	−21

Model It

You can write and evaluate an expression to find the exact value.

$$44.50 - 26.30 - 21.40 = 44.50 + (-26.30) + (-21.40)$$
$$= 44.50 + (-47.70)$$

➤ **Use the problem from the previous page to help you understand how to solve problems involving negative numbers.**

1 Look at the first **Model It**. What approximation do you get when you round the values to the nearest $5? What does this estimate tell you about the costs of Elena's order and return?

2 What approximation do you get when you round the values to the nearest $1? What does this estimate tell you about the costs of Elena's order and return?

3 Why might you want to estimate by rounding each value to the nearest $1 instead of to the nearest $5?

4 Is the cost of Elena's order more or less than her return? Exactly how much more or less?

5 How can finding an estimate help you check whether your answer is reasonable?

6 **Reflect** Think about all the models and strategies you have discussed today. Describe how one of them helped you better understand how to solve the **Try It** problem.

LESSON 14 Use the Four Operations with Negative Numbers **283**

Apply It

➤ **Use what you learned to solve these problems.**

7 Adriana is rock climbing. She started at an elevation of
−36.5 m relative to sea level, and will finish at an elevation of
$25\frac{3}{4}$ m. Her climb is now 80% complete. Estimate her current
elevation. Then find her actual elevation. Show your work.

SOLUTION _____

8 Glen, Andre, and Ramón share the cost of renting a vacation cottage. The total
cost is $960. Glen pays 30% of the total cost. Andre pays 0.45 of the total cost.
Ramón pays the rest. How much does Ramón pay? Show your work.

SOLUTION _____

9 Simplify $\frac{0.5(-77.8 - 11)}{-4}$. Show your work.

SOLUTION _____

Practice Solving Problems Using the Four Operations with Negative Numbers

➤ **Study the Example showing how to solve problems involving negative numbers. Then solve problems 1–4.**

Example

Estimate the value of 25 − 1.5(6.8 − 2.6). Then find the exact value.

To estimate, round each number to the nearest integer.

$$25 − 2(7 − 3) = 25 − 2(4)$$
$$= 25 − 8$$
$$= 17$$

The value is about 17.

Now find the exact value.

$$25 − 1.5(6.8 − 2.6) = 25 − 1.5(4.2)$$
$$= 25 − 6.3$$
$$= 18.7$$

1. Without finding the quotient, is the value of the expression $\left(-3\frac{1}{3} + 3\frac{1}{2}\right) \div \left(-\frac{1}{4}\right)$ *positive* or *negative*? Explain.

2. Simplify $\dfrac{-3(16 - 35 + 4)}{5}$. Show your work.

SOLUTION _____

3 A marine rescue center starts the year with 44 sea turtles. The table shows how the sea turtle population changes each month. At the end of April, the center returns $\frac{2}{3}$ of the sea turtles at the center to the sea. How many sea turtles are returned at the end of April? Show your work.

Month	January	February	March
Change in Population	−12	+16	−17

SOLUTION _____

4 Consider the expression $-6\frac{3}{5} - \left(-7\frac{4}{15}\right) + 2\frac{1}{5}$.

a. Estimate the value of the expression. Show your work.

SOLUTION _____

b. Find the exact value of the expression. Show your work.

SOLUTION _____

c. Use your estimate to explain if your answer to problem 4b is reasonable.

Refine Using the Four Operations with Negative Numbers

➤ **Complete the Example below. Then solve problems 1–9.**

Example

Simplify $\frac{1}{5}[4.5 + (-4)^3 - 5.5]$.

Look at how you could show your work using multiplication.

$$\frac{1}{5}[4.5 + (-4)^3 - 5.5] = \frac{1}{5}[4.5 + (-4)(-4)(-4) - 5.5]$$
$$= \frac{1}{5}[4.5 + (-64) - 5.5]$$
$$= \frac{1}{5}(4.5 - 5.5 - 64)$$
$$= \frac{1}{5}(-1 - 64)$$
$$= \frac{1}{5}(-65)$$

SOLUTION _____

CONSIDER THIS...
$(-4)^3 = (-4)(-4)(-4)$

PAIR/SHARE
What is a different sequence of steps you could use to evaluate the expression?

Apply It

1 As a block of ice melts, its weight changes from $1\frac{3}{4}$ lb to $\frac{1}{4}$ lb. This change takes $\frac{1}{4}$ h. The ice melts at a constant rate. At what rate does the weight of the ice change? Show your work.

CONSIDER THIS...
The rate is pounds per hour.

PAIR/SHARE
How would the rate be different if it took $\frac{1}{2}$ h instead of $\frac{1}{4}$ h for the weight of the ice to change to $\frac{1}{4}$ lb?

SOLUTION _____

2 Chase is a contestant on a game show. His scores in each of the first four rounds are shown below. Chase's final score is double his score after the four rounds. What is Chase's final score? Show your work.

Round	1	2	3	4
Score	−35	45	90	−15

CONSIDER THIS . . .
Chase's score after the first four rounds is the sum of the four scores.

SOLUTION _____

PAIR/SHARE
How can you check that your answer is correct?

3 Edward is scuba diving. He stops 14.3 m below the surface to look at a fish. Then he swims down 5.8 m to look at a reef. He then swims up 3.2 m. Which is the best approximation of Edward's current position relative to the ocean surface?

A 12 meters

B 11 meters

C −17 meters

D −23 meters

Dara chose B as the correct answer. How might she have gotten that answer?

CONSIDER THIS . . .
Should you add or subtract each number?

PAIR/SHARE
How can you tell whether the answer will be positive or negative without calculating the exact value?

4 The heights of the low tides for four days are −0.22 ft, 2.64 ft, −0.22 ft, and 2.64 ft. What is the mean height of the low tides? Show your work.

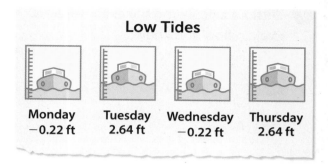

Low Tides

| Monday −0.22 ft | Tuesday 2.64 ft | Wednesday −0.22 ft | Thursday 2.64 ft |

SOLUTION _____

5 The result of which situation is best estimated by the integer −7?

A The temperature falls 1.9°F from 4.3°F.

B A hot-air balloon rises 4.1 m from the ground and then rises 2.3 m more.

C A submarine dives 3.8 ft below the surface of the ocean and then dives another 2.5 ft down.

D Laqueta has $3.85 and spends $2.45 on bread.

6 Consider the numbers below. Use two of the numbers to make the greatest sum, difference, product, and quotient possible.

$$-5\frac{1}{2} \quad 3.75 \quad -20.8 \quad 8 \quad -4 \quad 11\frac{1}{4}$$

Greatest sum: _____

Greatest difference: _____

Greatest product: _____

Greatest quotient: _____

7 Without calculating the exact value, is $\left(-\dfrac{5}{8}\right)^2 + 1$ *positive* or *negative*? Explain how you know.

8 Sarah has a savings account. This month she deposits four paychecks. Each paycheck is for $125.25. She makes four withdrawals to buy groceries. Each withdrawal is for $45. She also makes another withdrawal of $400. What is the total change in Sarah's account?

A −$1,279

B −$79

C $281

D $321

9 **Math Journal** Write a sum, difference, product, and quotient each with an approximate value of 6. The sum can only use decimals. The difference can only use mixed numbers. The product can only use negative numbers and at least one must be a fraction or decimal. The quotient should use only positive numbers and at least one should be a fraction or decimal.

✓ **End of Lesson Checklist**

☐ **INTERACTIVE GLOSSARY** Write a new entry for *approximate*. Write at least one synonym for *approximate*.

☐ **SELF CHECK** Go back to the Unit 3 Opener and see what you can check off.

Study an Example Problem and Solution

Math IN Action

SMP 1 Make sense of problems and persevere in solving them.

➤ **Read this problem involving operations with rational numbers. Then look at one student's solution to this problem on the following pages.**

Estimating Fuel

Captain Alita is an airline pilot. Her plane is approaching a thunderstorm. She needs to determine whether she has enough fuel to go around the thunderstorm and still reach her original destination.

Going around the storm will add 15 to 30 minutes to the estimated flight time. In addition, the amount of fuel needed for the next hour of flight after the detour will increase by 500 to 600 pounds.

Look at the portion of Captain Alita's flight plan shown below. Determine if she can safely reach her original destination by going around the thunderstorm or if she should land at a closer airport to refuel.

FLIGHT PLAN ✈

1. Departure Time:
3:25 PM ▼

2. Estimated Flight Time:
5 h 12 min

3. Fuel On Board:

Category	Pounds of Fuel
Trip	29,398
Reserve	7,241
Taxi	420
Total	37,069

4. Expected Change in Amount of Fuel on Board (per hour):
−5,450 to −5,325 pounds

5. Maximum Allowable Fuel Use:
$$\text{Trip} + \frac{\text{Reserve}}{5} + \text{Taxi}$$

Every commercial airplane gets hit by lightning about once per year. The electric current passes through the outer shell of the plane and usually exits at the tail, without endangering the passengers inside.

One Student's Solution

Problem-Solving Checklist ✓

- ☐ Tell what is known.
- ☐ Tell what the problem is asking.
- ☐ Show all your work.
- ☐ Show that the solution works.

First, I will determine the maximum, or greatest, amount of fuel the plane is allowed to use.

The flight plan includes an expression that represents this amount. I can evaluate this expression by substituting values for the trip fuel, reserve fuel, and taxi fuel.

$$\text{Trip} \quad + \quad \frac{\text{Reserve}}{5} \quad + \quad \text{Taxi}$$

$$29{,}398 \quad + \quad \frac{7241}{5} \quad + \quad 420$$

$$29{,}398 \; + \; 1{,}448.2 \; + \; 420$$

$$31{,}266.2$$

Captain Alita can use up to **31,266.2** pounds of fuel.

Next, I will estimate how much fuel the plane will use according to the original flight plan.

I can multiply to find the total change in fuel: change per hour × number of hours.

The change in fuel each hour should be between −5,450 pounds and −5,325 pounds. I will use −5,400 pounds per hour. I will multiply this value by the estimated flight time (in hours).

Estimated flight time: 5 h 12 min = $5\frac{12}{60}$ h

= 5.2 h

NOTICE THAT...
The fraction $\frac{12}{60}$ can be written as a decimal by using long division.

NOTICE THAT...
The change in fuel each hour is negative because the amount of fuel is decreasing.

 × =

change in fuel per hour   flight time in hours   total change in fuel
−5,400   **5.2**   **−28,080**

According to the original flight plan, the plane will use about **28,080** pounds of fuel.

Then, I will estimate how much additional fuel the plane will use to go around the thunderstorm.

The flight time will increase by 15 to 30 minutes. I will calculate the fuel use for an additional 20 minutes.

Additional time: 0 h 20 min $= \frac{20}{60}$ h

$$= \frac{1}{3} \text{ h}$$

I can multiply the change in fuel per hour by this time.

$$-5{,}400\left(\frac{1}{3}\right) = -1{,}800$$

> **NOTICE THAT . . .**
> The fraction $\frac{20}{60}$ is 0.33 . . . Using a fraction in the calculations instead of a decimal approximation gives a more precise answer.

The extra flight time changes the amount of fuel by about $-1{,}800$ pounds. I also need to account for the increased fuel use during the next hour after the detour. During this hour, fuel will decrease by an extra 500 to 600 pounds. I will use 550 pounds.

$$-1{,}800 + (-550) = -2{,}350$$

To go around the thunderstorm, the plane will use about **2,350** additional pounds of fuel.

> **NOTICE THAT . . .**
> Each decrease in the amount of fuel is represented with a negative number. Adding these amounts gives the total decrease in fuel that will result from the detour.

Now, I can estimate the total amount of fuel used during the flight if Captain Alita goes around the thunderstorm.

I can add the change in fuel according to the original flight plan to the additional change in fuel for the detour.

$$-28{,}080 + (-2{,}350) = -30{,}430$$

The plane will use a total of approximately **30,430** pounds of fuel.

Finally, I will compare the estimated total to the maximum amount of fuel the plane is allowed to use.

Captain Alita can use up to **31,266.2** pounds of fuel. The estimated total change in fuel is **−30,430** pounds.

$$31{,}266.2 + (-30{,}430) = 836.2$$

> **NOTICE THAT . . .**
> There will be about 836 pounds of fuel left over.

The plane has enough fuel to go around the thunderstorm and still safely land at the original destination.

Try Another Approach

➤ **There are many ways to solve problems. Think about how you might solve the Estimating Fuel problem in a different way.**

Estimating Fuel

Captain Alita is an airline pilot. Her plane is approaching a thunderstorm. She needs to determine whether she has enough fuel to go around the thunderstorm and still reach her original destination.

Going around the storm will add 15 to 30 minutes to the estimated flight time. In addition, the amount of fuel needed for the next hour of flight after the detour will increase by 500 to 600 pounds.

Look at the portion of Captain Alita's flight plan shown below. Determine if she can safely reach her original destination by going around the thunderstorm or if she should land at a closer airport to refuel.

FLIGHT PLAN

1. Departure Time:
3:25 PM ▼

2. Estimated Flight Time:
5 h 12 min

3. Fuel On Board:

Category	Pounds of Fuel
Trip	29,398
Reserve	7,241
Taxi	420
Total	37,069

4. Expected Change in Amount of Fuel on Board (per hour):
−5,450 to −5,325 pounds

5. Maximum Allowable Fuel Use:
$$\text{Trip} + \frac{\text{Reserve}}{5} + \text{Taxi}$$

Plan It

➤ **Answer these questions to help you start thinking about a plan.**

  a. What value will you use for the change in on-board fuel each hour? How do you know this value is within the expected range?

  b. If the flight time increases by 15 to 30 minutes, what is the new estimated flight time? How can you use this time (in hours) to help you solve the problem another way?

Solve It

➤ **Find a different solution for the Estimating Fuel problem. Show all your work on a separate sheet of paper. You may want to use the Problem-Solving Tips to get started.**

> **PROBLEM-SOLVING TIPS**
>
> **Math Toolkit** base-ten blocks, grid paper, hundredths grids, number lines
>
> **Key Terms**
>
> | integer | negative number | positive number |
> | estimate | repeating decimal | terminating decimal |
>
> **Models** You may want to use . . .
>
> • a picture, diagram, or table to organize your work.
>
> • negative numbers to model quantities that are decreasing.
>
> • expressions or equations to show relationships among quantities.

Reflect

Use Mathematical Practices As you work through the problem, discuss these questions with a partner.

• **Make an Argument** In this situation, is it better to overestimate or underestimate the plane's fuel use? Why?

• **Repeated Reasoning** What does each negative number in your work represent?

Discuss Models and Strategies

➤ **Read the problem. Write a solution on a separate sheet of paper. Remember, there can be lots of ways to solve a problem.**

Planning a Descent

Captain Alita is the pilot for Flight 127 from Chicago to Seattle. The plane is approaching Seattle, and she needs to plan a descent.

Read the radio conversation between Captain Alita and air traffic control (ATC). Then help Captain Alita calculate the following information required for the descent.

- The distance (in nautical miles) that the plane will travel forward during the descent

- The number of minutes the descent will take

- The plane's change in altitude (in feet) each minute of the descent

Radio Transcript	**Translation**
ATC: Flight 127, confirm ground speed and altitude.	Seattle air traffic control asks Flight 127 to identify its current ground speed (forward speed) and altitude.
CAPTAIN ALITA: 250 knots and 16,200 feet, Flight 127.	Flight 127 responds that it is currently traveling at a speed of 250 knots* at an altitude of 16,200 feet.
ATC: Flight 127, maintain ground speed. Seattle approach, descend 300 to 350 feet per nautical mile, and maintain 10,000.	Seattle air traffic control asks Flight 127 to keep the same ground speed, descend at a rate between 300 and 350 feet for every nautical mile it travels forward to an altitude of 10,000 feet, and then stay at that altitude.
CAPTAIN ALITA: Down to 10,000, Flight 127.	Flight 127 confirms that it will begin descending to 10,000 feet.

*One knot is equal to 1 nautical mile per hour. A nautical mile is slightly longer than a regular mile.

Plan It and Solve It

➤ **Find a solution to the Planning a Descent problem.**

Write a detailed plan and support your answer. Be sure to include:

- a rate of descent, in feet per nautical mile, for Flight 127.

- the forward distance, in nautical miles, the plane will travel during its descent to an altitude of 10,000 feet.

- the time, in minutes, the descent will take.

- the plane's change in altitude (in feet) each minute of the descent.

PROBLEM-SOLVING TIPS

 Math Toolkit grid paper, number lines

Key Terms

negative number	positive number	decimal
difference	product	quotient

Sentence Starters

- I can find the plane's total change in altitude during its descent by . . .

- I should use negative numbers to represent . . .

- I know that my answers are reasonable because . . .

Reflect

Use Mathematical Practices As you work through the problem, discuss these questions with a partner.

- **Reason Mathematically** How did you determine what value to use for the plane's rate of descent (feet per nautical mile)?

- **Be Precise** Why is it important to label each part of your final solution with units?

Pilots and air traffic controllers have their own flight-related language that replaces letters and numbers with code words. For example, they say *bravo* for the letter B and *niner* for the number nine.

Persevere On Your Own

➤ **Read the problem. Write a solution on a separate sheet of paper.**

Making a Cargo Plan

Captain Alita's next flight will travel from Los Angeles to Chicago. Her plane will carry cargo in addition to passengers and their baggage. Look at the information about Captain Alita's flight and the cargo that needs to be shipped from Los Angeles to Chicago.

Decide which cargo should go on Flight 910. Take all volume and weight restrictions into account, and try to carry as much cargo as possible.

Flight 910

Maximum payload (weight of passengers + baggage + cargo): **44,700 lb**

Weight of passengers + carry-on bags: **28,196 lb**

Weight of checked baggage: **3,757 lb**

Total volume of cargo holds: **1,041 ft³**

Volume of checked baggage: **747 ft³**

AIRLINE RESTRICTIONS

- Flights should carry no more than 80% of their maximum payload.

- Checked baggage travels in the cargo holds, but carry-on bags do not.

Trip:	Los Angeles to Chicago		
Type of Cargo	**Number of Containers**	**Volume of Each Container (ft³)**	**Weight of Each Container (lb)**
Electronics	3	18.4	$162\frac{3}{8}$
Flowers	4	12.2	$64\frac{1}{2}$
Fresh seafood	5	21	$148\frac{3}{4}$
Fruit	4	10.5	$295\frac{7}{8}$
Mail	7	17.9	225
Medicine	4	5.25	$48\frac{1}{4}$
Vegetables	5	10.1	$275\frac{1}{2}$

Solve It

➤ **Find a solution to the Making a Cargo Plan problem.**

- Make a plan for the cargo that Flight 910 should carry. Include the types of cargo and the number of containers of each type.

- Show that your plan meets the volume and weight restrictions for the flight.

- Explain how you decided which cargo to include on the flight.

Reflect

Use Mathematical Practices After you complete the problem, choose one of these questions to discuss with a partner.

- **Persevere** Did you try different combinations of cargo before deciding on a final plan? Explain.

- **Make an Argument** Could any more containers be added to your partner's cargo plan? Explain.

When transporting a herd of cattle, their natural release of warm methane gas and high body temperatures can set off the plane's smoke alarm.

In this unit you learned to . . .

Skill	Lesson
Multiply positive and negative integers.	11, 12
Divide positive and negative integers.	12
Multiply positive and negative fractions and decimals.	12
Divide positive and negative fractions and decimals.	12
Express rational numbers as terminating or repeating decimals.	13
Solve word problems with rational numbers.	14
Use math vocabulary and precise language to explain problems with rational numbers.	11–14

Think about what you have learned.

➤ **Use words, numbers, and drawings.**

1 Two things I learned in math are . . .

2 I am proud that I can . . .

3 I could use more practice with . . .

➤ Review the unit vocabulary. Put a check mark by items you can use in speaking and writing. Look up the meaning of any terms you do not know.

Math Vocabulary

- ☐ evaluate
- ☐ expression
- ☐ rational number

- ☐ reciprocal
- ☐ repeating decimals
- ☐ terminating decimals

Academic Vocabulary

- ☐ accurate
- ☐ calculation
- ☐ express
- ☐ justify
- ☐ reasonable

➤ This diagram shows a category and two subcategories. Label the boxes with titles for the category and subcategories from the unit vocabulary. Then add at least two numbers to each subcategory.

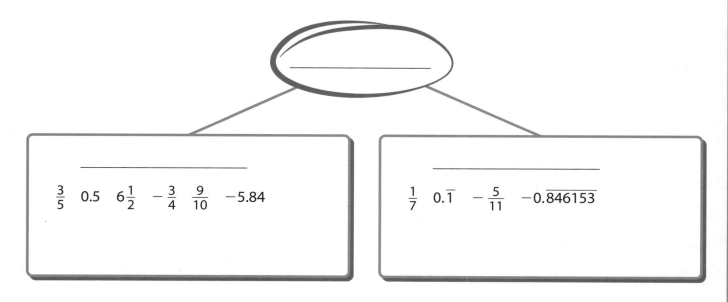

$\frac{3}{5}$ 0.5 $6\frac{1}{2}$ $-\frac{3}{4}$ $\frac{9}{10}$ -5.84

$\frac{1}{7}$ $0.\overline{1}$ $-\frac{5}{11}$ $-0.\overline{846153}$

➤ Use the unit vocabulary to complete the problems.

1 Explain why it is sometimes useful to approximate an answer and how you can find an approximate answer. Use at least two math or academic vocabulary terms in your explanation. Underline each term you use.

➤ **Use what you have learned to complete these problems.**

1 What is $-\frac{5}{6} \div -\frac{1}{3}$?

A $-\frac{5}{18}$

B $-\frac{5}{2}$

C $\frac{5}{2}$

D $\frac{5}{18}$

2 A small apple weighs $\frac{5}{16}$ lb. A digital scale shows the weight in decimal form. What weight, in pounds, does the scale show? Record your answer on the grid. Then fill in the bubbles.

3 Gualberto has a barrel that collects rainwater. As the rainwater evaporates, the height of the rainwater changes from 24.83 in. to 18.08 in. over a period of $5\frac{2}{5}$ days. What is the average change in the height of the rainwater each day? Show your work.

SOLUTION _____

4 Carla says that $(-5)(-7) = -35$, but she is incorrect. What is one change you can make to Carla's equation to make it correct? Explain your reasoning.

SOLUTION _____

_____

_____

5 The grocery store sells cheddar cheese at the deli counter. The weight of the cheddar cheese changes by -8 lb in 5 days. What rational number represents the average change in pounds of the cheddar cheese each day?

A -1.6

B -0.625

C 0.625

D 1.6

6 Rita and Fazil are working on a math project. Rita says that $\dfrac{\frac{5}{6}}{\frac{3}{2}}$ and 0.5 are not equal. Fazil says that $\dfrac{\frac{5}{6}}{\frac{3}{2}}$ and 0.5 are equal. Who is correct? Explain your reasoning.

SOLUTION _____

_____

_____

_____

7 Which expressions have a value less than 1? Choose all the correct answers.

A $-7 \cdot \dfrac{1}{2} - 4$

B $-7 \cdot \left(\dfrac{1}{2} - 4\right)$

C $-7 \cdot \dfrac{1}{2} \cdot (-4)$

D $-7 + \dfrac{1}{2} \cdot (-4)$

E $-7 \div \left(-\dfrac{1}{2}\right) + 4$

Performance Task

➤ **Answer the questions and show all your work on separate paper.**

A soap maker tracks costs of olive oil, coconut oil, and sodium hydroxide. The table below shows the cost of each ingredient last week and the change in cost per ounce. Find the new cost per ounce and complete the table. Round all values to the nearest cent.

Ingredient	Last Week's Cost	Change in Cost per Ounce	This Week's Cost per Ounce
Olive oil	$12.60 for 40 oz	+$0.03	
Coconut oil	$15.75 for 18 oz	−$0.13	
Sodium hydroxide	$0.75 for 0.5 oz	−$0.05	

To make a batch of soap, she needs the following ingredients:

30 oz olive oil

7 oz coconut oil

7 oz sodium hydroxide

Each batch makes 14 bars of soap.

The soap maker can buy each ingredient in any amount. She will make as many whole batches as possible using this week's costs and a budget of $150. Choose a sales price for one bar of soap and determine how much profit the soap maker will make this week if she sells all the bars that she makes.

Reflect

Use Mathematical Practices After you complete the task, choose one of the following questions to answer.

• **Make Sense of the Problem** How did you use the information in the table to find the new cost per ounce?

• **Be Precise** How did you know if an answer needed to be rounded?

Unit 4

Algebraic Thinking

Expressions, Equations, and Inequalities

✓ **Self Check**	Before starting this unit, check off the skills you know below. As you complete each lesson, see how many more skills you can check off!

I can . . .	Before	After
Find equivalent expressions.	☐	☐
Rewrite expressions in different forms.	☐	☐
Solve multi-step equations.	☐	☐
Solve problems using equations.	☐	☐
Solve inequalities.	☐	☐
Solve problems using inequalities.	☐	☐
Graph the solution set of an inequality.	☐	☐
Actively participate in discussions by asking questions and rephrasing or building on classmates' ideas.	☐	☐

➤ **Think about what you know about calculating with rational numbers. Look at each set of expressions and circle the expression that is not equivalent to the others.**

$-3(2x + 8)$	$-\frac{1}{3}y - 2y + 15x - 3y$
$-3 \cdot 2x + (-3 \cdot 8)$	$-10\frac{1}{3}y$
$-6x - 8$	$-5\frac{1}{3}y + 15x$
$-2(3x + 12)$	$-2\frac{1}{3}y + 15x - 3y$
$8 \cdot 3^2 + 5w$	
$24^2 + 5w$	
$8 \cdot 9 + 5w$	
$72 + 5w$	

Meet with a partner and compare answers. Discuss how you arrived at your answers. Then, in the last box, make your own set of four expressions and circle the one that is not equivalent to the others.

Dear Family,

This week your student is learning how to write equivalent expressions that have both variables and rational numbers.

Many situations can be represented with mathematical expressions. For example, suppose the price of a movie ticket is x dollars, and the price of a bag of popcorn is y dollars. The expression $x + y$ represents the cost of 1 ticket and 1 bag of popcorn. You can represent the cost of 2 tickets and 2 bags of popcorn with different expressions.

Three possible expressions are $x + y + x + y$, $2x + 2y$, and $2(x + y)$. These expressions are equivalent, or represent the same value.

$x + y + x + y$ $\qquad$ $2x + 2y$ $\qquad$ $2(x + y)$

Expand $2(x + y)$ $\qquad$ **Factor** $2x + 2y$

Your student will be solving problems like the one below.

Are $24x - 27 - 15x + 18 - 21x + 27$ and $-3(4x - 6)$ equivalent expressions?

➤ **ONE WAY** to check if the expressions are equivalent is to write both expressions without parentheses and then combine like terms.

$24x - 27 - 15x + 18 - 21x + 27$ $\qquad\qquad$ $-3(4x - 6)$

$(24x - 15x - 21x) + (-27 + 18 + 27)$ $\qquad$ $-12x + 18$

$-12x + 18$

➤ **ANOTHER WAY** is to write the first expression using parentheses, or factor.

$24x - 27 - 15x + 18 - 21x + 27$ $\qquad\qquad$ $-3(4x - 6)$

$(24x - 15x - 21x) + (-27 + 18 + 27)$

$-12x + 18$

$-3(4x - 6)$

Both ways show $24x - 27 - 15x + 18 - 21x + 27$ and $-3(4x - 6)$ are equivalent expressions.

 Use the next page to start a conversation about equivalent expressions.

Activity Thinking About Equivalent Expressions

➤ **Do this activity together to investigate equivalent expressions.**

Have you and a friend ever said things differently, but meant the same thing? Often expressions look or sound different but mean the same thing.

Some examples include:

- Six of one, or half a dozen of the other
- A mix of red and blue, or purple
- Quarter past 1, or 1:15

? What are other situations where you can express the same thing in different ways?

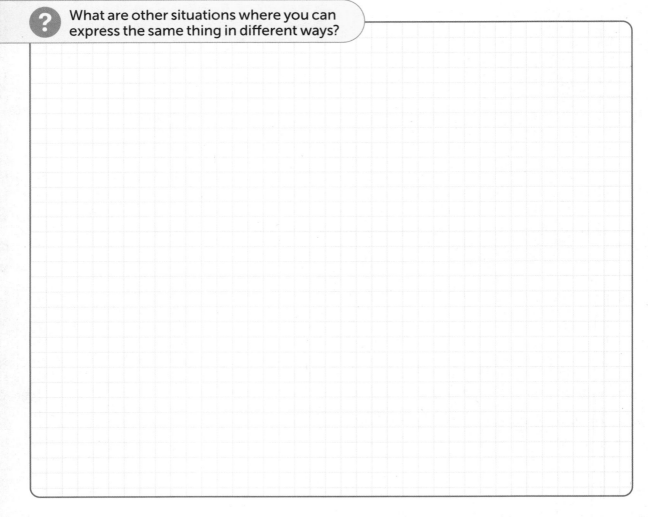

Explore Equivalent Expressions

Previously, you worked with equivalent expressions that have positive coefficients. In this lesson, you will work with equivalent expressions that have negative coefficients.

➤ **Use what you know to try to solve the problem below.**

In a certain video game, players earn bonus points after finishing a level. The number of bonus points is based on how many seconds, t, it takes the player to finish the level. The game uses the expression $-5.5 + 500 + 0.9t + \left(\frac{11}{2} - 1.9t\right)$ to determine the number of bonus points. Zahara finishes a level in 201 seconds. How many bonus points does she earn?

TRY IT   **Math Toolkit** grid paper, sticky notes

$$-5.5 + 500 + 0.9t + \left(\frac{11}{2} - 1.9t\right)$$

$$0.9 + (-1.9)$$

DISCUSS IT

Ask: What did you do first to determine how many bonus points Zahara earns?

Share: First, I . . . because . . .

Learning Target   SMP 1, SMP 2, SMP 3, SMP 4, SMP 5, SMP 6, SMP 7
Apply properties of operations as strategies to add, subtract, factor, and expand linear expressions with rational coefficients.

CONNECT IT

1 **Look Back** How many bonus points does Zahara earn? What is another expression the game could use to determine the number of bonus points she earns?

2 **Look Ahead** In the **Try It**, you evaluated an expression. Sometimes it can be helpful to find an equivalent expression to evaluate instead. One way to find an equivalent expression is to use the distributive property.

a. Sometimes you can use the distributive property to expand an expression. You can expand $-3(5 - x)$ into the equivalent expression $-15 + 3x$. Show how you can use the distributive property to expand $-4(-a + 2)$ to get an equivalent expression.

b. Sometimes you can use the distributive property to **factor** an expression. You can factor $3z - 6$ to get the equivalent expression $3(z - 2)$. Show how you can use the distributive property to factor $2g - 10$ to get an equivalent expression.

c. Can you factor $-2x + 6$ to get $-2(x - 3)$? Explain.

3 **Reflect** Explain why the expressions $-6(5 - k)$ and $6k - 30$ are equivalent.

Prepare for Writing Equivalent Expressions Involving Rational Numbers

1 Think about what you know about the terms of an expression. Fill in each box. Use words, numbers, and pictures. Show as many ideas as you can.

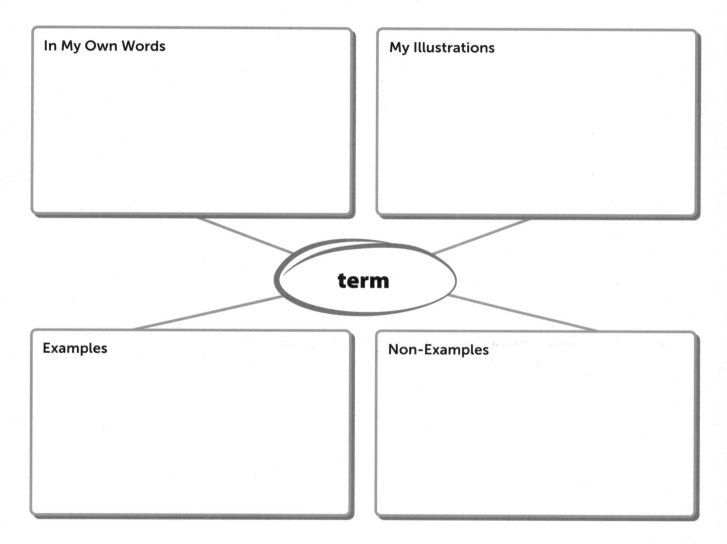

In My Own Words	My Illustrations

term

Examples	Non-Examples

2 Aiden says that equivalent expressions always have the same number of terms. Is Aiden correct? If he is, explain why. If he is not correct, give a counterexample.

3 Jake cuts out five-pointed stars. They are different sizes, but they all have the same shape. The side lengths within each star are the same. To find the perimeter of each star, Jake uses the expression $12\ell + \frac{1}{2} - 4\ell - 8.5 + 2\ell + 8$, where ℓ is the side length of the star.

a. Find the perimeter of a star with side length 6 inches. Show your work.

SOLUTION _____

b. Check your answer to problem 3a. Show your work.

Develop Expanding Expressions

➤ **Read and try to solve the problem below.**

Are $-\frac{1}{3}(-3m + 6 - 12 + 15m)$ and $2(1 - 2m)$ equivalent expressions?

Show why or why not.

Math Toolkit grid paper, sticky notes

DISCUSS IT

Ask: How did you get started figuring out whether the expressions are equivalent?

Share: I started by . . .

➤ **Explore different ways to find equivalent expressions.**

Are $-\frac{1}{3}(-3m + 6 - 12 + 15m)$ and $2(1 - 2m)$ equivalent expressions?

Show why or why not.

Solve It

You can combine like terms, then expand.

$-\frac{1}{3}(-3m + 6 - 12 + 15m)$

$-\frac{1}{3}(12m - 6)$

$-\frac{1}{3}(12m) - \left(-\frac{1}{3}\right)(6)$

$-4m + 2$

$2(1 - 2m)$

$2(1) - 2(2m)$

$2 - 4m$

$-4m + 2$

Solve It

You can expand, then combine like terms.

$-\frac{1}{3}(-3m + 6 - 12 + 15m)$

$-\frac{1}{3}(-3m) + \left(-\frac{1}{3}\right)(6) - \left(-\frac{1}{3}\right)(12) + \left(-\frac{1}{3}\right)(15m)$

$m - 2 + 4 - 5m$

$-4m + 2$

$2(1 - 2m)$

$2(1) - 2(2m)$

$2 - 4m$

$-4m + 2$

➤ **Use the problem from the previous page to help you understand how to find equivalent expressions.**

1 How do the **Solve Its** show that the expressions are equivalent?

2 How can expanding two expressions help show that the expressions are equivalent?

3 Is $-\frac{1}{3}(3 - m)$ equivalent to $-1 + \frac{1}{3}m$ or to $-1 - \frac{1}{3}m$? Explain.

4 How is expanding an expression with negative terms like expanding an expression with positive terms? How is it different?

5 **Reflect** Think about all the models and strategies you have discussed today. Describe how one of them helped you better understand how to determine whether expressions are equivalent.

Apply It

➤ **Use what you learned to solve these problems.**

6 Raúl says the expression $-25\left(\frac{1}{5}x - 20\right)$ is equivalent to $-5x - 500$. Do you agree? Explain why or why not.

7 Which expressions are equivalent to $-4(-25y + 4 + 50y - 8)$? Select all that apply.

A $-100y - 4$

B $-2(23y - 5 + 27y - 3)$

C $(100y + 32) - (200y + 16)$

D $-16 - 100y$

E $-(-100y + 16 + 200y - 32)$

F $-300y - 48$

8 Are the expressions $2(3x - 6)$ and $2(3x) - 6$ equivalent? Explain your reasoning.

Name:

Practice Expanding Expressions

➤ **Study the Example showing how to decide whether two expressions are equivalent. Then solve problems 1–5.**

Example

Is $-\frac{3}{4}(-8a - 12)$ equivalent to $6a + 9$?

You can start by expanding $-\frac{3}{4}(-8a - 12)$.

$-\frac{3}{4}(-8a - 12)$

$-\frac{3}{4}[-8a + (-12)]$

$\left(-\frac{3}{4}\right)(-8a) + \left(-\frac{3}{4}\right)(-12)$

$6a + 9$

You can rewrite $-\frac{3}{4}(-8a - 12)$ as $6a + 9$. So, the two expressions are equivalent.

1 Look at the Example. How do you know that $\left(-\frac{3}{4}\right)(-8a) + \left(-\frac{3}{4}\right)(-12)$ is equivalent to both $-\frac{3}{4}(-8a - 12)$ and $6a + 9$?

2 Bianca makes an error when she tries to write an expression equivalent to $12 + 15(3 - y) - 10y$. What is the error? Fix Bianca's error.

$12 + 15(3 - y) - 10y$

$12 + 45 + 15y - 10y$

$57 + 5y$

Vocabulary

equivalent expressions

two or more different expressions that always name the same value.

3 A square playground is surrounded by a sidewalk on all sides. The sidewalk is $2n + 3$ yd long on each side of the park. The sidewalk is 0.5 yd wide. Write two equivalent expressions for the perimeter of the playground. Show your work.

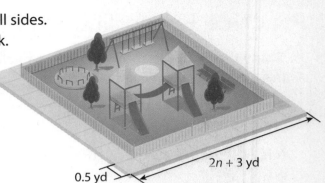

0.5 yd $2n + 3$ yd

SOLUTION _____

4 Is $-\frac{2}{3}(-12b - 6 + 9b - 18)$ equivalent to $2(b + 8)$? Show your work.

SOLUTION _____

5 Juanita says that $3.5[4d - (2)(1.5)]$ and $2[7d - (5)(1.05)]$ are equivalent. Is Juanita correct? Explain your reasoning.

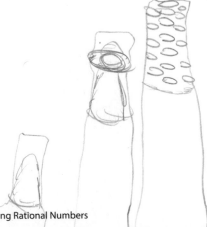

Develop Factoring Expressions

➤ **Read and try to solve the problem below.**

Are the expressions $24c - 36 + 12 - 12c + 36 - 48c$ and $-2(18c - 6)$ equivalent?
Show why or why not.

  Math Toolkit algebra tiles, grid paper

$$24c - 36 + 12 - 12c + 36 - 48c$$

$$-2\left(18c - 6\right)$$

DISCUSS IT

Ask: How did you reach that conclusion?

Share: First, I . . .

➤ **Explore different ways to determine whether expressions are equivalent.**

Are the expressions $24c - 36 + 12 - 12c + 36 - 48c$ and $-2(18c - 6)$ equivalent? Show why or why not.

Solve It

You can combine like terms and then expand the expression that has parentheses.

$24c - 36 + 12 - 12c + 36 - 48c$ $\qquad\qquad$ $-2(18c - 6)$

$(24c - 12c - 48c) + (-36 + 12 + 36)$ $\qquad$ $-36c + 12$

$-36c + 12$

Solve It

You can combine like terms and then factor.

$24c - 36 + 12 - 12c + 36 - 48c$ $\qquad\qquad$ $-2(18c - 6)$

$(24c - 12c - 48c) + (-36 + 12 + 36)$

$-36c + 12$

$-2(18c - 6)$

Solve It

You can factor each expression before combining like terms.

$24c - 36 + 12 - 12c + 36 - 48c$ $\qquad\qquad$ $-2(18c - 6)$

$12(2c - 3 + 1 - c + 3 - 4c)$ $\qquad\qquad$ $-2[-6(-3c + 1)]$

$12(-3c + 1)$ $\qquad\qquad$ $12(-3c + 1)$

➤ **Use the problem from the previous page to help you understand how to use the distributive property to find equivalent expressions.**

1 How does each of the Solve Its show that the expressions are equivalent?

2 In the third Solve It, the second expression is already in factored form. Why can it be factored again?

3 How is factoring an expression with negative terms similar to factoring an expression with positive terms? How is it different?

4 Combining like terms, expanding, and factoring are strategies you can use to write equivalent expressions. When might you want to use each of these strategies?

5 **Reflect** Think about all the models and strategies you have discussed today. Describe how one of them helped you better understand how to determine whether expressions are equivalent.

binbiity & Ace♠

Apply It

$$\frac{3}{4} + \frac{12}{1} = \frac{36}{4} =$$

➤ **Use what you learned to solve these problems.**

6 A cell phone company is having a sale. The expression

$12c + 12\left(\frac{3}{4}c\right) + 12\left(\frac{1}{2}c\right)$ shows the total cost for buying 3 phones

that each cost c dollars per month for 12 months.

Which expressions are equivalent to that expression? Select all that apply.

A $12(2.25c)$

B $12c + 12\frac{3}{4}c + 12\frac{1}{2}c$

C $12c + 8c + 6c$

D $37\frac{1}{4}c$

E $c(12 + 9 + 6)$

$12c + 12\left(\frac{3}{4}c\right) + 12\left(\frac{1}{2}c\right)$

$\boxed{12c + 9c + 6c}$

$27c$

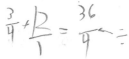

Cell Phone Sale Today!

1st Phone:
Full Cost

2nd Phone:
25% off

3rd Phone:
50% off

7 Are $(9g - 11 + 10g) - (12 - 11g + 13)$ and $-3(-10g + 12)$ equivalent expressions? Explain.

8 Is $2(6 - 3x) + x$ equivalent to $2(3x) + x + 12$? Show your work.

SOLUTION _____

Practice Factoring Expressions

➤ **Study the Example showing how to use factoring to write an equivalent expression. Then solve problems 1–6.**

Example

Consider the expression $(-3t + 3) + (2 - 2t) + (-4t + 4)$. Write an equivalent expression that is the product of two factors.

You can combine like terms. Then find a common factor.

$(-3t + 3) + (2 - 2t) + (-4t + 4)$

$(-3t - 2t - 4t) + (3 + 2 + 4)$

$-9t + 9$

$-9[t + (-1)]$

An equivalent expression is $-9(t - 1)$.

1 Write $-9t + 9$ as the product of two factors in a way that is not shown in the Example. Explain how you found it.

2 Write an expression equivalent to $6 - 4(3 - 6m) + 12m$ that is the product of two factors. Show your work.

SOLUTION _____

3 Is $1 + 4(3x - 10) - 12x$ equivalent to -39? Explain.

Vocabulary

equivalent expressions
two or more different expressions that always name the same value.

factor (noun)
a number, or expression within parentheses, that is multiplied.

factor (verb)
to rewrite an expression as a product of factors.

4 Olivia and Isabella each earn *d* dollars for each dog she walks. One day, Olivia walks 6 dogs and gets $8 in tips. That same day, Isabella walks 9 dogs and gets $12 in tips.

Dog Walking

Olivia

6 walks
$8 in tips

Isabella

9 walks
$12 in tips

a. Olivia writes $6d + 8 + 9d + 12$ to represent the amount they earn together. Isabella writes $5(3d + 4)$. Are their expressions equivalent? Show your work.

SOLUTION _____

b. Olivia and Isabella want to find out how much money they earn altogether. Suppose they earn $12 for each dog walk. Will you get a different amount if you evaluate Isabella's expression instead of Olivia's? Explain.

5 Are $\frac{1}{2}x + \frac{3}{4} - \frac{5}{8}x - \frac{7}{8}$ and $\frac{1}{8}(x + 1)$ equivalent expressions? Show your work.

SOLUTION _____

6 Show that $-0.75(-4f + 12)$ and $(5f + 9) - (2f + 18)$ are equivalent expressions.

Refine Writing Equivalent Expressions Involving Rational Numbers

➤ **Complete the Example below. Then solve problems 1–9.**

Example

Consider the expression $-\frac{3}{4}(-4f + 3g + 8f - 5g)$. **Write an equivalent expression that is the sum of two terms.**

Look at how you could rewrite an expression with more than one variable.

$-\frac{3}{4}(-4f + 3g + 8f - 5g)$

$-\frac{3}{4}(-4f + 8f + 3g - 5g)$

$-\frac{3}{4}(4f - 2g)$

SOLUTION _____

CONSIDER THIS . . .
To be like terms, the terms must have the same variables.

PAIR/SHARE
What would happen if you factored 4 out of $(4f - 2g)$?

Apply It

1 Are $0.5 - 3(-2x - \frac{1}{3} + 4 + 8x)$ and $-1.5(12x + 7)$ equivalent expressions? Show your work.

CONSIDER THIS . . .
Sometimes it is easier to see common factors after you combine like terms.

PAIR/SHARE
What is another way you could show that your answer is correct?

SOLUTION _____

2 Are the expressions $8(9 - 6x + 11)$ and $15 + \frac{3}{2}(-32x + 120) - 35$ both equivalent to $-16(3x - 10)$? Show your work.

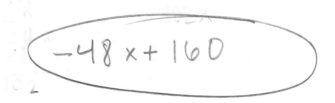

$$8(9 - 6x + 11)$$
$$72 - 48x + 88$$

$$-48x + 160$$

$$-16(3x - 10)$$

SOLUTION _____

3 Which expression is equivalent to $-3(10m - 2) + (3 + 6m - 3)$?

A $-24m + 6$

B $-24m - 6$

C $-48m + 6$

D $-18m$

Evelyn chose A as the correct answer. How might she have gotten that answer?

4 In front of a store, there is a row of parking spaces. Cars park parallel to one another, with the front of each car facing the store. Currently there are 10 compact spaces and 12 full size spaces. The store owners think they can repaint in the same space to fit 16 compact spaces and 9 full size spaces. The width of each type of space will not change. Are the store owners correct? Explain.

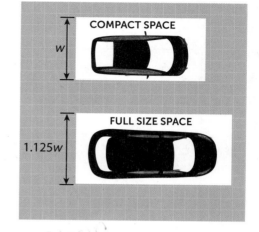

PARKING SPACE PLAN

COMPACT SPACE
w

FULL SIZE SPACE
$1.125w$

$10 + 12 = 22$
$16 + 9 = 25$

No, you need 3 more parking spaces.

$10w + 12(1.125)$
$22w$

$\times$ 22
2250
22500
24.750

5 The variable z represents a positive integer. Does $4 + 3(2z - 5)$ represent a number that is *greater than, less than,* or *equal to* $2(3z - 4)$? Show your work.

SOLUTION _____

6 Which expressions are equivalent to $\frac{1}{5}x(5y + 60)$? Select all that apply.

A $\frac{1}{5}(2xy + 20x + 3xy + 40x)$

B $xy + 60x$

C $y + 12x$

D $25xy + 300x$

E $13xy$

F $x(y + 12)$

7 Tell whether each statement is *True* or *False*.

	True	False
a. $6(-5a + 4)$ and $3(-10a + 8)$ are equivalent expressions.	○	○
b. $\frac{1}{6}(15a - 36)$ and $\frac{1}{2}a - (3a + 6)$ are equivalent expressions.	○	○
c. $-3a + 1.5$ and $-0.5(6a + 1.5)$ are equivalent expressions.	○	○
d. $-4(a - 4 + 2a + 8)$ and $-4(a - 4) - 4(2a + 8)$ are equivalent expressions.	○	○

8 Kazuko says the expressions $5x$ and $6 - x$ are equivalent expressions, because you can substitute 1 for x in both expressions and get the same result. Is Kazuko's reasoning correct? Explain.

9 **Math Journal** Start with the expression $12 - \frac{3}{4}\left(8f - \frac{5}{3} + 4f + \frac{2}{3}\right)$. Write an equivalent expression, and explain why it is equivalent. Then write an expression that is not equivalent and explain why it is not equivalent.

✔ **End of Lesson Checklist**

☐ **INTERACTIVE GLOSSARY** Find the entry for *factor* (verb). Add two things you learned about factoring in this lesson.

☐ **SELF CHECK** Go back to the Unit 4 Opener and see what you can check off.

Dear Family,

This week your student is exploring how rewriting an expression in an equivalent form can help them look at a situation in a different way.

Your student has already learned what it means for two expressions to be equivalent and how to represent a real-world situation with an expression.

You can often represent a situation with multiple equivalent expressions. The expression that you write depends on how you interpret the situation.

Your student will be modeling problems like the one below.

A swimming pool is being designed so that different sections can be used for different activities. The diagram of the pool gives the dimensions in meters.

You can model the total area of the pool with the expression $25(8) + 25x + 7(8) + 7x$. You can also model the area of the pool with the expression $(25 + 7)(8 + x)$.

What information does each expression provide?

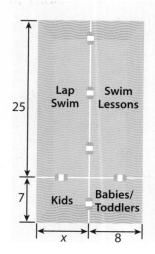

➤ **ONE WAY** to think about the total area is as the sum of the areas of the sections.

$$25(8) + 25x + 7(8) + 7x$$

This expression shows how the areas of the different sections make up the area of the whole pool. It shows that if the value of *x* changes, only the *Lap Swim* area and *Kids* area change. The *Swim Lessons* and *Babies/Toddlers* areas do not change.

➤ **ANOTHER WAY** to think about the total area of the pool is as a large rectangle.

$$(25 + 7)(8 + x)$$

This expression shows that the area of the whole pool is the product of the length and the width.

It shows that when *x* changes, both the width and the total area change.

 Use the next page to start a conversation about equivalent expressions.

Understand Reasons for Rewriting Expressions

Activity Thinking About Equivalent Expressions

➤ **Do this activity together to investigate reasons for rewriting expressions.**

Each situation below is represented with a pair of equivalent expressions.

Which expression do you like best for each situation? What question could that expression help you answer?

SITUATION 1

Four friends go to a fair. Each spends $25 for admission and $8.50 for lunch. These expressions show the total cost.

$4(25 + 8.50)$

$4(25) + 4(8.50)$

SITUATION 2

At a grocery store, each $3.75 box of cereal is on sale for $1.25 off. These expressions show the cost of b boxes.

$3.75b - 1.25b$

$2.5b$

 What are some other ways to think about these situations?

Explore Representing a Situation with Different Expressions

Model It

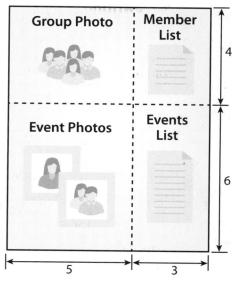

A page layout shows where different kinds of information will go on the page.

➤ **Complete the problem about writing equivalent numerical expressions.**

1 The yearbook team is designing the pages for school clubs so that the layouts are all the same. The dimensions shown are in inches. Different team members think about the total area of the page in different ways.

a. Paulo thinks of the area of the page as the product of the total length and the total width.
Complete Paulo's expression.

(_____ + 3) • (4 + _____)

b. Tamera thinks of the area of the page as the sum of the areas of the photo sections and the list sections.
Complete Tamera's expression. What does Tamera's expression let you see about the layout that Paulo's expression does not?

5(4 + _____) + _____(4 + 6)

c. Emily thinks of the area of the page as the sum of the areas of the four separate sections. Write an expression that represents Emily's way of thinking. What does Emily's expression let you see about the layout that neither Paulo's nor Tamera's expression did?

> **DISCUSS IT**
>
> *Ask:* How do you know that the expressions are equivalent?
>
> *Share:* I think it can be helpful to rewrite an expression in a different form because . . .

◎ **Learning Target**   SMP 2, SMP 3, SMP 7
Understand that rewriting an expression in different forms in a problem context can shed light on the problem and how the quantities in it are related.

Model It

➤ **Complete the problems about writing equivalent algebraic expressions.**

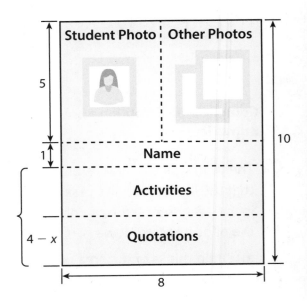

Student Photo | Other Photos

Name

Activities

Quotations

2 The yearbook team is also designing a page for each graduate. This page will have five different sections and will be 8 in. wide and 10 in. tall.

a. Look at the *Activities* and *Quotations* sections. Label the diagram to show the combined height of these two sections.

b. The height of the *Activities* sections can vary, depending on how many activities a student lists. Label the height of the *Activities* section.

c. Write two different expressions you could use to represent the combined area of the *Activities* and *Quotations* sections. What information about the sections does each expression show?

DISCUSS IT

Ask: Why might you want to use a variable to represent the height of the *Activities* section?

Share: I noticed . . . so I think . . .

3 **Reflect** Teresa writes $8(4) - 8x$ to represent the area of the *Quotations* section. Adnan writes $8(4 - x)$ to represent the area of the *Quotations* section. Explain what information each expression tells you.

Name:

Prepare for Reasons for Rewriting Expressions

1 Think about what you know about equivalent expressions. Fill in each box. Use words, numbers, and pictures. Show as many ideas as you can.

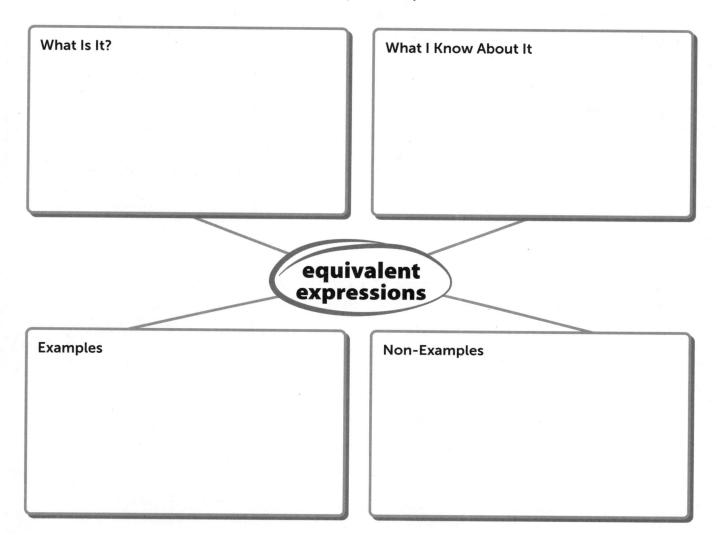

What Is It?	What I Know About It

equivalent expressions

Examples	Non-Examples

2 Why are 4(5) and 20 equivalent expressions?

➤ **Complete problems 3–4.**

3 The student government club makes a poster for a school dance. The dimensions shown are in inches. Different club members think about the total area of the poster in different ways.

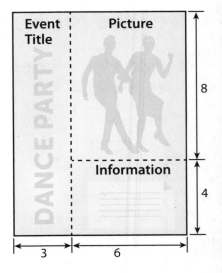

a. Brett thinks of the area of the poster as the product of the total length and the total width. Complete Brett's expression.

(_____ + 6) • (4 + _____)

b. Cai thinks of the area of the poster as the sum of the areas of the three separate sections. Write an expression that represents Cai's way of thinking. What does Cai's expression let you see about the layout that Brett's expression does not?

4 The science club designs a series of posters that all have the same four sections. Each poster measures 18 in. wide and 24 in. tall.

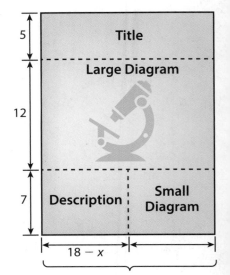

a. Look at the *Description* and *Small Diagram* sections. Label the diagram to show the combined width of these two sections.

b. The width of the *Small Diagram* section can vary, depending on the width of the diagram that must be shown. Label the width of the *Small Diagram* section.

c. Write two different expressions you could use to represent the combined area of the *Description* and *Small Diagram* sections. What information about the combined area does each expression show?

Develop Understanding of Representing a Situation with Different Expressions

Model It: Algebraic Expressions

➤ **Try these two problems involving rewriting algebraic expressions to represent a situation.**

1 Arturo's family hires 3 painters. Each painter charges $60 per hour. Arturo's family represents the charge for *x* hours of painting in different ways.

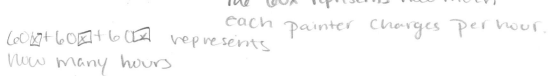

a. Arturo's father represents the situation with the expression $60x + 60x + 60x$. What does $60x$ represent? What does $60x + 60x + 60x$ represent?

The 60x represents how much each painter charges per hour.

60x + 60x + 60x represents how many hours

b. Arturo's mother represents the situation with the expression $180x$. What does $180x$ represent?

180 is the total

c. What information is in $60x + 60x + 60x$ that is not in $180x$? What information is in $180x$ that is not in $60x + 60x + 60x$?

2 Arturo writes the expression $480d + 480d + 480d$ to show how much the painters charge for *d* days of painting. Then he writes the equivalent expression $1,440d$. What information is in $480d + 480d + 480d$ that is not in $1,440d$? What information is in $1,440d$ that is not in $480d + 480d + 480d$?

DISCUSS IT

Ask: What information do you get from looking at each term of the expression?

Share: I think the expressions $480d + 480d + 480d$ and $1,440d$ help you interpret the situation differently because . . .

Model It: Two Variables

➤ **Try this problem about rewriting expressions with two variables.**

Adult   Child

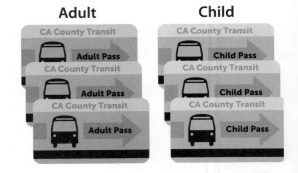

3 Leah buys 3 adult and 3 child bus passes for a trip. The cost of an adult pass is *a*. The cost of a child pass is *c*.

  a. Leah writes both 3(*a* + *c*) and 3*a* + 3*c*. Explain how each expression represents the cost of the bus passes.

  b. Leah learns that 2 more children will go on the trip. How can she modify 3(*a* + *c*) and 3*a* + 3*c* to include the cost of 2 more child passes?

> **DISCUSS IT**
>
> *Ask:* What is the relationship of (*a* + *c*) to the total cost of the bus passes?
>
> *Share:* In the expression . . . I can see that . . .

CONNECT IT

➤ **Complete the problems below.**

4 DeAndre spends the same number of hours awake every day. He writes 365(*a* − *s*) to represent how many more hours he spends awake, *a*, than asleep, *s*, in one year. DeAndre's mother says that he can also use 365*a* − 365(24 − *a*). What information is in DeAndre's expression that is not in his mother's? What information is in his mother's expression that is not in DeAndre's?

5 Estela brushes her teeth for *t* minutes twice a day. She uses the expression *t* · 2 · 365 to represent how many minutes she spends brushing her teeth each year. Write an equivalent expression. Then explain what information is in your expression that is not in the expression *t* · 2 · 365.

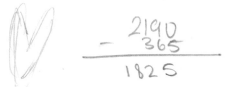

Name:

Practice Representing a Situation with Different Expressions

➤ **Study how the Example shows that equivalent expressions can provide different information about a situation. Then solve problems 1–3.**

Example

Ms. Patel orders posterboards and packs of stick-on letters for the science fair. Each posterboard costs $3, and each pack of stick-on letters costs $4. Ms. Patel represents the cost for x students with the expression $x(3 + 4)$. Then she represents it with the equivalent expression $7x$. What information does each expression tell you about the situation?

The expression $x(3 + 4)$ tells you the cost of one posterboard and one stick-on letter pack. It shows you how both the posterboard and the stick-on letter pack contribute to the total cost.

The expression $7x$ tells you that the cost per student is $7.

1 **a.** Mr. Gordon works with Ms. Patel from the Example. Mr. Gordon writes the expression $3x + 4x$ to represent the cost of ordering posterboards and stick-on letters for x students. What information does $3x + 4x$ tell you about the situation that the other expressions do not?

b. Suppose Mr. Gordon wants to buy 3 extra posterboards and 5 extra packs of stick-on letters. Write an expression that represents the cost of buying supplies for x students in addition to 3 extra posterboards and 5 extra packs of letters. Explain how your expression represents the new situation.

2 Nathan is making blueberry and pineapple kebabs. Each kebab needs the same number of blueberries, b, and the same number of pineapple pieces, p.

a. Nathan wants to check if he has enough of each type of fruit to make 12 kebabs. How can the expression $12b + 12p$ help him do that?

b. Nathan's friend Linda offers to help him make some of the kebabs. Nathan wants to set aside enough fruit for her to make 3 of the kebabs. How can you rewrite $12b + 12p$ so that it shows the fruit for Nathan's kebabs and the fruit for Linda's kebabs separately?

3 Noe sketches the design at the right. The small squares have side length a and the large squares have side length b. He writes the expression $2a^2 + 5ab + 2b^2$ to describe the area of his design. Then he changes his mind and writes $35a^2$.

What information is in the expression $2a^2 + 5ab + 2b^2$ that is not in $35a^2$? What information is in the expression $35a^2$ that is not in $2a^2 + 5ab + 2b^2$?

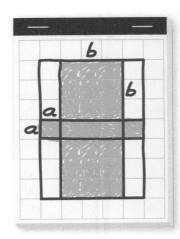

Refine Ideas About Reasons for Rewriting Expressions

Apply It

➤ **Complete problems 1–5.**

1 Interpret Two people describe a regular polygon. Brianna says that the polygon has side length 6.3 cm and perimeter 31.5 cm. Desiderio says the polygon has side length n and perimeter $5n$. Which person's description tells you how many sides the polygon has without doing any calculations? Why?

2 Evaluate A company sells rectangular pools. The length of each pool is 2 times the width, w. Jelani represents the perimeter of a pool to a customer as $6w$. Akiko represents the perimeter with the expression $2(2w + w)$. Explain what information each expression tells a customer.

3 Analyze The spirit club is sewing school flags for the pep rally. The club members want to find the amount of striped fabric they need for one flag. Avery says they can use the expression $5(4) + 7(4)$. Pedro says they can use the expression $(12 \cdot 8) \div 2$. Explain why both students are correct.

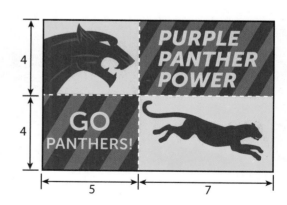

LESSON 16 Understand Reasons for Rewriting Expressions

4 The perimeter of an equilateral triangle is $6x - 6.3$.

PART A Find the side length of this triangle. Then draw a triangle and label its sides to represent this situation.

PART B Write an expression to represent the triangle's perimeter as the sum of its side lengths. Then write an expression to represent its perimeter as a product.

PART C Why might you want to represent the triangle's perimeter with one of the expressions you wrote in Part B, rather than with $6x - 6.3$?

5 **Math Journal** Look at the figure at the right. Explain one thing that representing the area of the figure as $9(x + 3) - 6x$ tells you about the situation. Then write an equivalent expression for the area. Explain what information is in your expression that is not in $9(x + 3) - 6x$.

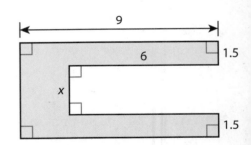

✓ End of Lesson Checklist

☐ **INTERACTIVE GLOSSARY** Write a new entry for *explain*. Tell what you do when you *explain* something.

Dear Family,

This week your student is exploring multi-step equations.

You can use a variable to represent an unknown quantity and write an equation with the variable to represent a situation. Then you can use reasoning to find the value of the unknown quantity. You can use a hanger diagram to reason about the value of an unknown quantity.

Your student will be reasoning about situations like the one below.

> For a party, Mr. Díaz buys 3 packs of confetti and a banner. He spends a total of $8. He knows that the banner cost $5, but does not remember the cost, c, of each pack of confetti. How can you represent this situation? How can you reason about the cost of each pack of confetti?

➤ **ONE WAY** is to use a hanger diagram.

The hanger diagram models this situation. The bar at the top is not tilted, showing the sides are balanced, or equal.

One way to reason about the cost, c, of each pack of confetti, is to cross off the same number of 1s from each side.

Now there are three c's on the left side and three 1s on the right side. That means each c is equal to 1.

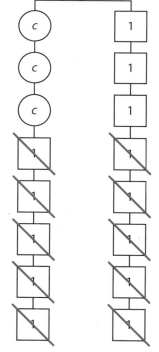

➤ **ANOTHER WAY** is to use an equation.

The equation $3c + 5 = 8$ models this situation.

One way to reason about the cost, c, of each pack of confetti is to first think about the value of $3c$. This means thinking about what plus 5 equals 8. Since 3 plus 5 equals 8, that means $3c$ equals 3.

You can then use the value of $3c$ to reason about the value of c. If 3 times c equals 3, then c equals 1.

Using either representation, you can reason that the cost of each pack of confetti is $1.

 Use the next page to start a conversation about multi-step equations.

Activity Thinking About Multi-Step Equations

➤ **Do this activity together to investigate modeling multi-step equations with hanger diagrams.**

Below are three hanger diagrams and three equations. Match each equation with the hanger diagram that models it.

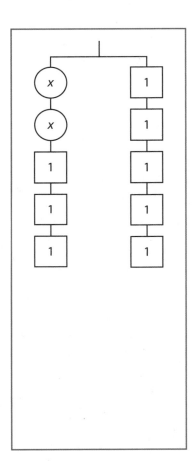

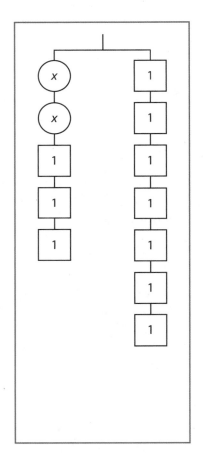

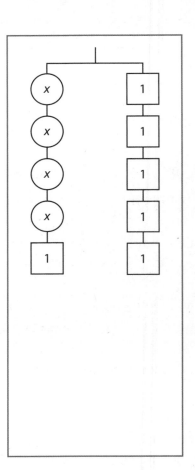

$2x + 3 = 7$

$4x + 1 = 5$

$2x + 3 = 5$

? How can you match the hanger diagram with the equation that it models?

? **UNDERSTAND:** How can you reason about equations to find the value of the unknown?

Explore Reasoning About Multi-Step Equations

Model It

➤ **Complete the problems about using hanger diagrams to reason about the value of an unknown in an equation.**

1 **a.** When the top bar in a hanger diagram is level, it means the hanger diagram is balanced. That means the value of what is on one side is equal to the value of what is on the other side. The hanger diagram at the right models the equation $3x = 6$. How can you use the diagram to find the value of x?

b. What does the hanger diagram show is the value of x?

2 The hanger diagram at the right models the equation $3x + 4 = 10$. You can use this diagram to find the value of x.

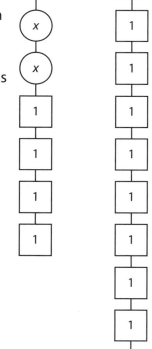

a. If you add or remove the same amount from both sides of the hanger diagram, it will stay balanced. What can you remove from both sides of the hanger so only variables are on the left side? Cross off what you can remove.

b. Fill in the blank to show the equation the hanger diagram now models.

$3x =$ _____

c. How can you use this hanger diagram to find the value of x?

DISCUSS IT

Ask: What does it mean if the bar in a hanger diagram is not level?

Share: When I cross off the 1s . . .

d. What does the diagram show is the value of x?

◎ **Learning Target** SMP 2, SMP 3, SMP 7
Use variables to represent quantities in a real-world or mathematical problem, and construct simple equations and inequalities to solve problems by reasoning about the quantities.

Model It

➤ **Complete the problems about using reasoning to solve equations.**

3 Instead of using a diagram, another way to solve an equation is to reason about its terms. Think about the equation $4w + 8 = 32$.

   a. You can think of $4w$ as the unknown quantity. How could you find the value of $4w$? What is the value of $4w$?

   b. How could you use the value of $4w$ to find the value of w? What is the value of w?

   c. How can you check that the value of w is correct?

4 Think about the equation $4w - 8 = 32$.

   a. The value of $4w$ is 40. How do you know this is true?

   b. The value of w is 10. How do you know this is true?

5 **Reflect** How is reasoning about the value of y the same in $5y + 10 = 25$ and $5y - 10 = 25$? How is it different?

Prepare for Multi-Step Equations

1 Think about what you know about an equation. Fill in each box. Use words, numbers, and pictures. Show as many ideas as you can.

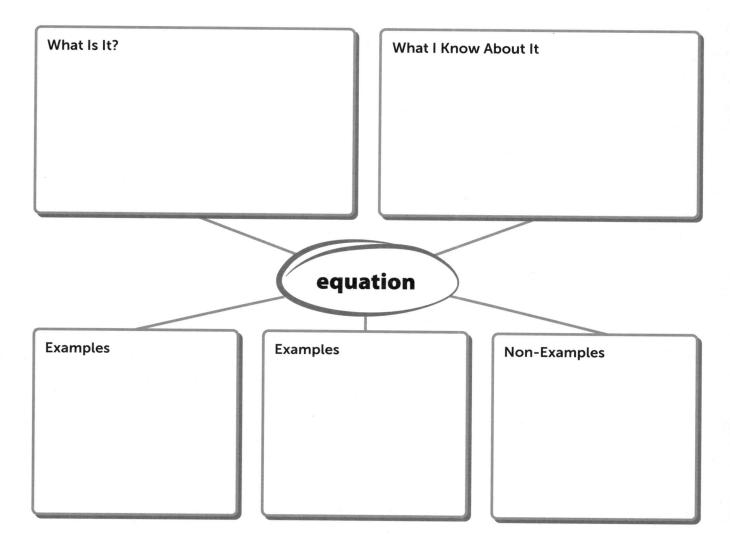

What Is It?

What I Know About It

equation

Examples

Examples

Non-Examples

2 Circle the equations. Justify your answer.

$x + 2$ $x + 2 = 4$ $x < 2$ $4 = x$ $5 + 7 = 12$

➤ **Complete problems 3–5.**

3 The hanger diagram models the equation $2b = 4$. Use the diagram to find the value of b. Show your reasoning.

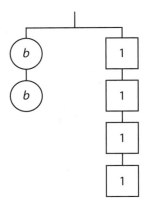

4 The hanger diagram models $2b + 2 = 6$. You can use this diagram to find the value of b.

a. What can you remove from both sides of the hanger diagram so only variables are on the left side? Cross off what you can remove.

b. Fill in the blank to show the equation the hanger diagram now models.

$2b =$ _____

c. How can you use the diagram to find the value of b?

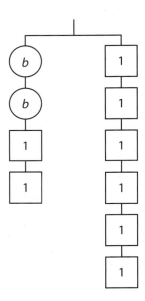

d. What does the diagram show is the value of b?

5 Think about the equation $3y - 9 = 24$.

a. The value of $3y$ is 33. How do you know this is true?

b. The value of y is 11. How do you know this is true?

Develop Understanding of Reasoning About Multi-Step Equations

Model It: Hanger Diagrams

➤ **Try these two problems involving using a hanger diagram to find an unknown value.**

1 The hanger diagram models the equation $3(x + 2) = 12$.

   a. How many groups of $x + 2$ are in the diagram and the equation? Explain your reasoning. Circle each group of $x + 2$ in the diagram.

   b. How can you figure out the value of each group of $x + 2$?

   c. How can you figure out the value of x?

2 Look at the hanger diagram.

   a. How many groups of $y + 6$ are there?

   b. Fill in the blank to show the equation the hanger diagram models.

   _____ $(y + 6) = 28$

   c. How can you figure out the value of each group of $y + 6$?

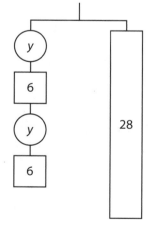

   d. How can you figure out the value of y?

> **DISCUSS IT**
>
> *Ask:* Why is it helpful to think of each side of the hanger diagram as having the same number of groups?
>
> *Share:* Noticing groups of the same size helps me because . . .

Model It: Equations

➤ **Try this problem about using reasoning to solve equations.**

3 **a.** Complete the equation to model *3 times the sum of k and 8 is 36.*

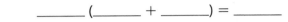

_____ (_____ + _____) = _____

b. You can think of $k + 8$ as the unknown quantity. How could you find the value of $k + 8$? What is the value of $k + 8$?

c. How could you use the value of $k + 8$ to find the value of k? What is the value of k?

d. How can you check that the value of k is correct?

> **DISCUSS IT**
>
> *Ask:* How does finding the value of $k + 8$ help you reason about the value of k?
>
> *Share:* Once I know the value of $k + 8$, then I can . . .

CONNECT IT

➤ **Complete the problems below.**

4 The hanger diagram models the equation $2(n + 7) = 24$. What could be the first step in using the diagram to find the value of n? What could be the first step reasoning about the equation to find the value of n? How are these steps the same or different?

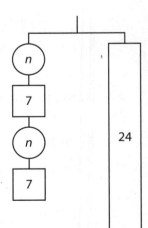

5 Explain how to find the value of y in the equation $6(y + 4) = 12$.

Practice Reasoning About Multi-Step Equations

➤ **Study how the Example shows how to use reasoning to find the value of an unknown in an equation. Then solve problems 1–6.**

> **Example**
>
> **The product of 4 and $(3 + x)$ is equal to 36. What is the value of x?**
>
> The equation $4(3 + x) = 36$ models this statement.
>
> *Think:* 4 times what number is 36?
>
> Since $4 \cdot 9$ equals 36, that means $(3 + x)$ equals 9.
>
> Since $3 + x = 9$, and $3 + 6 = 9$, that means x equals 6.

1 The sum of twice a number, n, and 14 is 30. Write an equation that models this statement. Then explain how you might use reasoning to find the value of n.

2 Is the value of $(y + 6)$ greater in $4(y + 6) = 48$ or $12(y + 6) = 48$? How do you know?

3 Ana wants to place 11 plants on 3 shelves. Each shelf holds the same number of plants. There are 2 plants that do not fit. Model this situation with an equation and a hanger diagram, where p is the number of plants that fit on each shelf.

4 Write an equation that hanger diagram models. How can you use the hanger diagram to find the value of *x*?

5 Write an equation to model the statement *the product of −8 and (y + 3) is 32.* How you can use the equation to reason about the value of *y*?

6 Jiro buys 2 rocks that each cost the same amount, *r*, and a magnifying glass that costs $5. The total cost is $9. Model this situation with an equation and a hanger diagram.

©Curriculum Associates, LLC   Copying is not permitted.

Refine Ideas About Multi-Step Equations

Apply It

➤ **Complete problems 1–5.**

1 **Examine** Hiroko is trying to find the value of d in $10d + 490 = 2{,}500$. He starts by correctly rewriting the equation as $10(d + 49) = 10(250)$. How could this help Hiroko figure out the value of d?

2 **Critique** Gavin says the hanger diagram shows that $2x - 4 = 8$ is the same as $2x = 4$. Jabari says the hanger diagram shows that $2x = 12$ is the same as $2x - 4 = 8$. Who is correct? Explain.

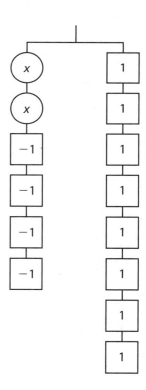

3 **Explain** To reason about the value of y in $\frac{1}{2}(2y + 4) = 14$, Lamont and Serafina each rewrite the equation. Lamont rewrites the equation as $2y + 4 = 28$. Serafina rewrites the equation as $y + 2 = 14$. Explain each person's strategy.

4 Consider the following equations:

$w + 4 = 25$

$3x + 4 = 25$

$7y + 4 = 25$

PART A What must be true about the values of w, $3x$, and $7y$?

PART B Which variable will have a greater value, w or y? Explain.

PART C Order w, x, and y from least to greatest. Explain.

5 **Math Journal** How can you reason about the equation $8b + 3 = 35$ to find the value of b?

✓ End of Lesson Checklist

☐ **INTERACTIVE GLOSSARY** Write a new entry for *reasoning*. Tell what you look for in an equation when you use reasoning to find an unknown value.

Dear Family,

This week your student is learning about writing and solving multi-step equations using algebraic approaches.

One way to solve word problems is by writing and solving an equation that represents the situation. A bar model may help you make sense of a problem. Then you can use it to write an equation to represent the situation.

A group of 5 friends go to a concert. Each friend buys a ticket that costs $30 and some buy a T-shirt that costs $15. In total the friends spend $195. How many T-shirts, x, did the friends buy?

Bar Model

195

| 30 | 30 | 30 | 30 | 30 | 15x |

Equation

$$15x + 150 = 195$$

There are often multiple ways to approach solving an equation. Your student will be solving problems like the one below.

A family buys 2 adult tickets and 4 child tickets to a high school basketball game. The family spends a total of $28 on tickets. The adult tickets cost $7 each. What is the cost, x, of each child ticket?

➤ **ONE WAY** to start finding the value of x is to subtract 14 from both sides of the equation.

$$4x + 14 = 28$$
$$4x + 14 - 14 = 28 - 14$$
$$4x = 14$$
$$\frac{4x}{4} = \frac{14}{4}$$
$$x = 3.5$$

➤ **ANOTHER WAY** to start is to divide both sides by 4.

$$4x + 14 = 28$$
$$\frac{4x + 14}{4} = \frac{28}{4}$$
$$x + 3.5 = 7$$
$$x + 3.5 - 3.5 = 7 - 3.5$$
$$x = 3.5$$

Using either method, $x = 3.5$. The cost of each child ticket is $3.50.

 Use the next page to start a conversation about equations.

Activity Thinking About Multi-Step Equations

➤ **Do this activity together to investigate using an equation to make sense to a situation.**

Have you ever taken a taxi to get somewhere? Many taxi companies charge per mile you travel plus a fee to start the trip! That means how much the ride costs is based on more than just how far you travel.

You can use an equation to think about the relationship between miles traveled and the cost of the taxi ride.

Cost of Taxi ($)	=	**Cost per Mile ($)**	×	**Number of Miles**	+	**Taxi Fee($)**

You can use this equation to figure out much a taxi ride will cost if you know how many miles long the trip is. You can also use this equation to figure out how many miles you can travel for a certain amount.

? What are other situations where a total depends on more than one thing?

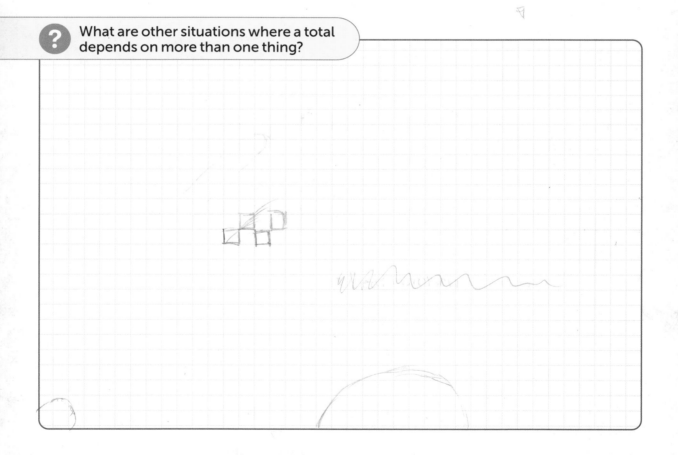

Explore Solving Multi-Step Equations

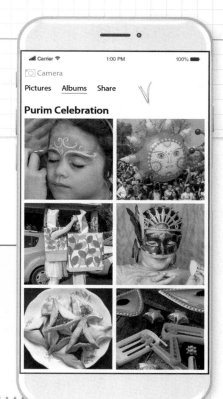

Previously, you learned how to reason about equations to find unknown values. In this lesson, you will learn about solving equations algebraically.

➤ **Use what you know to try to solve the problem below.**

Adela, Rachel, and Santo take pictures at a Purim celebration.
- Adela takes 7 more pictures than Rachel.
- Santo takes 4 times as many pictures as Adela.
- Santo takes 48 pictures.

How many pictures does Rachel take?

TRY IT   **Math Toolkit** algebra tiles, grid paper, number lines, sticky notes

$$\underline{\text{Santo}} \qquad \underline{\text{Adela} \quad \text{Rachel}}$$
$$48\,\text{pics} \qquad 12\,\text{pics} \quad 5\,\text{pics}$$

$$\boxed{4(7 + r) = 48}$$

$$\text{Equation } \mathcal{I}$$

DISCUSS IT

Ask: What did you do first to find the number of pictures Rachel takes? Why?

Share: I started by . . . because . . .

◎ **Learning Targets** SMP 1, SMP 2, SMP 3, SMP 4, SMP 5, SMP 6, SMP 7
Use variables to represent quantities and construct simple equations to solve problems.
- Solve word problems leading to equations of the form $px + q = r$ and $p(x + q) = r$, where p, q, and r are specific rational numbers. Solve equations of these forms fluently. Compare an algebraic solution to an arithmetic solution, identifying the sequence of the operations used in each approach.

CONNECT IT

1 **Look Back** How many pictures do Adela and Rachel each take? How do you know?

2 **Look Ahead** One way to find the number of photos Adela and Rachel each take is to reason about the quantities arithmetically. Another way is to solve an equation algebraically. Look at two ways you could find the unknown in the statement *the product of 6 and a number, n, plus 4 is 22.*

<table>
<tr><th>Arithmetic Approach</th><th>Algebraic Approach</th></tr>
<tr><td>Think: What number is 4 less than 22?</td><td>$6n + 4 = 22$</td></tr>
<tr><td>Step 1: $22 - 4 = 18$</td><td>Step 1: $6n + 4 - 4 = 22 - 4$</td></tr>
<tr><td>Think: What number times 6 is 18?</td><td>$6n = 18$</td></tr>
<tr><td>Step 2: $18 \div 6 = 3$</td><td>Step 2: $6n \div 6 = 18 \div 6$</td></tr>
<tr><td>The number is 3.</td><td>$n = 3$</td></tr>
</table>

a. How is Step 1 in the arithmetic approach like Step 1 in the algebraic approach?

b. How is Step 2 in the arithmetic approach like Step 2 in the algebraic approach?

c. Why do both approaches lead to the same solution?

3 **Reflect** How is the algebraic approach similar to the arithmetic approach? How is it different?

Prepare for Writing and Solving Multi-Step Equations

1 Think about what you know about the like terms in an expression. Fill in each box. Use words, numbers, and pictures. Show as many ideas as you can.

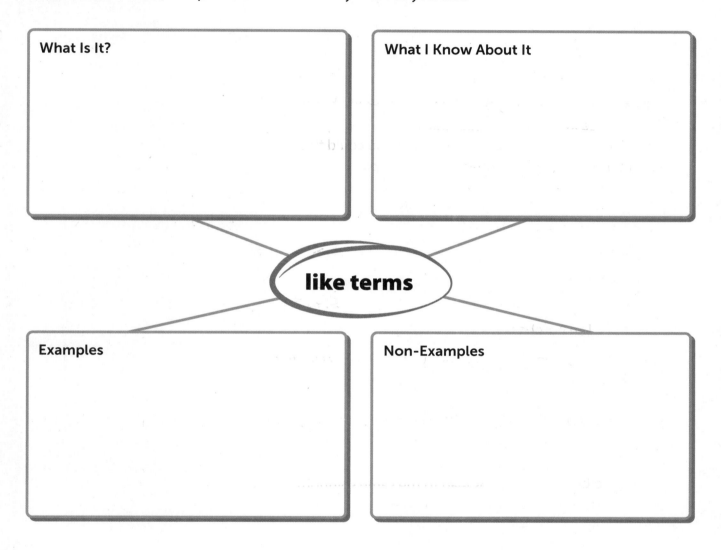

What Is It?

What I Know About It

like terms

Examples

Non-Examples

2 Rosa says $4x$ and $-6x$ are like terms, so they can be combined. Tiffany says $5a$ and $5b$ are like terms, so they can be combined. Is Rosa correct? Is Tiffany correct? Why or why not?

Rosa is correct, Tiffany is incorrect.

$4\underline{x}$, $-6\underline{x}$ have the same variables so they're like terms.

3 Kaley, Safara, and Daniel keep track of how many graphic novels they read over the summer.

- Kaley reads 6 graphic novels fewer than Safara.
- Daniel reads 3 times as many as Kaley.
- Daniel reads 30 graphic novels.

a. How many graphic novels does Safara read? Show your work.

Daniel	Kaley	Safara
Reads **3 times** as many graphic novels as Kaley	Reads **6 fewer** graphic novels than Safara	Reads **?** graphic novels

$$\underline{Kaley} \qquad \underline{Daniel} \qquad \underline{Safara}$$
$$10 \qquad\qquad 30 \qquad\qquad 16$$

$$3(s-6) = 30$$

$$4(7+r) = 48 \qquad 30 =$$

SOLUTION _____

b. Check your answer to problem 3a. Show your work.

Develop Writing and Solving Equations With Two or More Addends

4 times as many bricks for the arch

➤ **Read and try to solve the problem below.**

Noah is designing a set for a school theater production. He has 150 cardboard bricks. He needs to use some of the bricks to make a chimney and 4 times as many bricks to make an arch. He also saves 15 bricks in case some get crushed. How many cardboard bricks can he use to make the arch?

 TRY IT

 Math Toolkit algebra tiles, grid paper, number lines, sticky notes

Cardboard bricks	to make an arch	save incase ↑bricks some get crushed	Chimney
150	4x	15	x

150   4x + x = 5x ?

➤ **Explore different ways to find an unknown value in an equation that has two or more addends.**

Noah is designing a set for a school theater production. He has 150 cardboard bricks. He needs to use some of the bricks to make a chimney and 4 times as many bricks to make an arch. He also saves 15 bricks in case some get crushed. How many cardboard bricks can he use to make the arch?

Model It

You can draw a bar model to make sense of the problem.

Let x represent the number of bricks in the chimney.

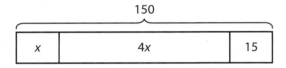

Use the model to write an equation.

$$x + 4x + 15 = 150$$
$$5x + 15 = 150$$

Model It

You can start solving the equation by isolating the x-term.

$$5x + 15 = 150$$
$$5x + 15 - 15 = 150 - 15$$
$$5x = 135$$

Model It

You can start solving the equation by dividing both sides by the same value.

$$5x + 15 = 150$$
$$\frac{(5x + 15)}{5} = \frac{150}{5}$$
$$x + 3 = 30$$

CONNECT IT

➤ **Use the problem from the previous page to help you understand how to solve an equation that has two or more addends.**

1 How many bricks can Noah use to make the arch?

2 Look at the first **Model It**. How does the bar model represent the situation?

3 Look at the second **Model It**. Why do you subtract 15 from both sides? What do you need to do next to find the value of *x*?

4 Look at the third **Model It**. Why do you divide all of the terms by 5?

5 Look at the second and third **Model Its**. How are the strategies for solving $5x + 15 = 150$ similar? How are they different?

6 Describe two ways you could solve the equation $2x + 12 = 8$.

7 **Reflect** Think about all the models and strategies you have discussed today. Describe how one of them helped you better understand how to solve the **Try It** problem.

LESSON 18 Write and Solve Multi-Step Equations   **361**

Apply It

➤ **Use what you learned to solve these problems.**

8 Solve $-21 = -\frac{1}{4}y + 6$. Show your work.

SOLUTION _____

9 A rectangular garden sits next to a house. There is fencing on three sides of the garden and the fourth side is the house. There is a total of 21.5 meters of fencing around the garden. The length of the garden along the house is 9 meters. Which equation can be used to find the width, *w*, of the garden in meters?

A $2w + 9 = 21.5$

B $2w + 18 = 21.5$

C $2w - 21.5 = 9$

D $2w + 21.5 = 9$

10 The total cost of a sketchpad and 6 pencils is $22.53. The sketchpad costs $9.99. Each pencil costs the same amount. How much does each pencil cost? Show your work.

SKETCH IT

$9.99

50 SHEETS QUALITY PAPER

SOLUTION _____

Name:

Practice Writing and Solving Equations With Two or More Addends

➤ **Study the Example showing how to solve a problem using an equation. Then solve problems 1–5.**

Example

Chloe is making a mural. She spends 6 hours designing it. She paints it during 3 sessions. Each session is the same number of hours long. In all, Chloe spends 24 hours making the mural. How many hours long, h, is each painting session?

You can represent the situation with an equation.

$$3h + 6 = 24$$

$$\frac{3h + 6}{3} = \frac{24}{3}$$

$$h + 2 = 8$$

$$h + 2 - 2 = 8 - 2$$

$$h = 6$$

Each painting session is 6 hours long.

---

1 Demarco has a piece of fabric 6 yd long. He uses a piece 3 yd long. He cuts the rest into strips that are each $\frac{3}{4}$ yd long. How many $\frac{3}{4}$ yd long strips are there? Show your work.

2 Solve $-7 = 12x - 16$. Show your work.

SOLUTION _____

SOLUTION _____

3 Liam makes soap sculptures of sea turtles. Each sculpture weighs $\frac{3}{8}$ pound. He ships them in a wooden box that weighs 2 pounds. The total weight of the box filled with the t sea turtles is 5 pounds. How many sea turtles are in the box? Show your work.

SOLUTION _____

4 Solve $-0.4k - 6 = 1.2$. Show your work.

SOLUTION _____

5 Claudia buys 12 postcards, 12 stamps, and 1 pen. The postcards cost twice as much as the stamps. The pen costs $1.50. The total cost is $14.10. How much does each postcard cost? Show your work.

SOLUTION _____

Develop Writing and Solving Equations with Grouping Symbols

Toronto
Current Temperature
25°C

NOW 3PM 4PM 5PM 6PM 7PM

25°C 25°C 25°C 24°C 23°C 23°C

Wednesday		25°C
Thursday		27°C
Friday		25°C
Saturday		27°C

➤ **Read and try to solve the problem below.**

Hugo is traveling in Toronto, Canada. His weather app shows the temperature is 25°C. Hugo writes the equation $25 = \frac{5}{9}(F - 32)$ to find the temperature in degrees Fahrenheit, F. What is the temperature in degrees Fahrenheit?

TRY IT

Math Toolkit grid paper, number lines, sticky notes

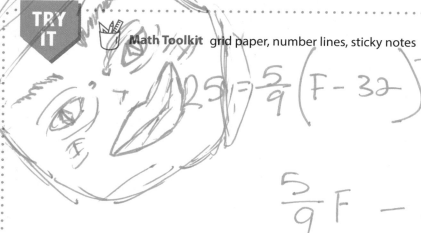

$$25 = \frac{5}{9}\left(F - 32\right)$$

$$\begin{array}{r} 32 \\ \times\ \frac{5}{9} \\ \hline 160 \end{array}$$

$$\frac{5}{9} \times \frac{32}{1} = \frac{160}{9}$$

$$\frac{5}{9}F - \frac{160}{9}$$

DISCUSS IT

Ask: Why did you choose that strategy to find the temperature in degrees Fahrenheit?

Share: I knew . . . so I . . .

➤ **Explore different ways to find an unknown value in an equation with grouping symbols.**

Hugo is traveling in Toronto, Canada. His weather app shows the temperature is 25°C. Hugo writes the equation $25 = \frac{5}{9}(F - 32)$ to find the temperature in degrees Fahrenheit, F. What is the temperature in degrees Fahrenheit?

Model It

You can use the distributive property to expand.

$$25 = \frac{5}{9}(F - 32)$$

$$25 = \frac{5}{9}(F) - \frac{5}{9}(32)$$

$$25 = \frac{5}{9}F - \frac{160}{9}$$

$$25 + \frac{160}{9} = \frac{5}{9}F - \frac{160}{9} + \frac{160}{9}$$

$$\frac{385}{9} = \frac{5}{9}F$$

Model It

You can divide each side by the coefficient $\frac{5}{9}$.

$$25 = \frac{5}{9}(F - 32)$$

$$25 \div \frac{5}{9} = \frac{5}{9}(F - 32) \div \frac{5}{9}$$

$$25 \cdot \frac{9}{5} = \frac{5}{9}(F - 32) \cdot \frac{9}{5}$$

$$45 = F - 32$$

©Curriculum Associates, LLC Copying is not permitted.

➤ **Use the problem from the previous page to help you understand how to solve an equation with grouping symbols.**

1 What is 25°C in degrees Fahrenheit?

2 Look at the first **Model It**. Describe the steps shown for solving the equation. What do you still need to do to find the value of *F*?

3 Look at the second **Model It**. Describe the steps shown for solving the equation. What do you still need to do to find the value of *F*?

4 Look at the **Model Its**. What was one advantage of distributing first? What was one advantage of dividing first?

5 Consider the equation $12 = b(2.5x + 15)$. What values of *b* might make you want to start solving the equation by distributing *b*? What values of *b* might make you want to start solving the equation by dividing by *b*?

6 **Reflect** Think about all the models and strategies you have discussed today. Describe how one of them helped you better understand how to write and solve an equation that includes grouping symbols.

Apply It

➤ **Use what you learned to solve these problems.**

7 Carolina fosters 5 puppies. For each puppy she buys a crate that costs c dollars and a leash that costs $20. She spends $475 total. Which equations model the situation? Select all that apply.

A $5c + 20c = 475$

B $5(c + 20) = 475$

C $5c + 100 = 475$

D $5c + 20 = 475$

E $c + 20 = 475$

8 Solve $-8 = \dfrac{k - 4}{-6}$. Show your work.

SOLUTION _____

9 The perimeter of a rectangular chicken coop is 30 feet. The width is w feet and the length is $w + 4$ feet. What are the length and width of the coop? Show your work.

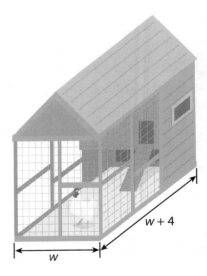

$w + 4$

w

SOLUTION _____

Practice Writing and Solving Equations with Grouping Symbols

➤ **Study the Example showing how to use an equation with grouping symbols to solve a problem. Then solve problems 1–5.**

Example

Lillie and her family donate money to charity at the end of each year. Lillie's brother donates $3 more than Lillie. Her parents donate 4.5 times as much as Lillie's brother. Lillie's parents donate $45. How much does Lillie donate?

You can represent the situation with an equation.

$d =$ Lillie's donation in dollars

$$4.5(d + 3) = 45$$

$$\frac{4.5(d + 3)}{4.5} = \frac{45}{4.5}$$

$$d + 3 = 10$$

$$d + 3 - 3 = 10 - 3$$

$$d = 7$$

Lillie donates $7.

---

1 Look at $4.5(d + 3) = 45$ from the Example.

a. What does $(d + 3)$ represent?

b. Why is $(d + 3)$ multiplied by 4.5?

c. How much does Lillie's brother donate?

2 Malik joins a gym. He gets $2 per month off the regular monthly rate for 3 months. Malik pays $49.50 for 3 months. What is the gym's regular monthly rate, r?
Show your work.

SOLUTION _____

_____

3 Luis is shopping for gifts. Mugs are on sale for $4 off the regular price, *p*. Luis buys 6 mugs. He pays a total of $54. What is the regular price of a mug? Show your work.

SOLUTION _____

4 Solve $\frac{3}{4}(5x - 3) + 8 = 17$. Show your work.

SOLUTION _____

5 Solve $-72 = 8(y - 3)$. Show your work.

SOLUTION _____

Refine Writing and Solving Multi-Step Equations

➤ **Complete the Example below. Then solve problems 1–8.**

Example

Solve $-0.25x + 7.5 = 15$.

Look at how you could show your work using multiplication.

$$-0.25x + 7.5 = 15$$
$$100(-0.25x + 7.5) = (100)15$$
$$-25x + 750 = 1,500$$
$$-25x + 750 - 750 = 1,500 - 750$$
$$-25x = 750$$

SOLUTION _____

CONSIDER THIS...
You can multiply both sides by a power of 10 to eliminate the decimals.

PAIR/SHARE
What is another way you could solve this problem?

Apply It

1 Solve $0 = -1.8y + 0.72$. Show your work.

CONSIDER THIS...
You can think of $0 = -1.8y + 0.72$ as having two addends.

PAIR/SHARE
How can you check your answer?

SOLUTION _____

2 Solve $\frac{2(n + 17)}{8} = \frac{3}{8}$. Show your work.

CONSIDER THIS ...
There is more than one way to think about this problem.

SOLUTION _____

PAIR/SHARE
How did you choose your first step?

3 Three siblings are born on the same date in consecutive years. The sum of their ages is 42. What is the age of the oldest sibling?

A 13

B 14

C 15

D 16

Victoria chose A as the correct answer. How might she have gotten that answer?

CONSIDER THIS ...
Consecutive integers follow each other, like 4, 5, 6. If the first integer is x, the next is $x + 1$, then $x + 2$, and so on.

PAIR/SHARE
How would the answer change if there were four siblings?

4 Leon pays $12.50 per month for a music subscription service. One month he also buys 6 songs from the service. Each song costs the same. His bill for that month is $17.84. In dollars, how much does he pay for each song?

5 One side of an isosceles triangle is $2x + 1$ ft long. The other two sides are both $3x - 1$ ft long. The perimeter of the triangle is 55 ft. What is the length of each side? Show your work.

SOLUTION _____

6 Khalid is solving the equation $8.5 - 1.2y = 6.7$. He gets to $1.8 = 1.2y$. Explain what he might have done to get to this equation.

7 Mora is preparing her pack for a hike. Her empty pack weighs $\frac{15}{16}$ pound. She adds some water bottles that each weigh $1\frac{1}{8}$ pound. Now Mora's pack weighs $6\frac{9}{16}$ pounds. How many bottles, b, does Mora add to her pack? Show your work.

SOLUTION _____

8 Solve $\frac{1}{2} + \frac{1}{3}w = \frac{1}{6}$. Show your work.

SOLUTION _____

9 **Math Journal** Damita says the equations $0.8x - 0.8 = 1.6$ and $\frac{4}{5}(x - 1) = 1\frac{3}{5}$ are the same. How can she show this, without solving the equations?

✓ **End of Lesson Checklist**

☐ **INTERACTIVE GLOSSARY** Write a new entry for *represent*. Write at least one synonym for *represent*.

☐ **SELF CHECK** Go back to the Unit 4 Opener and see what you can check off.

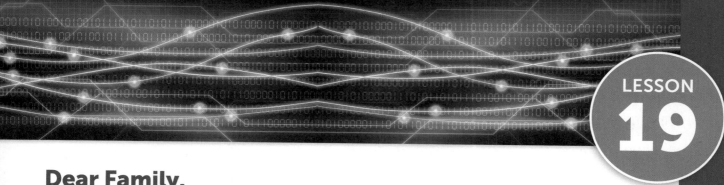

Dear Family,

This week your student is learning about solving problems with inequalities.

An inequality uses symbols to show the relationship between two expressions. The inequality symbols are greater than ($>$), greater than or equal to ($\geq$), less than ($<$), and less than or equal to ($\leq$).

You can use inequalities to represent situations in everyday life. Solving an inequality is similar to solving an equation. But when you multiply or divide each side of the inequality by a negative number, you reverse the inequality symbol.

$$-3x > 6$$
$$\frac{-3x}{-3} < \frac{6}{-3}$$
$$x < -2$$

Your student will be solving problems like the one below.

> The sum of -4 times x and 0.7 is at most 16.7. What are all the possible values of x?

➤ **ONE WAY** to show the possible values is to write and solve an inequality.

$$-4x + 0.7 \leq 16.7$$
$$-4x + 0.7 - 0.7 \leq 16.7 - 0.7$$
$$-4x \leq 16$$
$$\frac{-4x}{-4} \geq \frac{16}{-4}$$
$$x \geq -4$$

➤ **ANOTHER WAY** is to graph the solutions on a number line.

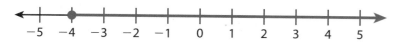

Both ways show that $x \geq -4$.

 Use the next page to start a conversation about inequalities.

Activity Thinking About Inequalities

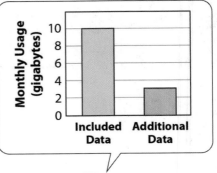

➤ **Do this activity together to investigate inequalities.**

Do you use data on a cellphone? You may have a maximum amount of data you can use without having to pay more.

Suppose a family data plan includes 10 gigabytes of shared data and costs $80 per month. Any additional data usage is billed at $15 per gigabyte. A certain family wants to spend at most $125 on their bill each month. You could use an inequality to find that the family can use at most 3 additional gigabytes of data.

? When else could you use an inequality to find a range of values?

Explore Solving Inequalities

Previously, you learned to write and solve equations. In this lesson, you will learn about writing and solving inequalities.

➤ **Use what you know to try to solve the problem below.**

The opposite of *x* is greater than or equal to 2.

What are two possible values of *x*? What are two values that *x* cannot be?

What is true about all possible values of *x*?

  TRY IT

Math Toolkit integer chips, number lines, sticky notes

DISCUSS IT

Ask: How can you tell whether a number is a possible value of *x*?

Share: I can check whether a number is a possible value of *x* by . . .

◎ **Learning Targets**   SMP 1, SMP 2, SMP 3, SMP 4, SMP 5, SMP 6, SMP 7
Use variables to represent quantities in a real-world or mathematical problem, and construct simple equations and inequalities to solve problems by reasoning about the quantities.
• Solve word problems leading to inequalities of the form $px + q > r$ or $px + q < r$, where p, q, and r are specific rational numbers. Graph the solution set of the inequality and interpret it in the context of the problem.

CONNECT IT

1 **Look Back** What is true about all the possible values of x?

2 **Look Ahead** In the **Try It**, you found all of the possible values of x. You could represent the situation with an inequality. Then you could solve the inequality to find all of the possible values of x. Solving an inequality is similar to solving an equation. The solution set of an inequality includes all values that make it true.

a. Solve the inequality $x + 2 > 6$ by subtracting 2 from both sides.

b. Solve the inequality $x - 2 > 6$.

c. Solve the inequality $2x > 6$.

d. Look at two different ways to solve $-x < 3$.

<table>
<tr><td align="center">Add x to Both Sides</td><td align="center">Multiply Both Sides by −1</td></tr>
<tr><td align="center">$-x < 3$</td><td align="center">$-x < 3$</td></tr>
<tr><td align="center">$-x + x < 3 + x$</td><td align="center">$-1 \cdot -x > -1 \cdot 3$</td></tr>
<tr><td align="center">$0 < 3 + x$</td><td align="center">$x > -3$</td></tr>
<tr><td align="center">$0 - 3 < 3 - 3 + x$</td><td></td></tr>
<tr><td align="center">$-3 < x$</td><td></td></tr>
</table>

Are the solutions the same for both ways? Explain.

e. Solve the inequality $-2x > 6$.

f. When you multiply or divide both sides of an inequality by a negative number, you must reverse the inequality sign. Why?

3 **Reflect** How is solving an inequality where the variable has a negative coefficient similar to solving an inequality where the variable has a positive coefficient? How is it different?

Name:

Prepare for Writing and Solving Inequalities

1 Think about what you know about inequalities. Fill in each box.
Use words, numbers, and pictures. Show as many ideas as you can.

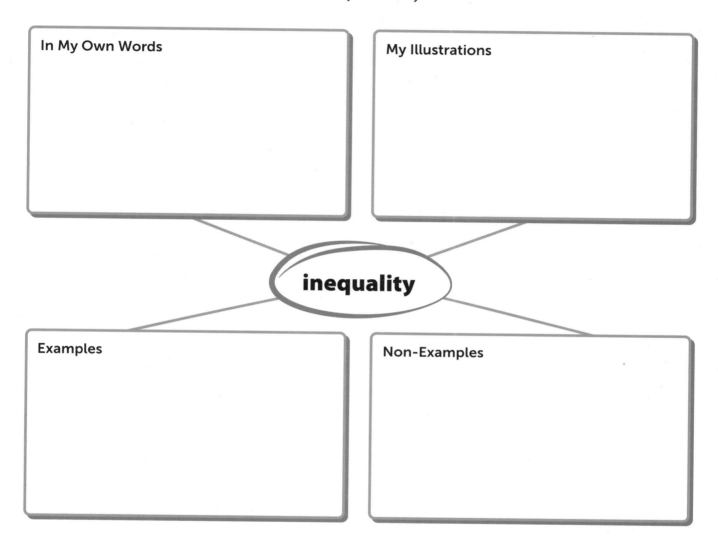

In My Own Words

My Illustrations

inequality

Examples

Non-Examples

2 Charles says that the number line shows all the values that make the inequality
$n \geq -1$ true. Do you agree with Charles? Explain.

3 The opposite of z is greater than 5.

    a. What are two possible values of z? What are two values that z cannot be? What must be true about all possible values of z? Show your work.

SOLUTION _____

_____

_____

    b. Check your answer to problem 3a. Show your work.

Develop Solving One-Step Inequalities

➤ **Read and try to solve the problem below.**

What solutions, if any, do the inequalities $-2t < 6$ and $r + 2 \geq 6$ share?

  Math Toolkit integer chips, number lines, sticky notes

DISCUSS IT

Ask: How did you begin to solve the problem?

Share: I started by . . .

➤ **Explore different ways to solve one-step inequalities.**

What solutions, if any, do the inequalities $-2t < 6$ and $r + 2 \geq 6$ share?

Analyze It

You can reason about the quantities.

The inequality $-2t < 6$ means the **opposite of 2t is less than 6.**

This is true when **2t is greater than −6.**

The inequality $r + 2 \geq 6$ means $r + 2 = 6$ or $r + 2 > 6$.

Model It

You can solve the inequalities algebraically.

$$-2t < 6 \qquad\qquad\qquad r + 2 \geq 6$$
$$\frac{-2t}{-2} > \frac{6}{-2} \qquad\qquad r + 2 - 2 \geq 6 - 2$$
$$t > -3 \qquad\qquad\qquad r \geq 4$$

Model It

You can graph the solution sets on number lines.

$-2t < 6$

$r + 2 \geq 6$

➤ **Use the problem from the previous page to help you understand how to solve one-step inequalities.**

1 Look at **Analyze It**. How is the reasoning about $-2t < 6$ related to the idea of multiplying both sides of the inequality by -1?

2 Look at the first **Model It**. How is solving $r + 2 \geq 6$ similar to solving $-2t < 6$? How is it different?

3 How does the second **Model It** show the values the solution sets of $r + 2 \geq 6$ and $-2t < 6$ share?

4 How can you check whether a number is in the solution set for both $r + 2 \geq 6$ and $-2t < 6$?

5 Consider the equation $-2t = 6$. How are finding the solution of $-2t = 6$ and finding the solution set of $-2t < 6$ similar? How are they different?

6 **Reflect** Think about all the models and strategies you have discussed today. Describe how one of them helped you better understand how to solve the **Try It** problem.

Apply It

➤ **Use what you learned to solve these problems.**

7 The sum of 43.5 and a number, *n*, is no greater than 50.
What are all possible values of *n*? Show your work.

SOLUTION _____

_____

8 Sebastián says that the graph below shows the solution set of the inequality
$2.5x \geq -20$. Do you agree? Explain.

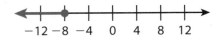

9 Solve the inequality $-48 < -8t$. Then graph the solution set. Show your work.

SOLUTION _____

Practice Solving One-Step Inequalities

➤ **Study the Example showing how to write and solve an inequality. Then solve problems 1–5.**

Example

The product of −3.5 and a number is no greater than 17.5. What are all the possible values of the number?

You can write an inequality to represent the situation. Then solve the inequality.

$$-3.5n \leq 17.5$$

$$\frac{-3.5n}{-3.5} \geq \frac{17.5}{-3.5}$$

$$n \geq -5$$

You can graph the solution set on a number line.

1 Explain why $3.5n \leq -17.5$ does not have the same solution set as $-3.5n \leq 17.5$.

2 Solve the inequality $x - 4 < -3$. Then graph the solution set. Show your work.

SOLUTION _____

3 The product of a number and 1.5 is less than the absolute value of the difference between 20 and 5. What are all the possible values of the number?
Show your work.

SOLUTION _____

4 Consider the inequalities $-\frac{1}{4}a > 3$ and $b - 12 > -3$. What values, if any, make both inequalities true? Show your work.

SOLUTION _____

5 Solve the inequality $x + 2\frac{1}{2} > -\frac{1}{2}$. Graph the solution set on a number line.
Show your work.

SOLUTION _____

Develop Solving Multi-Step Inequalities

➤ **Read and try to solve the problem below.**

The sum of −3 times a number and 0.3 is at most 6.3. What are all the possible values of the number?

 TRY IT

 Math Toolkit number lines, sticky notes

DISCUSS IT

Ask: Why did you choose that strategy to find the possible values of the number?

Share: I chose that strategy because . . .

➤ **Explore different ways to show the solution to inequalities.**

The sum of −3 times a number and 0.3 is at most 6.3. What are all the possible values of the number?

Model It

You can write an inequality to represent the situation.

sum of −3 times a number and 0.3 is at most **6.3**

$$-3n \quad + \quad 0.3 \quad \leq \quad 6.3$$

Model It

You can use the inequality to solve the problem.

Let *n* represent the unknown number.

$$-3n + 0.3 \leq 6.3$$
$$-3n + 0.3 - 0.3 \leq 6.3 - 0.3$$
$$-3n \leq 6$$
$$\frac{-3n}{-3} \geq \frac{6}{-3}$$

Model It

You can graph the solution set of the inequality.

$$-3n + 0.3 \leq 6.3$$

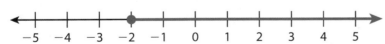

➤ **Use the problem from the previous page to help you understand how to write, solve, and graph inequalities.**

1 What are all possible values of the number?

2 Look at the second **Model It**. Describe the steps shown for solving $-3n + 0.3 \leq 6.3$.

3 Look at the third **Model It**. How does the number line show what numbers are in the solution set?

4 How else could you begin solving the inequality?

5 How is solving the inequality $-3n + 0.3 \leq 6.3$ similar to solving the equation $-3n + 0.3 = 6.3$? How is it different?

6 **Reflect** Think about all the models and strategies you have discussed today. Describe how one of them helped you better understand how to write, solve, and graph inequalities.

Apply It

➤ **Use what you learned to solve these problems.**

7 The sum of 12 times a number, *n*, and 4 is no more than 190. What are all the possible values of the number? Show your work.

SOLUTION _____

8 Which inequality's solution set is shown on the graph below?

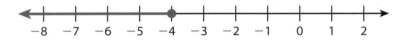

A $-2 \leq -1.5p - 8$

B $-2 \geq -1.5p - 8$

C $-2 \leq 1.5p - 8$

D $-2 \geq 1.5p - 8$

9 Graph the solution set for the inequality $\frac{x-2}{-3} \leq -\frac{5}{6}$. Show your work.

Name:

Practice Solving Multi-Step Inequalities

➤ **Study the Example showing how to write and solve an inequality. Then solve problems 1–5.**

Example

The sum of −5 times a number and 2.5 is no less than 22.5. What are all the possible values of the number?

You can write and solve an inequality to find the possible values of the number. Then you can show all the possible values on a number line.

Let n represent the number.

$$22.5 \leq -5n + 2.5$$

$$22.5 - 2.5 \leq -5n + 2.5 - 2.5$$

$$20 \leq -5n$$

$$\frac{20}{-5} \geq \frac{-5n}{-5}$$

$$-4 \geq n$$

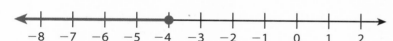

1 Explain why $-22.5 \geq 5n - 2.5$ has the same solution set as $22.5 \leq -5n + 2.5$.

2 Graph the solution set of $\frac{a}{2} + 5 > 4$. Show your work.

③ The product of $\frac{8}{9}$ and the sum of a number and -4 is less than or equal to 64.

What are all the possible values of the number? Show your work.

SOLUTION _____

④ Solve $-4\left(r - \frac{2}{3}\right) + 4 < -8$. Show your work.

SOLUTION _____

⑤ The value of 4 less than the product of 0.25 and x is greater than 6.
What are all the possible values of x? Show your work.

SOLUTION _____

Develop Writing and Solving Inequalities

➤ **Read and try to solve the problem below.**

Cameron has $200. He wants to buy a diploma frame for $44. He also wants to buy kente graduation stoles for himself and his friends. Each stole costs $24. How many kente stoles can Cameron buy?

Math Toolkit number lines

Kente stoles are worn by graduates to show pride in their African heritage.

➤ **Explore different ways to use inequalities to solve problems.**

Cameron has $200. He wants to buy a diploma frame for $44. He also wants to buy kente graduation stoles for himself and his friends. Each stole costs $24. How many kente stoles can Cameron buy?

Model It

You can model the situation with an inequality.

cost of the frame	+	cost of each stole	•	number of stoles	is at most	the amount Cameron has
↓		↓		↓	↓	↓
44	+	24	•	x	$\leq$	200

$$44 + 24x \leq 200$$
$$44 - 44 + 24x \leq 200 - 44$$
$$24x \leq 156$$
$$\frac{24x}{24} \leq \frac{156}{24}$$
$$x \leq 6.5$$

Solve It

You can use a number line to show the solution to the problem.

➤ **Use the problem from the previous page to help you understand how to use inequalities to solve problems.**

1 Interpret the inequality statement in Model It in the context of the problem.

2 Look at **Solve It**. Does the graph represent the inequality $x \leq 6.5$? Why or why not?

3 According to the graph, what is the solution to the problem? Why are only the whole numbers less than 6.5 part of the solution?

4 How do you graph the solution set of an inequality when that set includes only whole numbers?

5 **Reflect** Think about all the models and strategies you have discussed today. Describe how one of them helped you better understand how to use inequalities to solve problems.

Apply It

➤ **Use what you learned to solve these problems.**

6 A scuba diver is hired to take underwater photos. He begins swimming straight downward from an elevation of −5 meters relative to sea level. His elevation changes at a constant rate of 2.5 meters per minute. When he stops, his camera is still in a safe depth for use. For how many minutes could he have been swimming? Graph the solution set. Show your work.

Use only at elevations above
−30 meters

SOLUTION _____

7 Aiyana has $20.00 to buy photo frames. Each frame costs $4.50. She also wants to buy a box of nails for $2.25. Dylan models the situation with the inequality $20 \geq 4.5f + 2.25$. He says Aiyana can buy at most 4 frames. Did Dylan correctly interpret the solution? Explain.

8 Kennedy has 8 cups of flour. She covers the countertop and the rolling pin with $\frac{1}{2}$ cup of flour. Then she uses $2\frac{1}{4}$ cups of flour for each batch of biscuits she bakes. How many full batches of biscuits can Kennedy bake? Show your work.

SOLUTION _____

Practice Writing and Solving Inequalities

➤ **Study the Example showing how to interpret an inequality to solve a problem. Then solve problems 1–4.**

> Thrill Rides:
> **5 tokens**
> Kiddie Rides:
> **3 tokens**

Example

Akira buys 50 tokens at the carnival. He gives his sister tokens for 5 kiddie rides. He wants to use at least some of the remaining tokens for thrill rides. How many thrill rides could he go on?

You can write and solve an inequality to solve the problem.

t = number of thrill rides

$$5t + 3(5) \leq 50$$
$$5t + 15 \leq 50$$
$$5t + 15 - 15 \leq 50 - 15$$
$$5t \leq 35$$
$$\frac{5t}{5} \leq \frac{35}{5}$$
$$t \leq 7$$

Akira could go on 0, 1, 2, 3, 4, 5, 6, or 7 thrill rides.

---

1 Akira's sister from the Example is too small to ride alone. Akira must use tokens to go on the kiddie rides with her. Now how many thrill rides can he go on?

2 A truck holds at most 20,000 lb. There are 18 boxes on the truck. Each weighs 750 lb. How many additional boxes can the truck hold? Graph the solution. Show your work.

SOLUTION _____

3 Workers at an animal reserve are preparing a new exhibit for meerkats. The exhibit must include at least 6.5 m² of space for each meerkat. The area of the exhibit is 78 m². How many meerkats can the exhibit hold? Write, solve, and graph an inequality to find the possible numbers of meerkats. Show your work.

SOLUTION _____

4 A summer camp rewards campers and counselors with badges. The camp orders 200 badges. They plan to give 25 badges to counselors. They ordered at least 3 badges for each camper.

a. How many campers could be at the camp? Show your work.

SOLUTION _____

b. Are all of the values on the graph of $c \leq 58$ possible solutions? Explain.

Refine Writing and Solving Inequalities

➤ **Complete the Example below. Then solve problems 1–8.**

Example

Solve the inequality $-\frac{1}{3}(2x + 5) < x$.

Look at how you could show your work by solving an inequality with a variable on both sides.

$$-\frac{1}{3}(2x + 5) < x$$

$$-3\left(-\frac{1}{3}\right)(2x + 5) > -3x$$

$$2x + 5 > -3x$$

$$-2x + 2x + 5 > -3x - 2x$$

$$5 > -5x$$

SOLUTION _____

CONSIDER THIS...
Your solution will have a variable on only one side of the inequality symbol.

PAIR/SHARE
Why does the inequality symbol reverse?

Apply It

1 The water level in Rafael's fish tank must be at least 11 in. for his fish to be healthy. He starts with a water level of $11\frac{1}{2}$ in. Then the water level decreases $\frac{7}{8}$ in. Rafael adds water, but not enough for the fish to be healthy. How many inches of water could Rafael have added? Show your work.

CONSIDER THIS...
Could an inequality help you model this problem?

PAIR/SHARE
What is the maximum number of inches of water Rafael could add to the tank?

SOLUTION _____

2. Which solutions, if any, do the inequalities $-2(c - 4) \le -4$ and $\frac{1}{2}d - 6 > -4$ have in common? Show your work.

CONSIDER THIS ...
Number lines could help you compare the inequalities.

SOLUTION _____

_____

PAIR/SHARE
How can you check your answer?

3. An online company sells and ships T-shirts. The company has to pay extra to ship a package that weighs more than 13 oz. Before putting any T-shirts in the box, the package weighs 1.5 oz. Each T-shirt weighs 5 oz. Which number line best represents the possible numbers of T-shirts the company can ship in a package without paying extra for shipping?

CONSIDER THIS ...
What types of numbers make sense in this situation?

A

B

C

D

Hannah chose B as the correct answer. How might she have gotten that answer?

PAIR/SHARE
Would your answer change if each T-shirt weighed 4 oz instead of 5 oz? Explain.

4 The math team wants to visit the Museum of Mathematics to celebrate Pi Day. They have $210 to spend. They need to buy 14 student tickets and 1 adult ticket. A student ticket costs $12, and an adult ticket costs $17. The team also wants to buy sugar-free fruit pies. Each pie costs $6. How many whole pies can the team buy? Show your work.

Take home a pie on Pi Day

only $6.00

SOLUTION _____

5 Marta and Kareem each solved the inequality $-8(-3.5 + n) \leq -56$. Their work is shown below. Explain why both strategies are correct.

Marta	**Kareem**
$-8(-3.5 + n) \leq -56$	$-8(-3.5 + n) \leq -56$
$28 - 8n \leq -56$	$\dfrac{-8(-3.5 + n)}{-8} \geq \dfrac{-56}{-8}$
$28 - 28 - 8n \leq -56 - 28$	$-3.5 + n \geq 7$
$-8n \leq -84$	$-3.5 + 3.5 + n \geq 7 + 3.5$
$\dfrac{-8n}{-8} \geq \dfrac{-84}{-8}$	$n \geq 10.5$
$n \geq 10.5$	

6 Which is the solution of $3(t + 1) \leq 6t - 13.5$?

A $t \leq -5.5$

B $t \geq -5.5$

C $t \leq 5.5$

D $t \geq 5.5$

7 Antonio is in a bowling league. His goal is to score an average of at least 100 points per game. His scores so far are 105, 95, 97, 82, and 110. How many points can Antonio score in his next game to reach his goal? Show your work.

SOLUTION _____

8 **Math Journal** Write a word problem you can solve by writing and solving an inequality. Explain how to find the answer.

✓ **End of Lesson Checklist**

☐ **INTERACTIVE GLOSSARY** Write a new entry for *interpret*. Tell what you do when you *interpret* the meaning of a variable in a problem situation.

☐ **SELF CHECK** Go back to the Unit 4 Opener and see what you can check off.

Study an Example Problem and Solution

SMP 1 Make sense of problems and persevere in solving them.

➤ **Read this problem involving linear expressions and rational numbers. Then look at one student's solution to this problem on the following pages.**

Booking a Show

Jorge and Liam play in a band called J Plus L. The band needs to decide on a venue for their next show. Read this email from their agent about the band's options, and help them respond to their agent.

Delete　Archive　　Reply　Reply All　Forward

To: Jorge, Liam
Subject: Show for August 4th

Hey guys,

Here are the options for where we can book your next show. I think you would sell between 200 and 300 tickets at any of these venues.

	Venue	Ticket Price	Share of Ticket Sales		Section AA
CONCERT Live Music	Moonmint Music Hall	$22	20%		Row 3
	Legacy Park	$24	40%		
	Galaxy Theater	$28	30%		Seat 17

Remember that each venue takes a percent of the ticket sales, my fee is $\frac{1}{10}$ of the ticket sales, and $\frac{3}{20}$ of the ticket sales go to your manager. You keep the rest.

WHAT I NEED FROM THE BAND:

• Pick a venue.

• Write an expression that shows how much the band will make from the sale of t tickets. The expression should make it easy for me to see the price for a ticket and the amount that the venue, your manager, and I will make for every ticket sold.

• Write an equivalent expression that makes it easy for me to see how much the band will make for every ticket sold.

• Estimate how much the band will make in ticket sales from the show.

Thanks!

The sound of a drum depends on its size, shape, materials, and the striking technique of the drummer.

One Student's Solution

NOTICE THAT...
Each term of the expression provides information about the situation.

NOTICE THAT...
20% is the same as $\frac{20}{100}$, which means 20 hundredths, or 0.20.

First, I have to choose one of the venues for the band.

I will pick Moonmint Music Hall because it takes the smallest percent of the band's ticket sales.

The ticket price at Moonmint Music Hall is $22, and this venue takes 20% of the ticket sales.

Next, I will think about how I can write an expression for the amount the band will make from the sale of *t* tickets at a Moonmint show.

I know that the band has to pay part of the ticket sales to the venue, part to their agent, and part to their manager.

I can subtract each part from the total ticket sales to find the amount the band gets to keep.

total ticket sales − part to venue − part to agent − part to manager

Now, I will use the given information to write the expression.

total ticket sales	price per ticket times number of tickets, *t*	$22t$
part to venue	20% of ticket sales	$0.20(22t)$
part to agent	$\frac{1}{10}$ of ticket sales	$\frac{1}{10}(22t)$
part to manager	$\frac{3}{20}$ of ticket sales	$\frac{3}{20}(22t)$

Here is my expression:

Ticket Sales		Venue		Agent		Manager
$22t$	−	$0.20(22t)$	−	$\frac{1}{10}(22t)$	−	$\frac{3}{20}(22t)$

Then, I will rewrite the expression to make it easy to see the price for a ticket and how much the venue, agent, and manager each make for every ticket sold.

I can rewrite each term as the product of a number and t.

total ticket sales − part to venue − part to agent − part to manager

$$22t \quad - \quad 0.20(22t) \quad - \quad \frac{1}{10}(22t) \quad - \quad \frac{3}{20}(22t)$$

$$22t \quad - \quad 4.40t \quad - \quad 0.1(22t) \quad - \quad 0.15(22t)$$

$$22t \quad - \quad 4.40t \quad - \quad 2.20t \quad - \quad 3.30t$$

> **NOTICE THAT . . .**
> Because the expression represents an amount of money, it makes sense to rewrite the fractions as decimals.

The new expression shows that the price of a ticket is **$22** and that, for every ticket sold, the venue receives **$4.40**, the agent receives **$2.20**, and the manager receives **$3.30**.

Next, I will write another expression to make it easy to see how much the band makes for every ticket sold.

I can rewrite the previous expression as the product of a number and t.

$$22t - 4.40t - 2.20t - 3.30t$$

$$12.10t$$

> **NOTICE THAT . . .**
> All terms from the previous expression are like terms, so they can be combined.

For each ticket sold, the band members will make $12.10.

Finally, I will use my expressions to estimate how much the band will make in ticket sales from a show at Moonmint Music Hall.

I will use 250 tickets, since 250 is between 200 and 300 tickets.

$22t - 4.40t - 2.20t - 3.30t$	$12.10t$
$22(250) - 4.40(250) - 2.20(250) - 3.30(250)$	$12.10(250)$
$5,500 - 1,100 - 550 - 825$	$3,025$
$3,025$	

Both expressions have a value of 3,025. This helps to show that my calculations are correct and that the expressions I wrote are equivalent.

So, the band will make about $3,025 in ticket sales.

Try Another Approach

➤ **There are many ways to solve problems. Think about how you might solve the Booking a Show problem in a different way.**

Booking a Show

Jorge and Liam play in a band called J Plus L. The band needs to decide on a venue for their next show. Read this email from their agent about the band's options, and help them respond to their agent.

Delete   Archive | Reply   Reply All   Forward

To: Jorge, Liam
Subject: Show for August 4th

Hey guys,

Here are the options for where we can book your next show. I think you would sell between 200 and 300 tickets at any of these venues.

	Venue	Ticket Price	Share of Ticket Sales
	Moonmint Music Hall	$22	20%
	Legacy Park	$24	40%
	Galaxy Theater	$28	30%

Section AA

Row 3

Seat 17

Remember that each venue takes a percent of the ticket sales, my fee is $\frac{1}{10}$ of the ticket sales, and $\frac{3}{20}$ of the ticket sales go to your manager. You keep the rest.

WHAT I NEED FROM THE BAND:

• Pick a venue.

• Write an expression that shows how much the band will make from the sale of *t* tickets. The expression should make it easy for me to see the price for a ticket and the amount that the venue, your manager, and I will make for every ticket sold.

• Write an equivalent expression that makes it easy for me to see how much the band will make for every ticket sold.

• Estimate how much the band will make in ticket sales from the show.

Thanks!

Plan It

➤ **Answer these questions to help you start thinking about a plan.**

   a. Which venue will you pick? What value will you use for the number of tickets the band will sell at the show?

   b. How will you rewrite a percent or fraction as a decimal?

Solve It

➤ **Find a different solution for the Booking a Show problem. Show all your work on a separate sheet of paper. You may want to use the Problem-Solving Tips to get started.**

PROBLEM-SOLVING TIPS

Math Toolkit sticky notes

Key Terms

expression   variable   like terms

equivalent expression   coefficient   estimate

Questions

• How will you keep track of what each part of the expression represents?

• How can you check that the expressions you wrote are equivalent?

Reflect

Use Mathematical Practices   As you work through the problem, discuss these questions with a partner.

• **Use Structure** What does each form of the expression tell you about the band's expenses?

• **Reason Mathematically** How do you know that the amount the agent and manager make in ticket sales will always be less than the amount the band makes?

Discuss Models and Strategies

➤ **Read the problem. Write a solution on a separate sheet of paper. Remember, there can be lots of ways to solve a problem.**

Renting a Tour Van

Jorge and Liam want to rent a van for their band to use on a tour around Texas. Read through their notes, and help them finalize their plans.

J Plus L Texas Tour!

Rental Company Info:

Company	Daily Rate	Fee for Extra Miles	Van Gas Mileage
Sapling	$191.80	$0.25 for each mile over 500	24 miles per gallon
Raven Rentals	$171.72	$0.30 for each mile over 750	15 miles per gallon
Bridge King	$206.22	$0.35 for each mile over 1,000	19 miles per gallon

Other Info:

- The tour starts and ends in Houston. Each distance includes how far we will drive to reach each city and other stops we will make.

- Right now, gas in Texas ranges from $2.39 to $2.63 per gallon.

- Our budget for renting the van, including gas, is $1,100.

WHAT WE NEED TO DO:

- Choose a rental company.

- Determine how many miles we can drive without going over budget for a 5-day tour.

- Figure out if we can afford to keep Dallas as the last show on our tour or if we should end the tour a day early. If our last show is in Waco, we will drive about 215 miles back to Houston on Day 4.

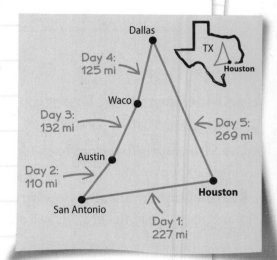

©Curriculum Associates, LLC Copying is not permitted.

Plan It and Solve It

➤ **Find a solution to the Renting a Tour Van problem.**

Write a detailed plan and support your answer. Be sure to include:

- the rental company you choose.

- the greatest number of miles the band can afford to drive on a 5-day tour.

- a statement about whether or not the band can afford to keep Dallas as the last show on the tour.

PROBLEM-SOLVING TIPS

 Math Toolkit number lines, sticky notes

Key Terms

expression	inequality	inverse operations
distributive property	term	expand
like terms	solution	

Questions

- What gas price will you use to make sure the band will not go over budget?

- How can you write an expression that represents the fee the band will pay for extra miles if they drive a total of *m* miles?

- If the band drives *m* miles, how many gallons of gas will they need? How can you write an expression to represent the cost for this number of gallons?

Reflect

Use Mathematical Practices As you work through the problem, discuss these questions with a partner.

- **Make Sense of Problems** What costs or fees contribute to the total amount the band will pay for the van during the tour?

- **Use a Model** How could an inequality help you solve this problem?

Persevere On Your Own

➤ **Read the problem. Write a solution on a separate sheet of paper.**

Choosing Merch(andise)

Jorge and Liam's band plans to set up a merchandise table at each show to sell items to fans. The flyer shows the items the band may sell.

The band's total budget for merchandise is $1,350. They want to order 100 T-shirts, 1,000 stickers, and one more item. Select one more item for the band to order, and determine how many of that item the band can afford.

Place Your ORDER NOW!

Free Shipping!

YOUR BAND LOGO HERE

Item	Design Fee	Cost per Item	Minimum Number of Items per Order	Quantity
T-shirt	N/A	$6.99	25	100
Sticker	N/A	$0.35	100	1,000
Button	$107	$0.30	100	
Guitar pick	$64	$0.37	100	
Hat	$149	$6.54	25	
Poster	$354	$0.20	25	
Tote bag	$72	$3.74	5	

✂

Orders over $1,000 pay only 95% of the purchase price! • All prices include tax.

Solve It

➤ **Find a solution to the Choosing Merch(andise) problem.**

- Determine whether the band's order will qualify to pay only 95% of the purchase price.

- Write and solve an inequality that shows how much of the band's merchandise budget will be left after they buy the T-shirts and stickers.

- Choose another merchandise item, and determine how many of that item the band can buy with the remaining money in their budget.

Reflect

Use Mathematical Practices After you complete the problem, choose one of these questions to discuss with a partner.

- **Be Precise** How did the context of this problem help you decide how to round your answers?

- **Critique Reasoning** Which merchandise item did your partner choose? Do you agree that the band could buy as many of that item as your partner says? Could they buy more? Explain.

In this unit you learned to . . .

Skill	Lesson
Find equivalent expressions.	**15**
Rewrite expressions in different forms.	**15, 16**
Solve multi-step equations.	**17, 18**
Solve problems using equations.	**18**
Solve inequalities.	**19**
Solve problems using inequalities.	**19**
Graph the solution set of an inequality.	**19**
Actively participate in discussions by asking questions and rephrasing or building on classmates' ideas.	**15–19**

Think about what you have learned.

➤ **Use words, numbers, and drawings.**

1 Three examples of what I learned are . . .

2 The hardest thing I learned to do is _____ because . . .

3 A question I still have is . . .

➤ **Review the unit vocabulary. Put a check mark by items you can use in speaking and writing. Look up the meaning of any terms you do not know.**

Math Vocabulary   **Academic Vocabulary**

☐ equation   ☐ inequality   ☐ combine

☐ equivalent expressions   ☐ like terms   ☐ consider

☐ expression   ☐ rational number   ☐ interpret

☐ factor (verb)   ☐ modify

➤ **Use the unit vocabulary to complete the problems.**

1 Give an example of an equation and an inequality. Then use at least two math or academic vocabulary terms to explain how equations and inequalities are the same and different. Underline each term you use.

2 Explain each step of solving the inequality. Use at least two math or academic vocabulary terms. Underline each term you use.

$$75(2x + 9) \le 30x - 165$$

$$150x + 675 \le 30x - 165 \quad \underline{\hspace{5cm}}$$

$$150x - 30x + 675 \le -165 \quad \underline{\hspace{5cm}}$$

$$120x + 675 \le -165 \quad \underline{\hspace{5cm}}$$

$$120x \le -840 \quad \underline{\hspace{5cm}}$$

$$x \le -7 \quad \underline{\hspace{5cm}}$$

➤ **Use what you have learned to complete these problems.**

1 A square's side length is represented by $2x - 1.8$. Its perimeter is 24 inches. Which equations represent the perimeter? Choose all the correct answers.

A $4(2x - 1.8) = 24$

B $8x - 7.2 = 24$

C $2(2x - 1.8) = 24$

D $2(2x - 1.8) + 2(2x - 1.8) = 24$

E $8x - 1.8 = 24$

2 Aaliyah teaches an exercise class. The class has 25 regular participants. Each participant uses 4 weights. Aaliyah writes the expression $4(25 - n)$ to represent the number of weights needed if n regular participants do not come to class. The gym manager represents the number of weights needed with the expression $100 - 4n$. What information does each expression tell you? Explain your reasoning.

SOLUTION _____

_____

_____

_____

_____

_____

_____

3 Solve $\frac{1}{4}(x - 16) = \frac{3}{4}$. Record your answer on the grid. Then fill in the bubbles.

4 Monica works at a fitness center. She sells 15 fitness class passes that each cost the same amount and one exercise mat that costs $18. The total amount of money she collects is $93. How much does each fitness class pass cost? Show your work.

SOLUTION _____

5 Which expression is equivalent to $-5(2g + 6) - 4g$?

A $10g - 30$ **B** $-10g - 34$ **C** $-14g + 6$ **D** $-14g - 30$

6 Graph $\dfrac{b}{-2} - 4 < -1$ on the number line below. Show your work.

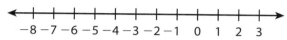

$$-8\ -7\ -6\ -5\ -4\ -3\ -2\ -1\ \ \ 0\ \ \ 1\ \ \ 2\ \ \ 3$$

SOLUTION _____

7 Daniel and Amber each solved the inequality $-4(1.5 + 2n) \geq -24$. Their work is shown below. Why are both strategies correct? Explain your reasoning.

Daniel	**Amber**
$-4(1.5 + 2n) \geq -24$	$-4(1.5 + 2n) \geq -24$
$-6 - 8n \geq -24$	$\dfrac{-4(1.5 + 2n)}{-4} \leq \dfrac{-24}{-4}$
$-6 - 8n + 6 \geq -24 + 6$	$1.5 + 2n \leq 6$
$-8n \geq -18$	$1.5 + 2n - 1.5 \leq 6 - 1.5$
$\dfrac{-8n}{-8} \leq -\dfrac{18}{-8}$	$2n \leq 4.5$
$n \leq 2.25$	$\dfrac{2n}{2} \leq \dfrac{4.5}{2}$
	$n \leq 2.25$

SOLUTION _____

_____

_____

_____

_____

Performance Task

➤ **Answer the questions and show all your work on separate paper.**

Backyard Paradise has hired you as their lead designer. Your first client wants a rectangular pool that is 20 feet by 40 feet. She would also like to install a fence around the pool that meets the following requirements:

- The fence must have a minimum perimeter of 300 feet.

- The distance from the pool to the fence must be the same on all sides of the pool.

- The maximum budget for the fence is $8,000.

The costs for different types of fencing are shown in the table.

Fence Type	Price (per foot)
Chain link	$14
Vinyl	$25
Wood	$22
Metal	$30

Describe two different fence options for the client. Include the type of fence, dimensions of the fence, and the total price. Prove that either option will satisfy all the requirements.

Reflect

Use Mathematical Practices After you complete the task, choose one of the following questions to answer.

- **Persevere** How would you compare using algebraic thinking to using guess-and-check approaches to create your design and plan a solution?

- **Use Reasoning** How did you visualize the fence and its dimensions?

Set 1 Write and Evaluate Algebraic Expressions

➤ **Write an algebraic expression and evaluate it to solve the problem. Show your work.**

1 A rectangle has side lengths $x + 2$ and $x - 1$. What is the perimeter of the rectangle when $x = 5$?

Set 2 Evaluate Expressions with Exponents

➤ **Evaluate the expressions at the specified value. Show your work.**

1 Evaluate m^3 for $m = \frac{3}{2}$.

2 Evaluate $6s^2$ for $s = \frac{2}{3}$.

3 Evaluate $n^4 \div 2$ for $n = \frac{2}{5}$.

Set 3 Absolute Value

➤ **Write $<$, $>$, or $=$ in each circle to make a true statement.**

1 -3 ◯ -9 and $|-3|$ ◯ $|-9|$

2 -9 ◯ 7 and $|-9|$ ◯ $|7|$

3 7 ◯ -2 and $|7|$ ◯ $|-2|$

4 11 ◯ -11 and $|11|$ ◯ $|-11|$

Set 4 Divide with Fractions

➤ **Divide. Show your work.**

1 $\frac{3}{2} \div \frac{1}{3}$

2 $3\frac{1}{2} \div 2\frac{3}{4}$

3 $4\frac{3}{4} \div \frac{3}{2}$

4 Three horses equally share $16\frac{1}{5}$ pounds of hay. How many pounds of hay does each horse receive?

Set 5 Percents

➤ **Solve the problems. Show your work.**

1 What is 25% of 140?

2 500 is 40% of what number?

Set 6 Solve One-Variable Equations

➤ **Solve each equation for x. Show your work.**

1 $x - 8 = 5$

2 $14 = x + 6$

3 $4x = 28$

Set 7 Solve Unit Rate Problems

➤ **Solve problems 1 and 2. Show your work.**

1 Bottled water costs $40 for 32 bottles. At this rate, what is the cost of 8 bottles of water?

2 Sandra collects trash along the shore. In the first 4 days, she finds 10 lb of trash. At this rate, how many pounds of trash will Sandra collect by day 15?

➤ **Convert the measurements in problems 3 and 4. Show your work.**

3 $12.80 per gallon = $? per cup

4 50 ft in 4 seconds = ? yards per minute

$12.80 per gallon = $ _____ per cup

50 ft in 4 seconds = _____ yards per minute

Set 8 Interpret Statements of Inequality

➤ **For the statements of inequality in problems 1–3, circle the value located farther to the right on the number line.**

1 $-11 < 0$

2 $-5 > -12$

3 $\frac{3}{8} < \frac{3}{4}$

➤ **Write an inequality to express each relationship described in problem 4.**

4 A temperature of 75°F is warmer than a temperature of 68°F. A temperature of -8°F is colder than a temperature of 0°F.

Set 9 Write Equations in Two Variables

➤ **Solve the problems. Show your work.**

1 The total cost of having a meal delivered to your house is equal to the cost of the meal plus the delivery fee of $5.

    a. Write an equation in two variables that shows how to use the total cost of the meal to find the cost of the meal before the delivery charge is applied.

    b. Which is the independent variable in your equation? _____

    c. Which is the dependent variable in your equation? _____

Set 10 Work with One-Variable Inequalities

➤ **Solve problems 1 and 2.**

1 Circle the values that are solutions of the inequality $16 > f$.

    -10 20   16   5 -25 30

2 Circle the values that are solutions of the inequality $j \geq -3$.

    -100 -3 0   5   100 -1

➤ **Write and graph an inequality to show the situation in problem 3.**

3 The temperature outside is no more than 4 °C.

Set 1 Find Unit Rates Involving Ratios of Fractions

➤ **Find the unit rate to solve the problems. Show your work.**

1 A jogger runs $1\frac{4}{5}$ miles in $\frac{1}{4}$ hour and continues jogging at the same rate.

What is the jogger's speed in miles per hour?

2 A recipe calls for $\frac{1}{4}$ teaspoon of baking powder for every $\frac{2}{3}$ cup of flour. How many

teaspoons of baking powder should be used for 1 cup of flour?

Set 2 Identify the Constant of Proportionality in Tables

➤ **Fill in the blanks.**

1 The table shows the cost of tickets to an event.

Number of Tickets	1	2	3	4	5	6
Cost (dollars)	6	12	18	24	30	36

The unit rate for dollars per ticket is _____.

The constant of proportionality for the relationship of cost in dollars to number

of tickets is _____.

2 The table shows the amounts of water and oats to make oatmeal.

Cups of Water	2	4	6	8	10	12
Cups of Oats	1	2	3	4	5	6

The constant of proportionality for the relationship of cups of water to

cups of oats is _____.

Set 3 Represent Proportional Relationships by Equations

➤ **Write an equation to represent each relationship. Show your work.**

1 A lemonade recipe calls for 1 cup of water for every $\frac{1}{3}$ cup of lemon juice. Write an equation to show the relationship between the amount of water, w, and lemon juice, j.

2 A salesperson earns $6 in $\frac{1}{2}$ hour. Write an equation to show the relationship between the money a salesperson earns, m, and the hours he works, h.

3 The distance a cyclist travels is proportional to the time she spends cycling. She travels 4 mi in $\frac{1}{4}$ hour. Write an equation to show the relationship between the distance she travels, d, and the hours she spends cycling, h.

Set 4 Identify Proportional Relationships

➤ **Calculate ratios to show whether each relationship is proportional. Show your work.**

1 The table compares the number of minutes a car has been driving and the number of signs it has passed.

Minutes	0	2	4
Signs	0	4	16

2 It costs $35 to hire a musician for 1 hour, $70 to hire a musician for 2 hours, and $105 to hire a musician for 3 hours.

Set 5 Interpret Graphs of Proportional Relationships

➤ **Fill in the blanks.**

1 The graph shows the proportional relationship between the hours Jacqueline works and the amount she earns.

The point (3, 60) represents that Jacqueline earns $ _____ in

_____ hours.

The point _____ shows that the unit rate is $ _____
per hour.

The constant of proportionality is _____ .

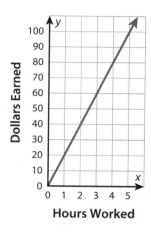

2 The graph shows the proportional relationship between the amount of popcorn kernels and the amount of popcorn that can be made.

The point _____ means that _____ cups of popcorn can be made with 0 tablespoons of popcorn kernels.

The constant of proportionality is _____ .

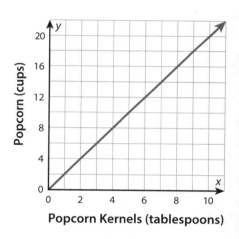

3 The graph shows the proportional relationship between the time, in minutes, and the distance, in miles, an athlete runs.

The point (20, 4) represents that the athlete runs _____

miles in _____ minutes.

The constant of proportionality is _____ .

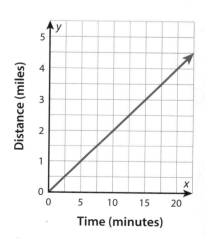

Set 6 Identify the Constant of Proportionality

➤ **Identify the constant of proportionality for each relationship.**

1 For every hour he spends doing homework, Denzel plays video games for $\frac{1}{4}$ hour. What is the constant of proportionality for the relationship between time playing video games and time doing homework? _____

2 For each cup of oats in a recipe, a baker adds $1\frac{1}{2}$ teaspoons of cinnamon. What is the constant of proportionality for the relationship between teaspoons of cinnamon and cups of oats? _____

Set 7 Solve Proportional Relationship Problems

➤ **Solve the problems. Show your work.**

1 The ratio of nonfiction books to fiction books on a shelf is 5 : 3. There are 12 fiction books on the shelf. How many books are on the shelf?

2 A recipe for 2 dozen muffins uses $\frac{2}{3}$ cup of walnuts. Greg has $\frac{4}{5}$ cup of walnuts. Does Greg have enough walnuts to make 3 dozen muffins?

3 To make purple paint, Sofia mixes $1\frac{1}{6}$ cups blue paint and $\frac{1}{3}$ cup red paint. How much red paint does Sofia need to make 4 cups of purple paint?

Set 1 Add Opposites

➤ **Complete the models to represent and solve each problem.**

1 The temperature on a winter morning is −3°F. In the afternoon, the temperature increases by 3°F. The expression (−3) + 3 represents the temperature at the end of the afternoon. What is the temperature at the end of the afternoon?

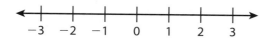

2 A diver is 8 feet below sea level. She swims up 8 feet. The expression −8 + 8 represents the diver's elevation relative to sea level. What is the diver's elevation relative to sea level now?

Set 2 Add with Negative Integers

➤ **Use the horizontal number line to fill in the blanks.**

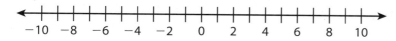

1 2 + 5 is located to the _____ of 2, and 2 + (−5) is located to the

_____ of 2.

2 −4 + 6 is located to the _____ of −4, and −4 + (−6) is located to the

_____ of −4.

3 −3 + 2 is located to the _____ of −3, and −3 + (−2) is located to the

_____ of −3.

4 8 + (−3) is located to the _____ of 3 and −8 + 3 is located to the

_____ of 3.

Set 3 Add with Negative Numbers

➤ **Add. Show your work.**

1 $6 + (-10)$

2 $-3 + (-4)$

3 $8 + (-6)$

4 $17.5 + (-22.3)$

5 $-3.2 + (-4.8)$

6 $\frac{1}{6} + \left(-\frac{2}{3}\right)$

7 $1\frac{3}{4} + \left(-2\frac{1}{4}\right)$

8 $-3\frac{1}{2} + 1\frac{1}{4}$

Set 4 Subtract with Negative Integers

➤ **Fill in the blanks.**

1 On a horizontal number line, $3 - 4$ is located to the _____ of 3 and

$3 - (-4)$ is located to the _____ of 3.

2 On a horizontal number line, $(-5) - (-2)$ is located to the _____ of -5

and $(-5) - 2$ is located to the _____ of -5.

3 The distance between _____ and _____ is $|2 - (-4)|$.

4 The distance between _____ and _____ is $|-5 - (-3)|$.

5 The difference $7 - (-3)$ is equivalent to the sum $7 +$ _____.

Set 5 Subtract with Negative Numbers

➤ **Subtract. Show your work.**

1 $1 - (-4)$

2 $-\frac{3}{5} - \left(\frac{2}{10}\right)$

3 $-15 - (-9)$

4 $-15.2 - (-12.8)$

5 $-1.5 - (-2.8)$

6 $-2 - (-5)$

7 $-2\frac{1}{2} - 3\frac{1}{2}$

8 $-2\frac{3}{5} - \left(\frac{2}{10}\right)$

Set 6 Add and Subtract Positive and Negative Numbers

➤ **Add or subtract. Show your work.**

1 $4 + (-8)$

2 $-58.4 + (-24.7)$

3 $-16 - (-25)$

4 $-36.2 - (-17.6)$

5 $-4\frac{2}{3} + 12$

6 $8.3 - (-6.8)$

Set 7 Identify the Constant of Proportionality in Graphs

➤ **Identify what the constant of proportionality from *x* to *y* represents in each graph.**

1 What is the constant of proportionality for the relationship between minutes of swimming and the number of laps shown in the graph?

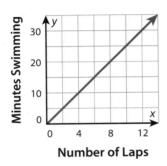

2 What is the constant of proportionality for the relationship between the number of tables and the number of people shown in the graph?

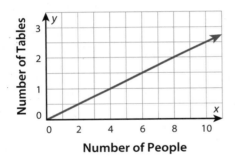

Set 8 Identify the Constant of Proportionality in Equations

➤ **Identify the constant of proportionality in each equation.**

1 What is the constant of proportionality in the equation $y = 5.4x$? _____

2 The equation $t = \frac{s}{5}$ gives the number of cups of tomatoes, *t*, required per cup of

salad, *s*. What is the constant of proportionality? _____

3 In *t* hours, a jogger runs $d = 6t$ miles. What is the constant of proportionality? _____

Cumulative Practice

Name: _____

Set 1 Multiplication with Negative Integers

➤ **Fill in the blanks with *negative, positive,* or *zero*.**

1 The product of two negative numbers is _____.

2 The product of a negative number and zero is _____.

3 The product of a negative number and a positive number is _____.

4 The product of a positive number and zero is _____.

5 The product of three negative numbers is _____.

6 The product of two negative numbers and a positive number is _____.

Set 2 Multiply with Negative Numbers

➤ **Multiply. Show your work.**

1 $4.5(-1.7)$

2 $-\frac{1}{2}\left(-3\frac{1}{3}\right)$

3 $-2\frac{2}{5}\left(-4\frac{3}{8}\right)$

4 $-5(0.6)$

5 $-\frac{4}{10}\left(\frac{3}{5}\right)$

6 $-4(-0.2)(-1.5)$

Set 3 Divide with Negative Numbers

➤ **Divide. Show your work.**

1 $-6 \div 0.2$

2 $-\frac{1}{2} \div \left(-\frac{2}{3}\right)$

3 $-4\frac{2}{3} \div 1\frac{5}{9}$

Set 4 Multiply and Divide Negative Rational Numbers

➤ **Multiply or divide. Show your work.**

1 $-7(-3.6)$

2 $-3\frac{1}{2} \div \left(-\frac{1}{4}\right)$

3 -24×0.03

4 $-\frac{2}{3}\left(3\frac{2}{3}\right)$

5 $-\frac{4}{5}\left(\frac{2}{3}\right) \div 1\frac{3}{5}$

6 $-6.4 \div (-8)$

Set 5 Express Fractions as Decimals

➤ **Express each fraction as a decimal. Show your work.**

1 $\frac{7}{8}$

2 $\frac{4}{5}$

3 $2\frac{7}{20}$

4 $\frac{5}{6}$

5 $3\frac{4}{9}$

6 $\frac{3}{11}$

Set 6 Express Fractions as Decimals in Word Problems

➤ **Solve the problems. Show your work.**

1 Qiana walks 2.89 miles. Will walks $2\frac{8}{9}$ miles. Who walks farther?

2 Dora's recipe calls for $\frac{5}{8}$ ounce of garlic. Dora's scale shows that she has cut up 0.58 ounce of garlic. How much more garlic does Dora need?

Set 7 Rational Numbers in Word Problems

➤ **Solve the problems. Show your work.**

1 Pedro makes a loaf of bread that weighs 24 ounces. He gives $\frac{1}{3}$ of the loaf to his sister and 20% of the loaf to his friend. He eats the rest himself. How much bread, in ounces, does Pedro eat?

2 Amy is scuba diving. She starts at -15.5 m relative to the ocean surface. She swims down 4.2 m. Then she swims up halfway to the surface. What is her position relative to the ocean surface?

Set 8 Add and Subtract Rational Numbers

➤ **Add or subtract. Show your work.**

1 $-2 - (-6.5)$

2 $-3.12 + 1.24$

3 $3\frac{1}{3} - 5\frac{2}{3}$

4 $-\frac{2}{5} + 3\frac{1}{5}$

5 $-7\frac{3}{4} - 2\frac{5}{8}$

6 $7.25 + (-1.17)$

Set 9 Find Unit Rates Involving Ratios of Fractions

➤ **Find the unit rate to solve each problem. Show your work.**

1 A baker uses $\frac{3}{4}$ teaspoon cinnamon for every $\frac{2}{3}$ can of pumpkin when making pumpkin muffins. How much cinnamon does the baker need for each can of pumpkin? Show your work.

2 Allison runs for $1\frac{3}{4}$ minutes and travels $\frac{1}{5}$ mile. What is her speed in miles per minute?

3 A butterfly is $1\frac{1}{2}$ inches long and $1\frac{2}{3}$ inches wide. Lashay makes a scale drawing of the butterfly that is 1 inch long. What is the width of his drawing?

Interactive Glossary/Glosario interactivo

English/Español	Example/Ejemplo	Notes/Notas

Aa

absolute value a number's distance from 0 on the number line. Absolute value is never negative.

valor absoluto distancia de un número desde 0 en la recta numérica. El valor absoluto nunca es negativo.

$|-3| = 3$

$|3| = 3$

---

acute angle an angle that measures more than 0° but less than 90°.

ángulo agudo ángulo que mide más de 0° pero menos de 90°.

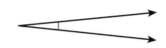

---

acute triangle a triangle that has three acute angles.

triángulo acutángulo triángulo que tiene tres ángulos agudos.

---

additive inverses two numbers whose sum is zero. The additive inverse of a number is the opposite of that number, i.e., the additive inverse of a is $-a$.

inverso aditivo dos números cuya suma es cero. El inverso aditivo de un número es el opuesto de ese número; por ejemplo, el inverso aditivo de a es $-a$.

-2 and 2

$\frac{1}{2}$ and $-\frac{1}{2}$

---

adjacent angles two non-overlapping angles that share a vertex and a side.

ángulos adyacentes dos ángulos que no se superponen y que comparten un vértice y un lado.

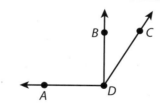

$\angle ADB$ and $\angle BDC$ are adjacent angles.

---

algorithm a set of routine steps used to solve problems.

algoritmo conjunto de pasos rutinarios que se siguen para resolver problemas.

```
      17 R 19
31)546
   − 31↓
     236
   − 217
      19
```

---

angle a geometric shape formed by two rays, lines, or line segments that meet at a common point.

ángulo figura geométrica formada por dos semirrectas, rectas o segmentos de recta que se encuentran en un punto común.

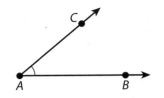

---

area the amount of space inside a closed two-dimensional figure. Area is measured in square units such as square centimeters.

área cantidad de espacio dentro de una figura bidimensional cerrada. El área se mide en unidades cuadradas, como los centímetros cuadrados.

6 units

Area = 30 units² · 5 units

---

associative property of addition regrouping the terms does not change the value of the expression.

propiedad asociativa de la suma reagrupar los términos no cambia el valor de la expresión.

$(a + b) + c = a + (b + c)$

$(2 + 3) + 4 = 2 + (3 + 4)$

---

associative property of multiplication regrouping the terms does not change the value of the expression.

propiedad asociativa de la multiplicación reagrupar los términos no cambia el valor de la expresión.

$(a \cdot b) \cdot c = a \cdot (b \cdot c)$

$(2 \cdot 3) \cdot 4 = 2 \cdot (3 \cdot 4)$

---

axis a horizontal or vertical number line that determines a coordinate plane. The plural form is *axes*.

eje recta numérica horizontal o vertical que determina un plano de coordenadas.

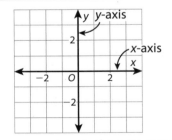

Bb

balance point the point that represents the center of a data set. In a two-variable data set, the coordinates of the balance point are the mean of each variable.

punto de equilibrio punto que representa el centro de un conjunto de datos. En un conjunto de datos de dos variables, las coordenadas del punto de equilibrio son la media de cada variable.

Data set: (1, 1), (3, 4), (5, 6), (7, 8)

$$\frac{1 + 3 + 5 + 7}{4} = 4$$

$$\frac{1 + 4 + 6 + 8}{4} = 4.75$$

Balance point: (4, 4.75)

---

base (of a parallelogram) a side of a parallelogram from which the height is measured.

base (de un paralelogramo) lado de un paralelogramo desde el que se mide la altura.

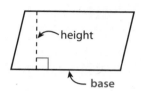

---

base (of a power) in a power, the number that is used as a repeated factor.

base (de una potencia) en una potencia, el número que se usa como factor que se repite.

---

base (of a three-dimensional figure) a face of a three-dimensional figure from which the height is measured.

base (de una figura tridimensional) cara de una figura tridimensional desde la que se mide la altura.

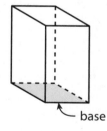

---

base (of a triangle) a side of a triangle from which the height is measured.

base (de un triángulo) lado de un triángulo desde el que se mide la altura.

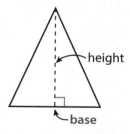

---

box plot a visual display of a data set on a number line that shows the minimum, the lower quartile, the median, the upper quartile, and the maximum. The sides of the box show the lower and upper quartiles and the line inside the box shows the median. Lines connect the box to the minimum and maximum values.

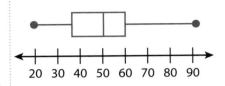

diagrama de caja representación visual de un conjunto de datos en una recta numérica que muestra el mínimo, el cuartil inferior, la mediana, el cuartil superior y el máximo. Los lados de la caja muestran los cuartiles inferior y superior y la recta del centro muestra la mediana. Las rectas conectan la caja con los valores mínimo y máximo.

Cc

center (of a circle) the point inside a circle that is the same distance from every point on the circle.

centro (de un círculo) punto dentro de un círculo que está a la misma distancia de todos los puntos del círculo.

circle a two-dimensional shape in which every point is the same distance from the center.

círculo figura bidimensional en que todos los puntos están a la misma distancia del centro.

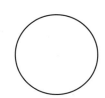

circumference the distance around the outside of a circle. It can be thought of as the perimeter of the circle.

circunferencia distancia alrededor del exterior de un círculo. Se puede considerar como el perímetro del círculo.

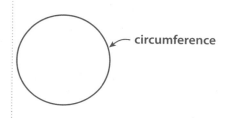

closed figure a two-dimensional figure that begins and ends at the same point.

figura cerrada figura bidimensional que comienza y termina en el mismo punto.

Closed figure   Open figure

cluster a group of data points that are close to each other.

agrupación conjunto de datos que están cerca unos de otros.

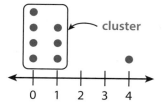

coefficient a number that is multiplied by a variable.

coeficiente número que se multiplica por una variable.

$5x + 3$

coefficient

English/Español	Example/Ejemplo	Notes/Notas
commission a fee paid for services, often a percent of the total cost. A salesperson who earns a commission often gets a percent of the total sale. **comisión** tarifa que se paga por servicios, que suele ser un porcentaje del costo total. Un vendedor que gana una comisión por lo general recibe un porcentaje de la venta total.	A 5% commission on $4,000 is 0.05($4,000), or $200.	
common denominator a number that is a common multiple of the denominators of two or more fractions. **denominador común** número que es múltiplo común de los denominadores de dos o más fracciones.	A common denominator for $\frac{1}{2}$ and $\frac{3}{5}$ is 10 because $2 \cdot 5 = 10$.	
commutative property of addition changing the order of the addends does not change the sum. **propiedad conmutativa de la suma** cambiar el orden de los sumandos no cambia el total.	$a + b = b + a$ $4.1 + 7.5 = 7.5 + 4.1$	
commutative property of multiplication changing the order of the factors does not change the product. **propiedad conmutativa de la multiplicación** cambiar el orden de los factores no cambia el producto.	$ab = ba$ $4(7.5) = 7.5(4)$	
compare to describe the relationship between the value or size of two numbers or quantities. **comparar** describir la relación que hay entre el valor o el tamaño de dos números o cantidades.	$-4 < 8.5$	

English/Español	Example/Ejemplo	Notes/Notas
complementary angles two angles whose measures sum to 90°. **ángulos complementarios** dos ángulos cuyas medidas suman 90°.	 ∠AEB and ∠BEC	
complex fraction a fraction in which the numerator is a fraction, the denominator is a fraction, or both the numerator and the denominator are fractions. **fracción compleja** fracción en la que el numerador es una fracción, el denominador es una fracción, o tanto el numerador como el denominador son fracciones.	$\dfrac{\frac{1}{2}}{\frac{3}{4}}$	
compose to make by combining parts. You can put together numbers to make a greater number or put together shapes to make a new shape. **componer** formar al combinar partes. Se pueden unir números para hacer un número mayor o unir figuras para formar una figura nueva.		
composite number a number that has more than one pair of whole number factors. **número compuesto** número que tiene más de un par de números enteros como factores.	16 is a composite number because 1 · 16, 2 · 8, and 4 · 4 all equal 16.	
compound event an event that consists of two or more simple events. **evento compuesto** evento que consiste en dos o más eventos simples.	Rolling a number cube twice	
constant of proportionality the unit rate in a proportional relationship. **constante de proporcionalidad** tasa unitaria en una relación proporcional.	Unit rate: $10 per hour Constant of proportionality for dollars per hours: 10.	

English/Español	Example/Ejemplo	Notes/Notas

convert to write an equivalent measurement using a different unit.

convertir escribir una medida equivalente usando una unidad diferente.

60 in. is the same as 5 ft.

---

coordinate plane a two-dimensional space formed by two perpendicular number lines called *axes*.

plano de coordenadas espacio bidimensional formado por dos rectas numéricas perpendiculares llamadas ejes.

---

corresponding terms terms that have the same position in two related patterns. For example, the second term in one pattern and the second term in a related pattern are corresponding terms.

términos correspondientes términos que tienen la misma posición en dos patrones relacionados. Por ejemplo, el segundo término en un patrón y el segundo término en un patrón relacionado son términos correspondientes.

Pattern A: 12, 18, 24, 30

Pattern B: 6, 9, 12, 15

---

cross-section a two-dimensional shape that is exposed by making a straight cut through a three-dimensional figure.

sección transversal figura bidimensional que se forma al hacer un corte recto a través de una figura tridimensional.

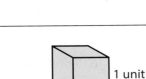

---

cube a rectangular prism in which each face of the prism is a square.

cubo prisma rectangular en el que cada cara del prisma es un cuadrado.

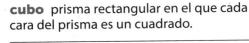

1 unit
1 unit
1 unit

English/Español	**Example**/Ejemplo	**Notes**/Notas
cylinder a three-dimensional figure with two parallel curved bases that are the same size. The bases are connected by a curved surface.		
cilindro figura tridimensional que tiene dos bases curvas paralelas que tienen el mismo tamaño. Las bases están conectadas por una superficie curva.		

Dd

data a set of collected information. Often numerical information such as a list of measurements.	Commute length (mi): 15, 22, 10.5, 21, 9.5	
datos conjunto de información reunida. Con frecuencia, información numérica como una lista de medidas.		
decimal a number containing a decimal point that separates a whole from fractional place values (tenths, hundredths, thousandths, and so on).	1.293	
decimal número que tiene un punto decimal que separa un entero de los valores posicionales fraccionarios (décimas, centésimas, milésimas, etc.).		
decompose to break into parts. You can break apart numbers and shapes.		
descomponer separar en partes. Se puede separar en partes números y figuras.		

English/Español	Example/Ejemplo	Notes/Notas
degree (°) a unit used to measure angles. **grado (°)** unidad que se usa para medir ángulos.	There are 360° in a circle.	
denominator the number below the line in a fraction that tells the number of equal parts in the whole. **denominador** número debajo de la línea en una fracción que indica el número de partes iguales que hay en el entero.	$\dfrac{3}{4}$	
dependent variable a variable whose value depends on the value of a related independent variable. **variable dependiente** variable cuyo valor depende del valor de una variable independiente relacionada.	$y = 5x$ The value of y depends on the value of x.	
diameter a line segment that goes through the center of a circle and has endpoints on the circle. Also, the distance across a circle through the center. **diámetro** segmento de recta que pasa por el centro de un círculo y tiene extremos en el círculo. También, la distancia de un lado al otro del círculo a través del centro.	diameter	
difference the result of subtraction. **diferencia** resultado de la resta.	16.75 − 15.70 1.05	
digit a symbol used to write numbers. **dígito** símbolo que se usa para escribir números.	The digits are 0, 1, 2, 3, 4, 5, 6, 7, 8, and 9.	
dimension length in one direction. A figure may have one, two, or three dimensions. **dimensión** longitud en una dirección. Una figura puede tener una, dos o tres dimensiones.	5 in. 2 in. 3 in.	

distribution a representation that shows how often values in a data set occur.

distribución representación que muestra la frecuencia con la que ocurren los valores en un conjunto de datos.

Pet	Frequency
Bird	7
Cat	12
Dog	8
Snake	3

---

distributive property multiplying each term in a sum or difference by a common factor does not change the value of the expression.

propiedad distributiva multiplicar cada término de una suma o diferencia por un factor común no cambia el valor de la expresión.

$$a(b + c) = ab + ac$$
$$5(4 + 2) = 5(4) + 5(2)$$

---

dividend the number that is divided by another number.

dividendo número que se divide por otro número.

$$22.5 \div 3 = 7.5$$

---

divisor the number by which another number is divided.

divisor número por el que se divide otro número.

$$22.5 \div 3 = 7.5$$

---

dot plot a data display that shows data as dots above a number line. A dot plot may also be called a *line plot*.

diagrama de puntos representación de datos que muestra datos como puntos sobre una *recta numérica*.

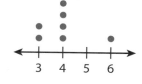

3 4 5 6

Ee

edge a line segment where two faces meet in a three-dimensional shape.

arista segmento de recta en el que dos caras se unen en una figura tridimensional.

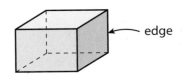

edge

---

equal having the same value, same size, or same amount.

igual que tiene el mismo valor, el mismo tamaño o la misma cantidad.

$50 - 20 = 30$

$50 - 20$ is equal to 30.

---

equation a mathematical statement that uses an equal sign (=) to show that two expressions have the same value.

ecuación enunciado matemático que tiene un signo de igual (=) para mostrar que dos expresiones tienen el mismo valor.

$x + 4 = 15$

---

equilateral triangle a triangle that has all three sides the same length.

triángulo equilátero triángulo que tiene los tres lados de la misma longitud.

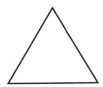

---

equivalent having the same value.

equivalente que tiene el mismo valor.

4 is equivalent to $\frac{8}{2}$.

---

equivalent expressions two or more expressions in different forms that always name the same value.

expresiones equivalentes dos o más expresiones en diferentes formas que siempre nombran el mismo valor.

$2(x + 4)$ is equivalent to $2x + 2(4)$ and $2x + 8$.

---

equivalent fractions two or more different fractions that name the same part of a whole or the same point on the number line.

fracciones equivalentes dos o más fracciones diferentes que nombran la misma parte de un entero o el mismo punto en la recta numérica.

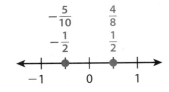

English/Español	Example/Ejemplo	Notes/Notas
equivalent ratios two ratios that express the same comparison. Multiplying both numbers in the ratio $a : b$ by a nonzero number n results in the equivalent ratio $na : nb$. **razones equivalentes** dos razones que expresan la misma comparación. Multiplicar ambos números en la razón $a : b$ por un número distinto de cero n da como resultado la razón equivalente $na : nb$.	$6 : 8$ is equivalent to $3 : 4$	
estimate (noun) a close guess made using mathematical thinking. **estimación** suposición aproximada que se hace por medio del razonamiento matemático.	$28 + 21 = ?$ $30 + 20 = 50$ 50 is an estimate of $28 + 21$.	
estimate (verb) to give an approximate number or answer based on mathematical thinking. **estimar** dar un número o respuesta aproximada basados en el razonamiento matemático.	$28 + 21$ is about 50.	
evaluate to find the value of an expression. **evaluar** hallar el valor de una expresión.	The expression $4.5 \div (1 + 8)$ has a value of 0.5.	
event a set of one or more outcomes of an experiment. **evento** conjunto de uno o más resultados de un experimento.	Experiment: rolling a number cube once Possible events: rolling an even number, rolling a 1	
experiment a repeatable procedure involving chance that results in one or more possible outcomes. **experimento** procedimiento repetible en el que se hacen pruebas y da uno o más resultados posibles.	Experiment: rolling a number cube once	

English/Español	Example/Ejemplo	Notes/Notas
experimental probability the probability of an event occurring based on the results from an experiment. **probabilidad experimental** probabilidad de que un evento ocurra con base en los resultados de un experimento.	A coin is flipped 30 times and lands heads up 17 times. The experimental probability of the coin landing heads up is $\frac{17}{30}$.	
exponent in a power, the number that shows how many times the base is used as a factor. **exponente** en una potencia, el número que muestra cuántas veces se usa la base como factor.	8^2 exponent	
exponential expression an expression that includes an exponent. **expresión exponencial** expresión que tiene un exponente.	$3x^3$	
expression a group of numbers, variables, and/or operation symbols that represents a mathematical relationship. An expression without variables, such as $3 + 4$, is called a *numerical expression*. An expression with variables, such as $5b^2$, is called an *algebraic expression*. **expresión** grupo de números, variables y/o símbolos de operaciones que representa una relación matemática. Una expresión sin variables, como $3 + 4$, se llama *expresión numérica*. Una expresión con variables, como $5b^2$, se llama *expresión algebraica*.	$\frac{32 - 4}{7}$ $3x + y - 9$	

Ff

face a flat surface of a solid shape.

cara superficie plana de una figura sólida.

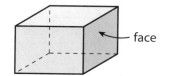

face

---

factor (noun) a number, or expression with parentheses, that is multiplied.

factor número, o expresión entre paréntesis, que se multiplica.

$4 \times 5 = 20$

factors

---

factor (verb) to rewrite an expression as a product of factors.

descomponer volver a escribir una expresión como producto de factores.

$12x + 42 = 6(2x + 7)$

---

factor pair two numbers that are multiplied together to give a product.

par de factores dos números que se multiplican para dar un producto.

$4 \times 5 = 20$

factor pair

---

factors of a number whole numbers that multiply together to get the given number.

factores de un número números enteros que se multiplican para obtener el número dado.

$4 \times 5 = 20$

4 and 5 are factors of 20.

---

formula a mathematical relationship that is expressed in the form of an equation.

fórmula relación matemática que se expresa en forma de ecuación.

$A = \ell w$

---

fraction a number that names equal parts of a whole. A fraction names a point on the number line and can also represent the division of two numbers.

fracción número que nombra partes iguales de un entero. Una fracción nombra un punto en la recta numérica y también puede representar la división de dos números.

---

frequency a numerical count of how many times a data value occurs in a data set.

frecuencia conteo numérico de cuántas veces ocurre un valor en un conjunto de datos.

Data set: 12, 13, 12, 15, 12, 13, 15, 14, 12, 12

Data Value	Frequency
12	5
13	2
14	1
15	2

Gg

gap an interval of the number line for which a distribution has no data values.

espacio intervalo de la recta numérica para el que una distribución no tiene valores.

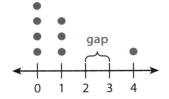

gratuity an amount added on to the cost of a service, often a percent of the total cost. Gratuity is often referred to as a *tip*.

propina cantidad que se suma al costo de un servicio; suele ser un porcentaje del costo total.

A gratuity of 18% on a $20 bill is 0.18($20), or $3.60.

English/Español	Example/Ejemplo	Notes/Notas
greatest common factor (GCF) the greatest factor two or more numbers have in common.	GCF of 20 and 30: $2 \cdot 5$, or 10 $$20 = 2 \cdot 2 \cdot 5$$ $$30 = 2 \cdot 3 \cdot 5$$	
máximo común divisor (M.C.D.) el mayor factor que dos o más números tienen en común.		
grouping symbol a symbol, such as braces {}, brackets [], or parentheses (), used to group parts of an expression that should be evaluated before others.	$3 \div (7 - 2) = 3 \div 5$ $$\frac{3}{7 - 2} = \frac{3}{5}$$	
símbolo de agrupación símbolo, como las llaves {}, los corchetes [] o los paréntesis (), que se usa para agrupar partes de una expresión que deben evaluarse antes que otras.		

Hh

English/Español	Example/Ejemplo	Notes/Notas
height (of a parallelogram) the perpendicular distance from a base to the opposite side.	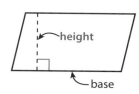	
altura (de un paralelogramo) distancia perpendicular desde una base hasta el lado opuesto.		
height (of a prism) the perpendicular distance from a base to the opposite base.	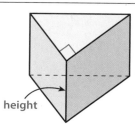	
altura (de un prisma) distancia perpendicular desde una base hasta la base opuesta.		

English/Español	Example/Ejemplo	Notes/Notas
height (of a triangle) the perpendicular distance from a base to the opposite vertex. **altura (de un triángulo)** distancia perpendicular desde una base hasta el vértice opuesto.	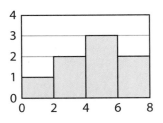	
hexagon a polygon with exactly 6 sides and 6 angles. **hexágono** polígono que tiene exactamente 6 lados y 6 ángulos.		
histogram a data display similar to a bar graph. A histogram groups the data into equal-size intervals. The height of each bar represents the number of data points in that group. **histograma** presentación de datos parecida a una gráfica de barras. Un histograma agrupa los datos en intervalos de igual tamaño. La altura de cada barra representa el número de datos que hay en ese grupo.		

Ii

identity property of multiplication
any number multiplied by 1 is itself.

propiedad de identidad de la multiplicación cualquier número multiplicado por 1 es el mismo número.

$3 \cdot 1 = 3$

independent variable a variable whose value is used to find the value of another variable. An independent variable determines the value of a dependent variable.

variable independiente variable cuyo valor se usa para hallar el valor de otra variable. Una variable independiente determina el valor de una variable dependiente.

$y = 5x$

The value of x is used to find the value of y.

inequality a mathematical statement that uses an inequality symbol $(<, >, \leq, \geq)$ to show the relationship between values of expressions.

desigualdad enunciado matemático que muestra con un símbolo de desigualdad $(<, >, \leq, \geq)$ la relación que existe entre los valores de las expresiones.

$4{,}384 > 3{,}448$
$x \geq -2$

integers the set of whole numbers and their opposites.

enteros (positivos y negativos) conjunto de números enteros y sus opuestos.

$-3, -1, 0, 2, 3$

interquartile range (IQR) the difference between the upper quartile and lower quartile.

rango entre cuartiles (REC) diferencia entre el cuartil superior y el cuartil inferior.

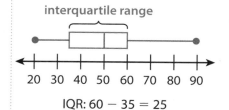

interquartile range

20 30 40 50 60 70 80 90

IQR: $60 - 35 = 25$

inverse operations operations that undo each other. For example, addition and subtraction are inverse operations, and multiplication and division are inverse operations.

$$300 \div 10 = 30$$
$$30 \times 10 = 300$$

operaciones inversas operaciones que se cancelan entre sí. Por ejemplo, la suma y la resta son operaciones inversas, y la multiplicación y la división son operaciones inversas.

---

isosceles triangle a triangle that has at least two sides the same length.

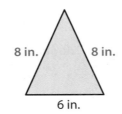

8 in.   8 in.

6 in.

triángulo isósceles triángulo que tiene al menos dos lados de la misma longitud.

Ll

least common multiple (LCM) the least multiple shared by two or more numbers.

LCM of 20 and 30: $2 \cdot 2 \cdot 3 \cdot 5$, or 60

$$20 = 2 \cdot 2 \cdot 5$$
$$30 = 2 \cdot 3 \cdot 5$$

mínimo común múltiplo (m.c.m.) el menor múltiplo que comparten dos o más números.

English/Español	Example/Ejemplo	Notes/Notas
like terms two or more terms that have the same variable factors.	$2x^2$ and $4x^2$	
términos semejantes dos o más términos que tienen los mismos factores variables.	1.2 and 5.1 $6xy$ and xy	
line a straight row of points that goes on forever in both directions.		
recta línea recta de puntos que continúa infinitamente en ambas direcciones.	⟷	
line of symmetry a line that divides a shape into two mirror images.		
eje de simetría línea que divide a una figura en dos imágenes reflejadas.		
line segment a straight row of points between two endpoints.		
segmento de recta fila recta de puntos entre dos extremos.	A ●————● B	
lower quartile the middle number between the minimum and the median in an ordered set of numbers. The lower quartile is also called the 1st quartile or Q1.	lower quartile	
cuartil inferior el número del medio entre el mínimo y la mediana en un conjunto ordenado de números. El cuartil inferior también se llama primer cuartil, o Q1.	20 30 40 50 60 70 80 90	

Mm

English/Español	Example/Ejemplo
markdown an amount subtracted from the cost of an item to determine the final price. The amount subtracted is often a percent of the cost. **reducción de precio** cantidad que se resta al costo de un artículo para determinar el precio final. La cantidad que se resta suele ser un porcentaje del costo.	A discount of $20 is the same as a markdown of $20.
markup an amount added to the cost of an item to determine the final price. The amount added is often a percent of the cost. **margen de ganancia** cantidad que se suma al costo de un artículo para determinar el precio final. La cantidad que se suma suele ser un porcentaje del costo.	A price increase of $25 is the same as a markup of $25.
maximum (of a data set) the greatest value in a data set. **máximo (de un conjunto de datos)** mayor valor en un conjunto de datos.	Data set: 9, 10, 8, 9, 7
mean the sum of a set of values divided by the number of values. This is often called the *average*. **media** suma de un conjunto de valores dividida por el número de valores. Suele llamarse *promedio*.	Data set: 9, 10, 8, 9, 7 Mean: $\dfrac{9 + 10 + 8 + 9 + 7}{5} = 8.6$
mean absolute deviation (MAD) the sum of the distances of each data point from the mean of the data set divided by the number of data points. It is always positive. **desviación media absoluta (DMA)** suma de las distancias de cada dato desde la media del conjunto de datos dividido por el número de datos. Siempre es positiva.	Data set: 9, 10, 8, 9, 7 Mean: 8.6 MAD: $\dfrac{0.4 + 1.4 + 0.6 + 0.4 + 1.7}{5} = 0.9$

English/Español	Example/Ejemplo	Notes/Notas
measure of center a single number that summarizes what is typical for all the values in a data set. Mean and median are measures of center.	Data set: 9, 10, 8, 9, 7 Mean: 8.6 Median: 9	
medida de tendencia central único número que resume qué es típico para todos los valores en un conjunto de datos. La media y la mediana son medidas de tendecia central.		
measure of variability a single number that summarizes how much the values in a data set vary. Mean absolute deviation and interquartile range are measures of variability.	Data set: 9, 10, 8, 9, 7 MAD: 0.9 IQR: 1	
medida de variabilidad único número que resume cuánto varían los valores en un conjunto de datos. La desviación media absoluta y el rango entre cuartiles son medidas de variabilidad.		
median the middle number, or the halfway point between the two middle numbers, in an ordered set of values.	Data set: 9, 10, 8, 9, 7 7, 8, 9, 9, 10	
mediana el número del medio, o punto intermedio entre los dos números del medio, de un conjunto ordenado de valores.		
minimum (of a data set) the least value in a data set.	Data set: 9, 10, 8, 9, 7	
mínimo (de un conjunto de datos) valor mínimo en un conjunto de datos.		
multiple the product of a given number and any other whole number.	4, 8, 12, 16 are multiples of 4.	
múltiplo producto de un número dado y cualquier otro número entero.		

English/Español	Example/Ejemplo	Notes/Notas
multiplicative comparison a comparison that tells how many times as many.	$\frac{1}{2} \times 6 = 3$ tells that 3 is $\frac{1}{2}$ times as many as 6 and that 3 is 6 times as many as $\frac{1}{2}$.	
comparación multiplicativa comparación que indica cuántas veces más.		
multiplicative inverse a number is the multiplicative inverse of another number if the product of the two numbers is 1.	3 and $\frac{1}{3}$	
inverso multiplicativo un número es el inverso multiplicativo de otro número si el producto de los dos números es 1.		

Nn

negative numbers numbers that are less than 0. They are located to the left of 0 on a horizontal number line and below 0 on a vertical number line.

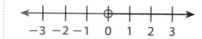

números negativos números que son menores que 0. Se ubican a la izquierda del 0 en una recta numérica horizontal y debajo del 0 en una recta numérica vertical.

---

net a flat, "unfolded" representation of a three-dimensional shape.

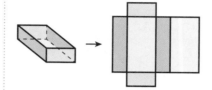

modelo plano representación plana "desplegada" de una figura tridimensional.

---

numerator the number above the line in a fraction that tells the number of equal parts that are being described.

$\dfrac{3}{4}$

numerador número que está sobre la línea en una fracción y que indica el número de partes iguales que se describen.

Oo

obtuse angle an angle that measures more than 90° but less than 180°.

ángulo obtuso ángulo que mide más de 90° pero menos de 180°.

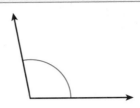

obtuse triangle a triangle that has one obtuse angle.

triángulo obtusángulo triángulo que tiene un ángulo obtuso.

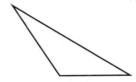

opposite numbers numbers that are the same distance from 0 on the number line but in opposite directions. Opposite numbers have the same numeral, but opposite signs. The opposite of a number is also called the *additive inverse* of that number.

-3 and 3

$-\dfrac{8}{15}$ and $\dfrac{8}{15}$

números opuestos números que están a la misma distancia del 0 en la recta numérica pero en direcciones opuestas. Los números opuestos son el mismo número, pero con el signo opuesto. El opuesto de un número también se llama *inverso de suma* de ese número.

Order of Operations a set of rules that state the order in which operations should be performed to evaluate an expression.

orden de las operaciones conjunto de reglas que establecen el orden en el que deben hacerse las operaciones para evaluar una expresión.

Working from left to right:

1. Grouping symbols
2. Exponents
3. Multiplication/Division
4. Addition/Subtraction

ordered pair a pair of numbers, (x, y), that describes the location of a point in the coordinate plane. The x-coordinate gives the point's horizontal distance from the y-axis, and the y-coordinate gives the point's vertical distance from the x-axis.

par ordenado par de números, (x, y), que describen la ubicación de un punto en el plano de coordenadas. La coordenada x da la distancia horizontal del punto desde el eje y, y la coordenada y da la distancia vertical del punto desde el eje x.

(x, y)

x-coordinate y-coordinate

origin the point (0, 0) in the coordinate plane where the *x*-axis and *y*-axis intersect.

origen el punto (0, 0) en el plano de coordenadas donde el eje *x* y el eje *y* se intersecan.

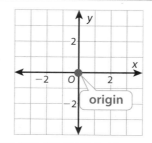

outcome one of the possible results of a chance experiment.

resultado uno de los efectos posibles de un experimento aleatorio.

Experiment: Rolling a number cube once

All possible outcomes: 1, 2, 3, 4, 5, 6

outlier a data value that is much greater or much less than most of the other values in the data set. An outlier seems to not quite fit with the rest of the data points.

valor atípico dato que es mucho mayor o mucho menor que la mayoría de los otros valores del conjunto de datos. Un valor atípico parece no ajustarse al resto de los datos.

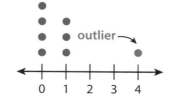

Pp

parallel (‖) always the same distance apart and never meeting.	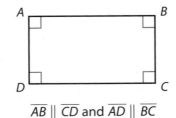
paralelos (‖) que están siempre a la misma distancia y nunca se encuentran.	$\overline{AB} \parallel \overline{CD}$ and $\overline{AD} \parallel \overline{BC}$
parallel lines lines that are always the same distance apart and never intersect.	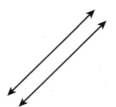
rectas paralelas rectas que siempre están a la misma distancia y nunca se intersecan.	
parallelogram a quadrilateral with opposite sides parallel and equal in length.	
paralelogramo cuadrilátero que tiene lados opuestos paralelos y de la misma longitud.	
partial products the products you get in each step of the partial-products strategy. You use place value to find partial products.	218×6 Partial products: 6×200, or 1,200, 6×10, or 60, and 6×8, or 48
productos parciales productos que se obtienen en cada paso de la estrategia de productos parciales. Se usa el valor posicional para hallar productos parciales.	
partial quotients the quotients you get in each step of the partial-quotient strategy. You use place value to find partial quotients.	$2,124 \div 4$ Partial quotients: $2,000 \div 4$, or 500, $100 \div 4$, or 25, and $24 \div 4$, or 6
cocientes parciales cocientes que se obtienen en cada paso de la estrategia de cocientes parciales. Se usa el valor posicional para hallar cocientes parciales.	

English/Español	Example/Ejemplo	Notes/Notas
partial sums the sums you get in each step of the partial-sums strategy. You use place value to find partial sums.	$124 + 234$ Partial sums: $100 + 200$, or 300, $20 + 30$, or 50, and $4 + 4$, or 8	
sumas parciales totales que se obtienen en cada paso de la estrategia de sumas parciales. Se usa el valor posicional para hallar sumas parciales.		

| **partial-products strategy** a strategy used to multiply multi-digit numbers. | $\begin{array}{r} 218 \\ \times \quad 6 \\ \hline 48 \\ 60 \\ +\ 1{,}200 \\ \hline 1{,}308 \end{array}$ $\begin{array}{l} (6 \times 8 \text{ ones}) \\ (6 \times 1 \text{ ten}) \\ (6 \times 2 \text{ hundreds}) \end{array}$ | |
| **estrategia de productos parciales** estrategia que se usa para multiplicar números de varios dígitos. | | |

| **partial-quotients strategy** a strategy used to divide multi-digit numbers. | $\begin{array}{r} 6 \\ 25 \\ 500 \\ 4\overline{)2{,}125} \\ -\ 2{,}000 \\ \hline 125 \\ -\ 100 \\ \hline 25 \\ -\ 24 \\ \hline 1 \end{array}$ | |
| **estrategia de cocientes parciales** estrategia que se usa para dividir números de varios dígitos. | The quotient 531 is the sum of partial quotients (6, 25, and 500) and the remainder (1). | |

| **partial-sums strategy** a strategy used to add multi-digit numbers. | $\begin{array}{r} 312 \\ +\ 235 \\ \hline \end{array}$ | |
| **estrategia de sumas parciales** estrategia que se usa para sumar números de varios dígitos. | Add the hundreds. $\quad 500$
Add the tens. $\qquad\ \ 40$
Add the ones. $\qquad +\ \ \ 7$
$\qquad\qquad\qquad\ \ 547$ | |

| **peak** in a distribution, the shape formed when many data points are at one value or group of values. | 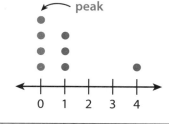 | |
| **pico** en una distribución, la figura que se forma cuando los puntos de muchos datos están en un valor o grupo de valores. | | |

English/Español	Example/Ejemplo	Notes/Notas
pentagon a polygon with exactly 5 sides and 5 angles. **pentágono** polígono que tiene exactamente 5 lados y 5 ángulos.		
per *for each* or *for every*. The word *per* can be used to express a rate, such as $2 per pound. **por** *por cada*. La palabra *por* se puede usar para expresar una tasa, como $2 por libra.	A price of $2 per pound means for every pound, you pay $2.	
percent per 100. A percent is a rate per 100. A percent can be written using the percent symbol (%) and represented as a fraction or decimal. **porcentaje** por cada 100. Un porcentaje es una tasa por cada 100. Un porcentaje se puede escribir usando el símbolo de porcentaje (%) y se representa como fracción o decimal.	15% can be represented as $\frac{15}{100}$ or 0.15.	
percent change the amount of change compared to the original (or starting) amount, expressed as a percent. Percent change $= \frac{\text{amount of change}}{\text{original amount}} \times 100$ **cambio porcentual** cantidad de cambio en comparación con la cantidad original (o inicial) que se expresa como porcentaje. Cambio porcentual $=$ $\frac{\text{cantidad de cambio}}{\text{cantidad original}} \times 100$	Saturday: 250 people Sunday: 300 people Change from Saturday to Sunday: $300 - 250 = 50$ Percent change: $\frac{50}{250} \times 100 = 20\%$	

percent decrease the percent change when a quantity decreases from its original amount.

Percent decrease =

$\dfrac{\text{amount of decrease}}{\text{original amount}} \times 100$

Saturday: 250 people

Sunday: 200 people

Change from Saturday to Sunday: 250 − 200 = 50

Percent change:

$\dfrac{50}{250} \times 100 = 20\%$

There is a 20% decrease from Saturday to Sunday.

disminución porcentual cambio porcentual cuando una cantidad disminuye desde su cantidad original. Disminución porcentual =

$\dfrac{\text{cantidad de disminución}}{\text{cantidad original}} \times 100$

percent error the difference between the correct value and the incorrect value compared to the correct value, expressed as a percent.

Percent error = $\dfrac{\text{amount of error}}{\text{correct value}} \times 100$

A bag of flour weighs 4.5 lb. It should weigh 5 lb.

Percent error:

$\dfrac{5 - 4.5}{5} \times 100 = 10\%$

error porcentual diferencia que hay entre el valor correcto y el valor incorrecto en comparación con el valor correcto, expresada como porcentaje.

Error porcentual = $\dfrac{\text{cantidad de error}}{\text{valor correcto}} \times 100$

percent increase the percent change when a quantity increases from its original amount.

Percent increase =

$\dfrac{\text{amount of increase}}{\text{original amount}} \times 100$

Saturday: 250 people

Sunday: 300 people

Change from Saturday to Sunday: 300 − 250 = 50

Percent change:

$\dfrac{50}{250} \times 100 = 20\%$

There is a 20% increase from Saturday to Sunday.

incremento porcentual cambio porcentual cuando una cantidad se incrementa desde su cantidad original.

Aumento porcentual =

$\dfrac{\text{cantidad de incremento}}{\text{cantidad original}} \times 100$

English/Español	Example/Ejemplo	Notes/Notas
perimeter the distance around a two-dimensional shape. The perimeter is equal to the sum of the lengths of the sides. **perímetro** distancia alrededor de una figura bidimensional. El perímetro es igual a la suma de las longitudes de los lados.	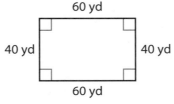 Perimeter: 200 yd (60 yd + 40 yd + 60 yd + 40 yd)	
perpendicular (⊥) meeting to form right angles. **perpendicular (⊥)** unión donde se forman ángulos rectos.	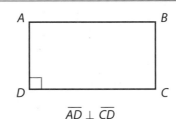 $\overline{AD} \perp \overline{CD}$	
perpendicular lines two lines that meet to form a right angle, or a 90° angle. **rectas perpendiculares** dos rectas que se encuentran y forman un ángulo recto, o ángulo de 90°.	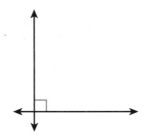	
pi (π) in a circle, the quotient $\frac{circumference}{diameter}$. Common approximations are 3.14 and $\frac{22}{7}$. **pi (π)** en un círculo, el cociente de $\frac{circumferencia}{diámetro}$. Las aproximaciones communes son 3.14 y $\frac{22}{7}$.	$\pi \approx 3.14$ or $\frac{22}{7}$	
place value the value of a digit based on its position in a number. **valor posicional** valor de un dígito que se basa en su posición en un número. Por ejemplo, el 2 en 3.52 está en la posición de las centésimas y tiene un valor de 2 centésimas, o 0.02.	The 2 in 3.52 is in the hundredths place and has a value of 2 hundredths or 0.02.	

English/Español	Example/Ejemplo	Notes/Notas
plane figure a two-dimensional figure, such as a circle, triangle, or rectangle. **figura plana** figura bidimensional, como un círculo, un triángulo o un rectángulo.		
plane section a two-dimensional shape that is exposed by making a straight cut through a three-dimensional figure. **sección plana** figura bidimensional que se expone al hacer un corte recto a través de una figura tridimensional.	plane section	
point a single location in space. **punto** ubicación única en el espacio.	*A*	
polygon a two-dimensional closed figure made with three or more straight line segments that meet only at their endpoints. **polígono** figura bidimensional cerrada formada por tres o más segmentos de recta que se encuentran solo en sus extremos.		
population the entire group of interest. Samples are drawn from populations. **población** grupo entero de interés. Las muestras se obtienen de las poblaciones.	Sample: 10 students from each Grade 8 homeroom in a school Population: All Grade 8 students in the school	
positive numbers numbers that are greater than 0. They are located to the right of 0 on a horizontal number line and above 0 on a vertical number line. **números positivos** números que son mayores que 0. Se ubican a la derecha del 0 en una recta numérica horizontal y sobre el 0 en una recta numérica vertical.	−3 −2 −1 0 1 2 3	

English/Español	Example/Ejemplo	Notes/Notas
power an expression with a base and an exponent. **potencia** expresión que tiene una base y un exponente.	8^2	
power of 10 a number that can be written as a product of 10s. **potencia de 10** número que se puede escribir como el producto de 10.	100 and 1,000 are powers of 10 because $100 = 10 \times 10$ and $1,000 = 10 \times 10 \times 10$.	
prime number a whole number greater than 1 whose only factors are 1 and itself. **número primo** número entero mayor que 1 cuyos únicos factores son 1 y sí mismo.	2, 3, 5, 7, 11, 13	
prism a three-dimensional figure with two parallel bases that are the same size and shape. The other faces are parallelograms. A prism is named by the shape of the base. **prisma** figura tridimensional que tiene dos bases paralelas que tienen el mismo tamaño y la misma forma. Las otras caras son paralelogramos. La base determina el nombre del prisma.		
probability a number between 0 and 1 that expresses the likelihood of an event occurring. **probabilidad** número entre 0 y 1 que expresa la posibilidad de que ocurra un evento.		

English/Español	Example/Ejemplo	Notes/Notas
product the result of multiplication.	$3 \cdot 5 = 15$	
producto resultado de la multiplicación.		
proportional relationship the relationship between two quantities where one quantity is a constant multiple of the other quantity. If the quantities x and y are in a proportional relationship, you can represent that relationship with the equation $y = kx$, where the value of k is constant (unchanging).	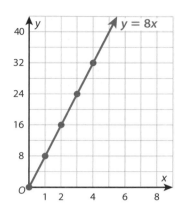	
relación proporcional relación que existe entre dos cantidades en la que una cantidad es un múltiplo constante de la otra. Si las cantidades x y y están en una relación proporcional, esa relación se puede representar con la ecuación $y = kx$, en la que el valor de k es constante (no cambia).		

Qq

quadrants the four regions of the coordinate plane that are formed when the *x*-axis and *y*-axis intersect at the origin.

cuadrantes las cuatro regiones del plano de coordenadas que se forman cuando los ejes *x* y *y* se intersecan en el origen.

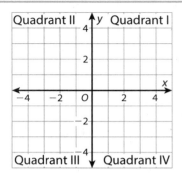

quadrilateral a polygon with exactly 4 sides and 4 angles.

cuadrilátero polígono que tiene exactamente 4 lados y 4 ángulos.

quotient the result of division.

$$22.5 \div 3 = 7.5$$

cociente resultado de la división.

Rr

radius (of a circle) a line segment from the center of a circle to any point on the circle. Also, the distance from the center to any point on a circle.

radio (de un círculo) segmento de recta desde el centro de un círculo hasta cualquier punto en el círculo. Además, la distancia desde el centro hasta cualquier punto en un círculo.

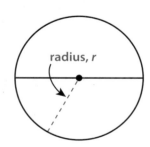

random sample a sample in which every element in the population has an equal chance of being selected.

muestra aleatoria muestra en la que todos los elementos de la población tienen la misma probabilidad de ser elegidos.

The names of all of the students in the school are placed in a hat. Without looking, 30 names are selected. The 30 students are a random sample of the population.

---

range the difference between the greatest value (maximum) and the least value (minimum) in a data set.

rango diferencia entre el mayor valor (máximo) y el menor valor (mínimo) en un conjunto de datos.

Data set: 9, 10, 8, 9, 7

Range: $10 - 7 = 3$

---

rate a ratio tells the number of units of one quantity for 1 unit of another quantity. Rates are often expressed using the word *per*.

tasa razón que indica el número de unidades de una cantidad para 1 unidad de otra cantidad. Las razones suelen expresarse usando la palabra *por*.

5 miles per hour

2 cups for every 1 serving

---

ratio a way to compare two quantities when there are *a* units of one quantity for every *b* units of the other quantity. You can write the ratio in symbols as *a* : *b* and in words as *a to b*.

razón manera de comparar dos cantidades cuando hay *a* unidades de una cantidad por cada *b* unidades de la otra cantidad. Se puede escribir la razón en símbolos como *a* : *b* y en palabras como *a a b*.

4 circles : 2 triangles

---

rational number a number that can be expressed as the fraction $\frac{a}{b}$ where *a* and *b* are integers and $b \neq 0$. Rational numbers include integers, fractions, repeating decimals, and terminating decimals.

número racional número que se puede expresar como la fracción $\frac{a}{b}$ en la que *a* y *b* son enteros y $b \neq 0$. Los números racionales incluyen los enteros, las fracciones, los decimales periódicos y los decimales finitos.

$\frac{3}{4}, -\frac{1}{8}, -3, 0, 1.2$

---

ray a part of a line that has one endpoint and goes on forever in one direction.

semirrecta parte de una recta que tiene un extremo y continúa infinitamente en una dirección.

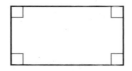

reciprocal for any nonzero number a, the reciprocal is $\frac{1}{a}$. The reciprocal of any fraction $\frac{a}{b}$ is $\frac{b}{a}$. Zero does not have a reciprocal. The reciprocal of a number is also called the *multiplicative inverse* of that number.

recíproco para cualquier número a distinto de cero, el recíproco es $\frac{1}{a}$. El recíproco de cualquier fracción $\frac{a}{b}$ es $\frac{b}{a}$. El cero no tiene recíproco. El recíproco de un número también se llama *inverso multiplicativo* de ese número.

The reciprocal of $\frac{4}{5}$ is $\frac{5}{4}$.

The reciprocal of $\frac{1}{6}$ is 6.

The reciprocal of -8 is $-\frac{1}{8}$.

rectangle a quadrilateral with 4 right angles. Opposite sides of a rectangle are the same length.

rectángulo cuadrilátero que tiene 4 ángulos rectos. Los lados opuestos de un rectángulo tienen la misma longitud.

rectangular prism a prism where the bases are rectangles.

prisma rectangular prisma en el que las bases son rectángulos.

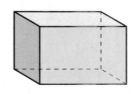

reflection a transformation that flips (reflects) a figure across a line to form a mirror image.

reflexión transformación que gira (refleja) una figura del otro lado de una línea para formar una imagen reflejada.

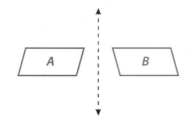

remainder the amount left over when one number does not divide another number a whole number of times.

$7 \div 2 = 3\,R\,1$

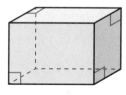

remainder

residuo cantidad que queda cuando un número no divide a otro un número entero de veces.

---

repeating decimals decimals that repeat the same digit or sequence of digits forever. A repeating decimal can be written with a bar over the repeating digits.

$0.\overline{3}$

$2.5\overline{1}$

decimal periódico decimales que repiten el mismo dígito o secuencia de dígitos infinitamente. Un decimal periódico se puede escribir con una barra sobre los dígitos que se repiten.

---

rhombus a quadrilateral with all sides the same length.

rombo cuadrilátero que tiene todos los lados de la misma longitud.

---

right angle an angle that measures 90°.

ángulo recto ángulo que mide 90°.

---

right prism a prism where each base is perpendicular to the other faces. In a right prism, the faces that are not bases are rectangles.

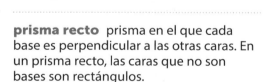

prisma recto prisma en el que cada base es perpendicular a las otras caras. En un prisma recto, las caras que no son bases son rectángulos.

English/Español	Example/Ejemplo	Notes/Notas
right rectangular prism a right prism where the bases and other faces are all rectangles. **prisma rectangular recto** prisma recto en el que las bases y las otras caras son rectángulos.		
right triangle a triangle with one right angle. **triángulo rectángulo** triángulo que tiene un ángulo recto.		
right triangular prism a right prism where the bases are triangles and the other faces are rectangles. **prisma triangular recto** prisma recto en el que las bases son triángulos y las otras caras son rectángulos.		
round to approximate the value of a number by finding the nearest ten, hundred, or other place value. **redondear** aproximar el valor de un número hallando la decena, la centena u otro valor posicional más cercano.	48 rounded to the nearest ten is 50.	

Ss

sample a part of a population.

muestra parte de una población.

Population: All students in the school

Sample: Three students in each homeroom

---

sample space the set of all possible unique outcomes for an experiment.

espacio muestral conjunto de todos los resultados posibles de un experimento.

Experiment: Rolling a number cube

Sample space: 1, 2, 3, 4, 5, 6

---

scale tells the relationship between a length in a drawing, map, or model to the actual length.

escala indica la relación que hay entre una longitud en un dibujo, un mapa o un modelo y la longitud real.

Scale from a map to actual distances in a town:

1 in. to 20 mi

---

scale (on a graph) the value represented by the distance between one tick mark and the next on a number line.

escala (en una gráfica) valor representado por la distancia que hay entre una marca y la siguiente en una recta numérica.

−10 −5 0 5 10 15 20
scale = 5

---

scale drawing a drawing in which the measurements correspond to the measurements of the actual object by the same scale.

dibujo a escala dibujo en el que las medidas se corresponden con las medidas del objeto real según la misma escala.

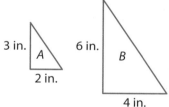

3 in. A 2 in. 6 in. B 4 in.

△A : △B is 1 : 2.

---

scale factor the factor you multiply all the side lengths in a figure by to make a scale copy.

factor de escala factor por el que se multiplican todas las longitudes laterales en una figura para hacer una copia a escala.

Scale from a map to the actual distance: 1 in. to 20 mi

Scale factor from distances on the map to the actual distances: 20

English/Español	Example/Ejemplo	Notes/Notas
scalene triangle a triangle that has no sides the same length. **triángulo escaleno** triángulo que no tiene lados de la misma longitud.	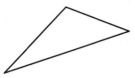	
side a line segment that forms part of a two-dimensional shape. **lado** segmento de recta que forma parte de una figura bidimensional		
simple interest a percent of an amount that is borrowed or invested. **interés simple** porcentaje de una cantidad que se toma prestada o se invierte.	$I = Prt$ I = interest P = principal (amount borrowed or invested) r = interest rate t = time	
skewed left when most of the data points of a distribution are clustered near the greater values. **asimétrica a la izquierda** cuando la mayoría de los datos de una distribución se agrupan cerca de los valores más altos.	**Skewed Left** 	
skewed right when most of the data points of a distribution are clustered near the lesser values. **asimétrica a la derecha** cuando la mayoría de los datos de una distribución se agrupan cerca de los valores más bajos.	**Skewed Right** 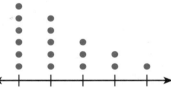	
solution of an equation a value that can be substituted for a variable to make an equation true. **solución de una ecuación** valor que puede sustituir a una variable para hacer que una ecuación sea verdadera.	The value 5 is the solution of the equation $19 = 4x - 1$ because $19 = 4(5) - 1$.	

English/Español	Example/Ejemplo	Notes/Notas
solution of an inequality a value that can be substituted for a variable to make an inequality true. **solución de una desigualdad** valor que puede sustituir a una variable para hacer que una desigualdad sea verdadera.	All values of x less than 5 ($x < 5$) are solutions of the inequality $5x < 25$.	
square a quadrilateral with 4 right angles and 4 sides of equal length. **cuadrado** cuadrilátero que tiene 4 ángulos rectos y 4 lados de la misma longitud.		
statistical question a question that can be answered by collecting data that are expected to vary. **pregunta estadística** pregunta que se puede responder reuniendo datos que se espera que varíen.	What is the typical amount of rain in April?	
straight angle an angle that measures 180°. The sides of a straight angle form a straight line. **ángulo llano** ángulo que mide 180°. Los lados de un ángulo llano forman una línea recta.	A B C $\angle ABC$ is a straight angle.	
sum the result of addition. **total** resultado de la suma.	$24 + 35 = 59$	
supplementary angles two angles whose measures sum to 180°. **ángulos suplementarios** dos ángulos cuyas medidas suman 180°.	$\angle WXZ$ and $\angle ZXY$ are supplementary angles.	

English/Español	Example/Ejemplo	Notes/Notas

surface area the sum of the areas of all the faces of a three-dimensional figure.

área total suma de las áreas de todas las caras de una figura tridimensional.

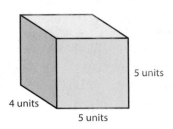

5 units

4 units

5 units

Surface Area: 2(4)(5) + 2(4)(5) + 2(5)(5) = 130 units²

---

symmetric when a distribution has the same shape on both sides of a middle point.

simétrico cuando una distribución tiene la misma forma en ambos lados de un punto que está en el medio.

Symmetric

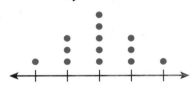

Tt

tax a percent of income or of the cost of goods or services paid to the government.

impuesto porcentaje del ingreso o del costo de bienes o servicios que se paga al gobierno.

A 7% sales tax on a purchase of $40 is $2.80

---

term a number, a variable, or a product of numbers, variables, and/or expressions. A term may include an exponent.

término número, variable o el producto de números, variables y/o expresiones. Un término puede tener un exponente.

$4x + 9 + y^2$

term

| --- | --- | --- |

terminating decimals decimals that end, or end in repeated zeros.

decimal finito decimal en el que termina un número, o que termina en ceros repetidos.

0.25
5.6
−7.125

theoretical probability the probability of an event occurring based on what is expected to happen.

probabilidad teórica probabilidad de que ocurra un evento según lo que se espera que suceda.

There are two equally likely outcomes to flipping a coin: heads up or tails up.

The theoretical probability of the outcome heads up is $\frac{1}{2}$, or 50%.

three-dimensional solid, or having length, width, and height. For example, a cube is three-dimensional.

tridimensional sólido, o que tiene longitud, ancho y altura. Por ejemplo, un cubo es tridimensional.

height
width
length

trapezoid (exclusive) a quadrilateral with exactly one pair of parallel sides.

trapecio (exclusivo) cuadrilátero que tiene exactamente un par de lados paralelos.

trapezoid (inclusive) a quadrilateral with at least one pair of parallel sides.

trapecio (inclusivo) cuadrilátero que tiene al menos un par de lados paralelos.

tree diagram a visual that shows all possible outcomes of an experiment.

diagrama de árbol representación visual que muestra todos los resultados posibles de un experimento.

There are 8 possible outcomes from flipping a coin 3 times.

English/Español	Example/Ejemplo	Notes/Notas
trial a single performance of an experiment. **ensayo** ejecución única de un experimento.	Rolling a number cube once	
triangle a polygon with exactly 3 sides and 3 angles. **triángulo** polígono que tiene exactamente 3 lados y 3 ángulos.		
triangular prism a prism where the bases are triangles. **prisma triangular** prisma en el que las bases son triángulos.		
two-dimensional flat, or having measurement in two directions, like length and width. For example, a rectangle is two-dimensional. **bidimensional** plano, o que tiene medidas en dos direcciones, como longitud y ancho. Por ejemplo, un rectángulo es bidimensional.	width length	

Uu

unit fraction a fraction with a numerator of 1. Other fractions are built from unit fractions.	
	$\frac{1}{5}$
fracción unitaria fracción que tiene un numerador de 1. Otras fracciones se construyen a partir de fracciones unitarias.	

unit rate the numerical part of a rate. For the ratio $a : b$, the unit rate is the quotient $\frac{a}{b}$.	
	Rate: 3 miles per hour
	Unit rate: 3
tasa por unidad parte numérica de una tasa. Para la razón $a : b$, la tasa por unidad es el cociente $\frac{a}{b}$.	

unknown the value you need to find to solve a problem.	
	$20.5 + x = 30$
incógnita valor que hay que hallar para resolver un problema.	

upper quartile the middle number between the median and the maximum in an ordered set of numbers. The upper quartile is also called the 3rd quartile or Q3.	
	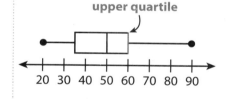
cuartil superior número del medio entre la mediana y el máximo en un conjunto ordenado de números. El cuartil superior también se llama tercer cuartil, o Q3.	

Vv

variability how spread out or close together values in a data set are.

variabilidad la dispersión o cercanía de los valores en un conjunto de datos.

Gavin's Handstand Times

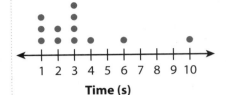

Time (s)

There is high variability in Gavin's handstand times.

---

variable a letter that represents an unknown number. In some cases, a variable may represent more than one number.

variable letra que representa un número desconocido. En algunos casos, una variable puede representar más de un número.

$$3x + 9 = 90$$

---

vertex the point where two rays, lines, or line segments meet to form an angle.

vértice punto en el que dos semirrectas, rectas o segmentos de recta se encuentran y forman un ángulo.

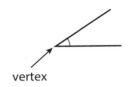

vertex

---

vertical angles opposite angles formed when two lines intersect. Vertical angles how the same measure.

ángulos opuestos por el vértice ángulos opuestos que se forman cuando se intersecan dos rectas. Los ángulos opuestos por el vértice tienen la misma medida.

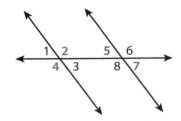

∠5 and ∠7

∠2 and ∠4

---

volume the amount of space inside a solid figure. Volume is measured in cubic units such as cubic inches.

volumen cantidad de espacio dentro de una figura sólida. El volumen se mide en unidades cúbicas como las pulgadas cúbicas.

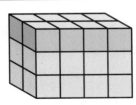

volume: 24 units^3

Ww

whole numbers the numbers 0, 1, 2, 3, 4, . . . Whole numbers are nonnegative and have no fractional part.

números enteros los números 0, 1, 2, 3, 4, . . . Los números enteros no son negativos y no tienen partes fraccionarias.

0, 8, 187

Xx

x-axis the horizontal number line in the coordinate plane.

eje x recta numérica horizontal en el plano de coordenadas.

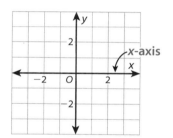

x-coordinate the first number in an ordered pair. It tells the point's horizontal distance from the y-axis.

coordenada x primer número en un par ordenado. Indica la distancia horizontal del punto al eje y.

(x, y)

Interactive Glossary/Glosario interactivo

Yy

y-axis the vertical number line in the coordinate plane.

eje y recta numérica vertical en el plano de coordenadas.

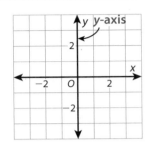

y-coordinate the second number in an ordered pair. It tells the point's vertical distance from the x-axis.

coordenada y el segundo número en un par ordenado. Indica la distancia vertical del punto al eje x.

(x, y)

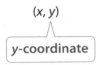

Zz

zero pair two numbers whose sum is zero. Opposite numbers form a zero pair.

par cero dos números cuya suma es cero. Los números opuestos forman un par cero.

−3 and 3 form a zero pair.

1.2 and −1.2 form a zero pair.

Credits

Acknowledgment

Common Core State Standards © 2010. National Governors Association Center for Best Practices and Council of Chief State School Officers. All rights reserved.

Photography Credits

Cover: Bo1982/Shutterstock, Lorri Kajenna/Shutterstock, Exotic vector/Shutterstock, Jorge Salcedo/Shutterstock
Back Cover: 71 Rawpixel.com/Shutterstock; 398 Cathy Withers-Clarke/Shutterstock
Text: ii, 58, 125, 359 New Africa/Shutterstock; ii, 95 Enrique Ramos/Shutterstock, Alena Brozova/Shutterstock; iii, 186 pictoplay/Shutterstock, 3DMI/Shutterstock; iv, 252 Danita Delmont/Shutterstock, Le Do/Shutterstock; v, 312 YamabikaY/Shutterstock; v, 335 visivastudio/Shutterstock, Gino Santa Maria/Shutterstock; v, 403 Chutima Chaochaiya/Shutterstock; vi, 420 jaroslava/Shutterstock; vi, 452 RemarkEliza/Shutterstock; vii, 593 nour eddine salhi/Shutterstock; viii, 695 design56/Shutterstock; viii, 705 iStock.com/Dmytro Aksonov; 1, 97 DimiSotirov/Shutterstock; 3 Romolo Tavani/Shutterstock; 4 Danita Delimont/Alamy Stock Photo; 8 The Metropolitan Museum of Art, New York, Rogers Fund, 1907, stevemart/Shutterstock; 12 alslutsky/Shutterstock; 14 Double-Matt/Shutterstock, Kamira/Shutterstock; 16 Witold Skrypczak/Alamy Stock Photo; 20 sergeykot/Shutterstock; 22 paul prescott/Shutterstock; 30 NaughtyNut/Shutterstock; 31 Oleksandra Naumenko/Shutterstock; 32 Courtesy of the Library of Congress, LC-USF33-030783-M2, dimitris_k/Shutterstock; 36 DWI YULIANTO/Shutterstock; 37 Fourleaflover/Shutterstock; 38 Dzmitrock/Shutterstock; 40 Fredy Thuerig/Shutterstock; 42 terekhov igor/Shutterstock; 45 Serg Salivon/Shutterstock, Kriengsuk Prasroetsung/Shutterstock; 47 Sandra Cunningham/Shutterstock, Yarygin/Shutterstock; 48 Nata-Lia/Shutterstock; 49 Melissa Sue/Shutterstock; 50 Susan Schmitz/Shutterstock; 55 onairda/Shutterstock; 59 Antonio V. Oquias/Shutterstock; 61 My Good Images/Shutterstock; 64 Production Perig/Shutterstock, Petr Nad/Shutterstock; 65 Binh Thanh Bui/Shutterstock; 66 Gabriela ZZ/Shutterstock.com; 81 Baloncici/Shutterstock; 83 Tiger Images/Shutterstock, Vasileios Karafillidis/Shutterstock, NIPAPORN PANYACHAROEN/Shutterstock, marekuliasz/Shutterstock; 86 Alchie/Shutterstock, Leigh Lather/Shutterstock, Steve Cukrov/Shutterstock; 87 iStock.com/skynesher; 88 Kamenetskiy Konstantin/Shutterstock; 99 rjmiguel/Shutterstock; 102 B Brown/Shutterstock; 106 Andrey Eremin/Shutterstock; 108 iStock.com/4x6, Ververidis Vasilis/Shutterstock; 112 elnavegante/Shutterstock; 114 Fat Jackey/Shutterstock.com; 118 NazaBasirun/Shutterstock, Joe MoJo/Shutterstock, MookSmile/Shutterstock, donatas1205/Shutterstock; 119, 122 bazzier/Shutterstock, Kittichai/Shutterstock; 119 Lisa F. Young/Shutterstock; 124 stuar/Shutterstock, Steve Cukrov/Shutterstock; 126 Pixel-Shot/Shutterstock; 127 pfluegler-photo/Shutterstock, Sasin Paraksa/Shutterstock; 133, 181 Stocktrek Images, Inc./Alamy Stock Photo; 135 Paulo Miguel Costa/Shutterstock; 137 delcarmat/Shutterstock; 142 Eugene Onischenko/Shutterstock; 144 curiosity/Shutterstock; 146 Mike Price/Shutterstock, kubais/Shutterstock; 147 Darren J. Bradley/Shutterstock, VIS Fine Art/Shutterstock; 149 Josef Hanus/Shutterstock; 152 glenda/Shutterstock, Marian Weyo/Shutterstock, Branko Jovanovic/Shutterstock; 153 photoschmidt/Shutterstock; 154 iStock.com/Willowpix; 156 Paulo Oliveira/Alamy Stock Photo; 158 Michelle Holihan/Shutterstock; 160 idreamphoto/Shutterstock; 162 Moonlightphoto/Shutterstock, M. Unal Ozmen/Shutterstock; 164 danilo ducak/Shutterstock, scubadesign/Shutterstock; 168 D Stevenson/Shutterstock; 169 BERNATSKAIA OKSANA/Shutterstock, GalapagosPhoto/Shutterstock; 171 Daboost/Shutterstock, Lec Neo/Shutterstock; 174 Somchai Som/Shutterstock; 175 Rynio Productions/Shutterstock, George Fairbairn/Shutterstock; 182 Sergey Novikov/Shutterstock; 187 nolie/Shutterstock; 188 Tomas Ragina/Shutterstock; 191 benchart/Shutterstock; 194 kopbs2/Shutterstock; 196 Valentyna Chukhlyebova/Shutterstock, Checubus/Shutterstock; 197 Ty Hartlipp/Shutterstock; 198 iStock.com/MATJAZ SLANIC; 201 S.Bachstroem/Shutterstock; 203 Hal Brindley/Shutterstock, Steinar/Shutterstock; 207 Shaun Jeffers/Shutterstock; 208 Macrovector/Shutterstock, Vectorpocket/Shutterstock; 209 salajean/Shutterstock; 211 Anna Om/Shutterstock, reisegraf.ch/Shutterstock, Filip Fuxa/Shutterstock; 217, 275 Tamakhin Mykhailo/Shutterstock; 219 tsuneomp/Shutterstock; 231 Sky Cinema/Shutterstock; 233 FrameAngel/Shutterstock; 236 Steve Bower/Shutterstock, Volodymyr Goinyk/Shutterstock; 238 Johnny Adolphson/Shutterstock; 240 GoProPk/Shutterstock; 243 IrinaK/Shutterstock; 244 Michael J. Munster/Shutterstock.com; 246 Polushkina Svetlana/Shutterstock; 248 Subphoto/Shutterstock; 253 grynold/Shutterstock, tishomir/Shutterstock; 254 Matee Nuserm/Shutterstock, Vadarshop/Shutterstock; 260 ONiONA_studio/Shutterstock; 262 Izf/Shutterstock, Kenneth Sponsler/Shutterstock; 265 bonchan/Shutterstock, almaje/Shutterstock, gowithstock/Shutterstock, greisei/Shutterstock, givaga/Shutterstock; 266 Viktory Panchenko/Shutterstock; 268 AngieYeoh/Shutterstock; 270 Andrey Suslov/Shutterstock;

273 Anton Starikov/Shutterstock, Fedorov Ivan Sergeevich/Shutterstock; 277 Jacob Boomsma/Shutterstock; 280 Gary C. Togoni/Shutterstock, Flipser/Shutterstock; 281 cugdem/Shutterstock; 282 Gilmanshin/Shutterstock.com; 284 Greg Epperson/Shutterstock; 286 Ed Jenkins/Shutterstock; 291 szpeti/Shutterstock; 297 Media_works/Shutterstock; 298 aapsky/Shutterstock; 299 ifong/Shutterstock, Dudarev Mikhail/Shutterstock; 305, 353 dwphotos/Shutterstock; 307 Stock-Asso/Shutterstock; 308 antpkr/Shutterstock, Photick/Shutterstock; 309 Macrovector/Shutterstock; 312 aopsan/Shutterstock; 329 TORWAISTUDIO/Shutterstock; 330 Gts/Shutterstock; 338 Evdokimov Maxim/Shutterstock; 341 stockcreations/Shutterstock; 342 iStock.com/vernonwiley; 350 IB Photography/Shutterstock, Sergey Lavrentev/Shutterstock; 354 Miro Vrlik Photography/Shutterstock.com; 355 ChameleonsEye/Shutterstock, Michael Jacobs/Alamy Stock Photo, Avi Rozen/Shutterstock, RnDmS/Shutterstock.com, ungvar/Shutterstock, Jewish Content Images/Shutterstock; 359 Dmod/Shutterstock, Lakeview Images/Shutterstock, Photo Melon/Shutterstock; 360 vilax/Shutterstock, Pencil_man17/Shutterstock, Design tech art/Shutterstock, Mile Atanasov/Shutterstock, Thornton/Shutterstock; 362 voyata/Shutterstock, Volodymyr Burdiak/Shutterstock; 364 FreshStock/Shutterstock, Zadiraka Evgenii/Shutterstock, IhorL/Shutterstock; 366 Protasov AN/Shutterstock; 370 In Green/Shutterstock; 373 Rinrinnn/Shutterstock; 375 nmedia/Shutterstock; 376 TATSIANAMA/Shutterstock; 393 iStock.com/ilbusca, TerraceStudio/Shutterstock; 394 Photo by @_WILLPOWER_ from nappy.co; 396 Rich Carey/Shutterstock; 401 Oksana Mizina/Shutterstock, Oil and Gas Photographer/Shutterstock; 409 gresei/Shutterstock, Petr Malyshev/Shutterstock, weissdesign/Shutterstock, astudio/Shutterstock, gusenynch/Shutterstock, razvart/Shutterstock, astudio/Shutterstock, RATOCA/Shutterstock; 410, 755 Africa Studio/Shutterstock; 410 vander/Shutterstock, Pixfiction/Shutterstock, andrea crisante/Shutterstock, Shablon/Shutterstock; 411 BublikHaus/Shutterstock, Ajintai/Shutterstock; 417, 447 Roka Pics/Shutterstock; 419 Eclipse Production/Shutterstock; 420 Mette Sig/Shutterstock; 424 MRProduction/Shutterstock; 426 Mikbiz/Shutterstock.com; 428 Vladyslav Starozhylov/Shutterstock; 431 Youshij Yousefzadeh/Shutterstock; 432 Richard Levine/Alamy Stock Photo; 434 Pan_Da/Shutterstock.com, pittaya/Shutterstock.com; 436 Ljupco Smokovski/Shutterstock; 437 niroworld/Shutterrstock, GrashAlex/Shutterstock; 438 Ljupco Smokovski/Shutterstock; 442 Daniel Fung/Shutterstock, GrandeDuc/Shutterstock, Sergey Nivens/Shutterstock; 449, 488 Oleksiy Mark/Shutterstock; 454 Jeffrey M Horler/Shutterstock, Gregory E. Clifford/Shutterstock.com;

456 kojihirano/Shutterstock; 458 Aleksandr Simonov/Shutterstock; 459 Roman Samokhin/Shutterstock, doomu/Shutterstock; 460 ducu59us/Shutterstock; 462 Milkovasa/Shutterstock, iamlukyeee/Shutterstock; 467 AlenKadr/Shutterstock, Andrew Burgess/Shutterstock, Mehmet Cetin/Shutterstock; 469 Lucky Business/Shutterstock; 481 Pakhnyushchy/Shutterstock, Jure Divich/Shutterstock; 482 donfiore/Shutterstock, Z.Kim/Shutterstock; 486 Cultura Creative (RF)/Alamy Stock Photo; 493 Eivaisla/Shutterstock, Jiri Hera/Shutterstock, Trygve Funjelsen/Shutterstock; 494 iStock.com/jordacheir; 498 wk1003mike/Shutterstock; 502 markku murto/art/Alamy Stock Photo, LLP collection/Alamy Stock Photo, Historic Collection/Alamy Stock Photo; 503 AwayIGI/Shutterstock; 512 violetblue/Shutterstock, Eric Isselee/Shutterstock, NosorogUA/Shutterstock; 514 Han maomin/Shutterstock; 523 Prokrida/Shutterstock; 525, 528 CampCrazy Photography/Shutterstock, space_heater/Shutterstock; 525 space_heater/Shutterstock; 530 F1online digitale Bildagentur GmbH/Alamy Stock Photo; 531 Paul Glendell/Alamy Stock Photo; 532 Duncan Selby/Alamy Stock Photo; 533 rbrown10/Shutterstock; 539, 629 Jordan Tan/Shutterstock; 541 Pete Saloutos/Shutterstock; 556 Ammily CP/Shutterstock; 558 Vadim Georgiev/Shutterstock; 560 Tei Sinthip/Shutterstock, Mary Swift/Shutterstock; 564 nuwatphoto/Shutterstock; 569 laura.h/Shutterstock; 574 Hit1912/Shutterstock.com; 576 Kostsov/Shutterstock, Ojele/Shutterstock; 578 PinkBlue/Shutterstock; 589 loskutnikov/Shutterstock, Beata Becla/Shutterstock; 591 Tim UR/Shutterstock, Igors Rusakovs/Shutterstock, MasterQ/Shutterstock, Alexeysun/Shutterstock; 592 Krasula/Shutterstock; 596 Inara Prusakova/Shutterstock; 602 Binh Thanh Bui/Shutterstock, EggHeadPhoto/Shutterstock, Simone Andress/Shutterstock; 605 Alexandra Lande/Shutterstock; 607 Kris Wiktor/Shutterstock; 608 archideaphoto/Shutterstock; 624 Kostenko Maxim/Shutterstock; 629 Phatthanit/Shutterstock; 635 The Metropolitan Museum of Art, New York, Gift of Mr. and Mrs. J. J. Klejman, 1966; 636 Kirsty Bisset/Shutterstock; 640 Tawansak/Shutterstock; 656 donatas1205/Shutterstock; 657 iStock.com/huseyintuncer; 663 Cynthia Shirk/Shutterstock; 665 Naypong Studio/Shutterstock, paulista/Shutterstock, Mike Flippo/Shutterstock; 671, 673 TOMO/Shutterstock; 682 Monkey Business Images/Shutterstock; 685 Milosz Bartoszczuk/Shutterstock; 686 Bahadir Yeniceri/Shutterstock, studiovin/Shutterstock; 697, 698 MISTER DIN/Shutterstock; 700 SS pixels/Shutterstock, Sandeep Gore/Shutterstock; 702 Nearbirds/Shutterstock; 707 allstars/Shutterstock, Lorelyn Medina/Shutterstock; 708 ronstik/Shutterstock, Vladimir Wrangel/Shutterstock; 716 biagacis/Shutterstock; 717 Yuriy Redkin/Shutterstock;